Astrophysical Quantities

Astrophysical Quantities

BY

C. W. ALLEN

Perren Professor of Astronomy
in the University of London

Second Edition

UNIVERSITY OF LONDON
The Athlone Press
1963

Published in 1955 by
THE ATHLONE PRESS
UNIVERSITY OF LONDON
at 2 Gower Street, London, w.c.1

Distributed by Constable & Co Ltd
12 Orange Street, London, w.c.2

U.S.A.
Oxford University Press Inc
New York

Printed in Great Britain by
WILLIAM CLOWES AND SONS LTD
London and Beccles

PREFACE TO FIRST EDITION

THE intention of this book is to present the essential quantitative inforation of astrophysics in a form that can be readily used. Questions relating to the material included and the form adopted are discussed in the introductory chapter.

The information is as up to date as possible, but the approved values of astrophysical constants change from year to year and there can be no finality about the last digit of most of the values quoted. It is to be expected, then, that some users will wish to pencil in amended values to suit later results or to agree with their own opinions. The author hopes that readers will let him know of any errors or faulty values that are contained. From consideration of such advice, and from the use of new results, it should be possible to progress towards the ideal of recording an accurate value for every quantity.

It has not been possible to give adequate acknowledgement in the references to all the sources of information. The references quoted are mostly to recent papers, since earlier ones can be traced from these. Use has been made of many handbooks, text-books, and tabulations which are quoted in the references. The comprehensive Landolt-Börnstein tables became available during the late stages of preparation, and these were used for checking and filling in gaps. However, it is not thought that the existence of such tabulations restricts in any way the need for the present volume.

The author's thanks are due to Dr. A. Hunter, Dr. P. A. Sweet and Dr. R. H. Garstang for reading the manuscript and proofs, and for many suggestions.

April 1955   C. W. A.

PREFACE TO SECOND EDITION

THE second edition has provided an opportunity to reassess all the original data and bring it up to date by the introduction of new material. A small increase in total size was perhaps inevitable but it has been kept to a minimum. The style is essentially the same.

The author's thanks are due to Dr. R. H. Garstang for original data and to Mr. M. Friedjung and Mr. R. J. Salisbury for clerical help.

November 1962   C. W. A.

CONTENTS

CHAPTER 1

INTRODUCTION

§ 1. Requirements

PROGRESS in any of the physical sciences is very closely linked with a determination of the precise values of the quantities concerned. Extensive labour and very much care have been put into the measurement of some of these essential quantities, and in the end the user may obtain the advantage of all this effort simply by reading the number that represents the final value. Thus an enormous economy of expression can be effected by writing a final result and omitting mention of the long chapter of events that led up to it.

The present work is concerned with final results, and we have to consider how these can be most effectively extracted from the available information and then presented for use. It is found that the necessary procedure becomes fairly clearly defined once we have decided what are the more important of the various user requirements. These requirements are listed below together with the steps and policy found necessary to meet them.

Material to be included

The purpose of *Astrophysical Quantities* is to present the quantitative framework on which astrophysics is being built. To do this the book should contain all experimental and theoretical values, constants, and conversion factors that are fundamental to astrophysical arguments. The extent to which individual items should be described, e.g. individual stars or spectrum lines, depends on whether such description is necessary for an appreciation of the whole range of such items. It is generally found that a finite and quite small number of data is sufficient to put the ideas of any branch of astrophysics onto a quantitative basis. The following work is intended to be an assembly of such data.

Ready availability

First consideration has been given to presenting the data in a form in which they can be readily found, understood, and used. For this purpose it is essential that all individual results be reduced to one adopted 'best value', or to an averaged smooth curve. The detailed procedure used for weighting the individual results to obtain the adopted value cannot be described in full as this would take up too much space and detract from the systematic presentation of the numerical results themselves. Brief remarks on the averaging procedure are sometimes given, but more generally the reader must rely on the references for any more critical examination of the data.

It is not possible to quote values in all units and normally only one is given. In order to maintain general usefulness it is therefore essential to have conversion factors at hand, and some attention has been paid to this requirement. The conversions are often expressed as formulae and to this extent it has been necessary to insert a number of the more general formulae of astrophysics. However there is no attempt to set out a complete table of basic astrophysical formulae and those included are intended only as a reminder of the inter-relations between the quantities involved.

Avoidance of ambiguity

If one were to avoid ambiguity at all costs it would require a complete definition of every quantity involved. This would not be well suited to a work whose main aim is to give quantitative values, and it has been assumed instead that the quantities mentioned are already understood. Dangers of ambiguity, however, arise from the multiplicity of rather similar units and quantities, and efforts are directed mainly at resolving misunderstandings of this sort. In particular the numerical factors 2 and π are often troublesome, and the definitions given are intended to clear such points.

Another possible source of ambiguity is connected with the multiple meaning of symbols. To counter this difficulty the numbered sections are self-contained as regards terminology, and it should not be necessary to look outside a section for the explanation of a quantity mentioned in it. Certain well-known symbols, however, are used without repeated explanation, and these are collected in § 7.

Other questions of ambiguity in the meaning of symbols and of table and diagram headings are discussed in § 4.

Conciseness

Compactness of tabulation is quite essential in this work, not only to keep the size within reason, but also to allow a more useful presentation. For this purpose the intervals of the arguments are made fairly large, and simple graphical interpolation can be used for intermediate values. Empirical formulae are often used in preference to tables.

A set of reference numbers is used in each section and the references collected at the end.

Generality and completeness

So much progress in astrophysics is dependent on pressing beyond the present boundaries that it becomes necessary to give all data over as wide an argument as possible. Data for the extreme conditions are often not known accurately and must be regarded as provisional. The same applies to a great many quantities that are not directly observable, but they are included where possible. When various estimates differ greatly the results quoted are generally a compromise.

Selected examples are often given of those items that are too numerous for listing completely. When the values describing a certain item vary considerably a mean value is sometimes given.

Accuracy and errors

It would be useful if a statement of the likely error could be attached to every value quoted, but there is no consistent way of deriving such information for most of the data. Error values are given only to the more fundamental quantities, and some of these errors are dependent rather vaguely on the inter-agreement of different estimates. The $\pm$ symbol implies standard error [s.e.] ($= 1 \cdot 4826 \times$ probable error [p.e.]). However, it is intended that the quoted errors should include all sources of departure from the absolute true value. The quoted errors are not necessarily derivable from internal agreement.

Throughout the book some attempt has been made to give an indication of the error by quoting the correct number of digits. The intention is that the standard error should be between 1 and 9 in the last digit.

Versatility and consistency

The absolute values of astrophysical quantities constitute a live and ever-changing subject, and it is necessary to cater for numerical changes. For this reason tabulations are used in preference to diagrams which must be redrawn whenever a value is changed.

For some astronomical undertakings internal consistency among the constants is a matter of major importance. However, it is only possible to produce a set of consistent data by an exhaustive analysis of all information available at a certain date. Once a new value of any constant is accepted an elaborate reshuffle of the values is generally necessary. A strict adherence to consistency would therefore cause a tendency to cling to old-established values and exclude new information. In the present work, on the other hand, the intention is to use new information wherever available. When such new information demands a clear-cut change in other constants the change has been made, but in other cases the change of dependent constants will await further analysis. The inconsistency errors so caused will not usually be greater than the probable error and therefore will not be serious. It is not expected that the values quoted here would be used without modification for an elaborate calculation in which internal consistency was vital.

There are a few constants that have been used so widely that they have achieved the status of conversion factors. These are sometimes quoted, even though they may not now be considered the best values.

Sources of information

There are several reasons for giving the references to the sources of information. They enable the reader to check any data as regards numerical value or meaning. This may be particularly necessary in the present case where the original information is frequently modified to conform to the plan of the tabulation. The references also enable the reader to extend the information to other details not catered for in the present tabulations. Finally, they give some credit to the original worker. Unfortunately it is not possible to give any adequate consideration to the last point since it would require references out of all proportion to the available space. Instead the main endeavour has been to refer to the more recent work on each topic so that through these the earlier work can be traced. The First Edition of *Astrophysical Quantities* (*A.Q.* 1) is quoted extensively and the references at the end of *A.Q.* 1 sections are not usually repeated. The freest use has been made of summary articles in various branches of astrophysics and the references are often directed to these rather than to original work. In the physical sections many data have been obtained from handbooks and tabulations.

Calculation aids

There is no intention of supplying tables for extended routine calculations. A few tables of this type are included (e.g. refraction, precession, and black body radiation tables), but they are intended rather as a means of indicating the values involved than for routine use.

§ 2. General Plan

The subdivisions of the book are almost independent. In any work that deals with a great number of varied concepts it becomes a problem to indicate where each one is defined, and this problem is accentuated when it may be required to extract isolated values as rapidly as possible. It is to cope with this situation that the work is divided into sections (§§) which are self-contained as regards symbols, definitions, and references. There is very little reading matter in any one section, and hence the search for an explanation should be rapid. The size of any section is governed by these considerations.

The tables and diagrams are not numbered separately, but each table or diagram is placed within the appropriate section. The symbols used at the head of a table are described within the section and not necessarily described again in the table. In this respect the script of a section may be regarded as an extended heading to the table.

The references are collected as near to the end of each section as allowed by the tabulation. Often some consideration of smoothness, consistency with other data, extension of material, accuracy, tabular interval, or unit used will effect some change in the figure quoted. A reference number in italics [*123*] implies that the data are taken exclusively from the reference without modification. A reference number not in italics [123] implies only that the reference has been consulted for obtaining the data published. In some sections it is found preferable to list references at the end without attempting to indicate how individual figures were obtained from them.

It is intended that names of chapters and sections should be sufficient for the location of most of the material. For more obscure quantities an index is available. A value may be quoted more than once if that is called for by the arrangement.

The sections §§ 7, 12, 22, 93 may be consulted for symbols, contractions, etc. that are used frequently without redefinition.

§ 3. Quantitative Significance of Symbols

When symbols are to be used for expressing quantitative values it is essential to make it clear whether (*a*) the symbol represents a number which has still to be multiplied by the units before it equals the quantity, or (*b*) the symbol represents the quantity itself. Both systems have some disadvantages.

The difficulty with the first system (*a*) is that a new symbol must be defined for every set of units used. We would not be able to say, for example,

$$\text{density } \rho = 5 \cdot 2 \, \mathcal{M}_\odot \, \text{parsec}^{-3} = 3 \cdot 5 \times 10^{-22} \, \text{g cm}^{-3},$$

but would have to define two symbols for the density. Furthermore, the definition would have to be made in the text, which means that the equation would not be self-contained. The system would therefore lead to clumsy expression which could not be tolerated in the present work.

Instead we adopt the second system (*b*), sometimes known as the Stroud system or quantity calculus [1, 2], and we may write, for example,

$$s = 12 \, \text{cm} = 0 \cdot 12 \, \text{m} = 0 \cdot 394 \, \text{ft}.$$

In simple cases this leads to no mathematical or dimensional ambiguity. For example, in the familiar acceleration equation

$$s = ut + \tfrac{1}{2}at^2$$

we might have the numerical values

$$72 \text{ cm} = 6 \text{ cm s}^{-1} \, 3 \, s + \tfrac{1}{2} \times 12 \text{ cm s}^{-2} \, 9 \text{ s}^2,$$

and we find the dimensions cancel, leaving a clear numerical relation.

However there are some difficulties which should be faced before this system is adopted completely. Consider the case of the Stefan equation

$$\mathscr{F} = \sigma T^4.$$

In order to make the dimensions cancel it is necessary to give the constant σ the dimensions erg cm^{-2} s^{-1} degree^{-4}. One could be quite logical and always give the constants those dimensions that would reduce the quantity equation to a numerical equation. However, this would only add to the confusion, as can be seen if we consider the empirical form of the Rayleigh extinction equation

$$a_\lambda = 0 \cdot 008 \, 2 \, \lambda^{-4 \cdot 05}.$$

To make this complete the numerical constant $0 \cdot 008 \, 2$ must be multiplied by the dimensions cm$^{-1} \, \mu^{4 \cdot 05}$ (where μ = microns). Besides being a very confusing dimension, there is no practical place to write the dimension in the equation. Furthermore, the idea is too unconventional to be useful here. A better method, which we adopt in the present work, is to add the dimensions of those quantities that require them; thus

$$a_\lambda = 0 \cdot 008 \, 2 \, \lambda^{-4 \cdot 05} \quad [a_\lambda \text{ in cm}^{-1}, \lambda \text{ in } \mu].$$

The information in the square brackets then converts the quantities a_λ and λ into numbers. It will be noticed that the algebraic significance of the word 'in' within the square brackets is that the quantity should be 'divided by' the unit. Sometimes, however, the bracket expressions are only a helpful guide. For instance [e in E.S.U.] means that the electrostatic system of units is to be used for the charge e and it must imply (unless otherwise mentioned) that the C.G.S. system is used for the other quantities. Where any expression still appears to be ambiguous it might be assumed that the C.G.S. system is intended.

[1] J. B. HENDERSON, Math. Gaz., 12, 99, 1924.
[2] G. N. COPLEY, Nature, 188, 254, 1960.

§ 4. Headings

Since astrophysics deals with some very large and very small numbers, great use must be made of the powers of 10 in expressing the values. For this purpose it is important to avoid any ambiguity of the sign of the index, and therefore the relation between the heading, the power of ten, the units, and the tabular number must be clearly understood.

The following is an example of a common fault:

Tabular heading $v \times 10^{-8}$ cm/sec
Tabulated numbers   T.

In this case v is a velocity, but it is ambiguous from the heading whether

velocity $= T \times 10^{-8}$ cm/sec
or   velocity $= T \times 10^{8}$ cm/sec.

It is also ambiguous whether v is intended to represent the actual velocity or a number which has to be multiplied by a unit to give the velocity.

In order to use a table (or diagram) quantitatively one has always to construct an equation of the type

quantity $=$ (tabular value) $\times$ (power of 10) $\times$ (unit).

As in any other equation, it is essential that we know on which side of the equation each factor falls, and our headings should be constructed in a way that makes this perfectly clear. In the tabulations that follow we keep as close to this equation as possible by putting the heading or symbol that describes the quantity above the line, and all the factors of the right-hand side of the equation below the line. The line separating the heading from the table is then analogous to the $=$ sign. However, it will not be necessary to read this explanation in order to use the tables without risk of ambiguity.

This procedure has the natural advantage that large numbers have positive indices of 10 and small numbers negative indices. We make an occasional exception to this rule when the quantity concerned is in wide use or has the status of a standard unit. For example, we use the heading $10^{6}W/\lambda$ [W = equivalent width, λ = wavelength] which is not ambiguous.

On the borders of diagrams it is sometimes even more difficult to avoid the same type of ambiguity. As an actual example we quote the diagram border

$$T_e \ (^{\circ}\text{K} \times 10^{-6}).$$

This leaves it uncertain whether the temperatures plotted are of the order 10^{-6} °K or 10^{6} °K. The following forms, however, are unambiguous and satisfactory:

$$T_e \ (\text{unit} = 10^{6} \ ^{\circ}\text{K}),$$
$$v \ (\text{in } 10^{8} \text{ cm/s}),$$
$$\log \rho \ (\rho \text{ in g cm}^{-3}).$$

§ 5. Logarithmic Quantities

In astrophysics great use is made of coefficients of diminution of intensity. These may be expressed in magnitude, exponential, or decadic scales, and these coefficients have the character of dimensions in the equations that arise. There is a danger of not knowing which scale is used unless it is stated with the units. We therefore adopt the notations

$$\text{mag} = \text{magnitude interval,}$$

$$\text{exp} = \text{exponential interval,}$$

$$\text{dex} = \text{interval in powers of 10,}$$

which are inter-related as follows:

$$1 \cdot 085 \ 7 \ \text{mag} = 1 \cdot 000 \ 0 \ \text{exp} = 0 \cdot 434 \ 29 \ \text{dex,}$$

$$2 \cdot 500 \ 0 \ \text{mag} = 2 \cdot 302 \ 6 \ \text{exp} = 1 \cdot 000 \ 00 \ \text{dex.}$$

We could, for example, express the absorption a of s.t.p. ozone at 6000 Å as

$$a = 0 \cdot 068 \ \text{dex/cm} = 0 \cdot 157 \ \text{exp/cm} = -0 \cdot 170 \ \text{mag/cm.}$$

This would follow the policy of putting as much information as possible into the equation. In this form it is preferable to speak of the absorption rather than the absorption coefficient. When the word coefficient is mentioned it immediately raises the question whether the coefficient is exponential or decadic.

The term *dex* in the above notation has been introduced to meet the needs of convenience [1]. Dex converts the number before it into its 10-based antilogarithm. The term can be used for a typographically convenient method of expressing large numbers, as in the example $10^{39} = 39$ dex. It can also be used to introduce verbal simplicity into statements on probable errors, ranges, and variations. The following hypothetical statements illustrate its use: (*a*) the probable error of the density of matter in the universe is $\pm 1 \cdot 5$ dex, (*b*) the frequency range of useful radio-astronomy observations is $3 \cdot 2$ dex, and (*c*) the increase in the distance scale of extra-galactic nebulae as a result of recent researches is $0 \cdot 68$ dex.

Other logarithmic units frequently used for special purposes are:

octave   ($= 0 \cdot 301 \ 03$ dex) for frequency on a binary scale,

decibel   ($= 0 \cdot 100 \ 00$ dex) for noise power on a tenth-decadic scale,

neper [2] ($= 0 \cdot 434 \ 29$ dex) for radiation amplitude on an exponential scale.

If decibels and nepers are both used for radiation then

$$1 \ \text{decibel} = 0 \cdot 115 \ 13 \ \text{nepers.}$$

[1] C. W. ALLEN, *Observatory*, **71**, 157, 1951.
[2] G. McK. ALLCOCK, *The Physics of the Ionosphere*, Report Phys. Soc., p. 14, 1955.

§ 6. Representative Measurements

It is necessary to devise comparative measurements of nearly all objects and phenomena of astronomy no matter what their shape or degree of irregularity.

The position of an object can usually be defined by its centre-of-gravity or by some analogous concept.

For the measurement of size of the more regular objects in the space x it is usual to quote the distance x_{ab} between the points x_a and x_b where some intensity factor $f(x) = mf(x_o)$. Here x_o is the position of maximum intensity and the arbitrarily chosen fraction m is often $\frac{1}{2}$ or $1/e$. This size measurement may be denoted the whole-m-width. If the object is symmetrical in x sometimes the half-measurement from x_o to x_a or x_b is used and therefore denoted the half-m-width. The half-width often used for spectrum lines usually means the whole-$\frac{1}{2}$-width (§ 33). Analogous designations may readily be defined in two or more dimensions. Another measurement, $\int_{-\infty}^{+\infty} f(x)\, dx / f(x_o)$, may also be used and could be denoted equivalent width with respect to the maximum intensity.

For the measurement of the size of an irregular object there is no appropriate value of $f(x_o)$ available. However the size may be defined unambiguously from the distance x_{cd} between the points x_c and x_d such that

$$\int_{x_o}^{x_d} f(x)\, dx = \tfrac{1}{2} \int_{-\infty}^{+\infty} f(x)\, dx$$

and

$$\int_{-\infty}^{x_c} f(x)\, dx = \int_{x_d}^{\infty} f(x)\, dx = \tfrac{1}{4} \int_{-\infty}^{+\infty} f(x)\, dx.$$

In order to give the correct value for a finite uniform length we use $2x_{cd}$ to define the representative length of the object. Similarly in two dimensions, if $2r$ is the diameter of that circle that contains half the total flux from an object then $2\sqrt{(2)}r$ is called the representative diameter.

The measurement of an object whose intensity $f(x)$ varies monotonically with x is usually in terms of a scale height H, such that $f(x)/f(x+H) = e$ (or $1/e$). The advantage of this measurement is that the integral of $f(x)$ from x_1 to ∞ (or $-\infty$) is $Hf(x_1)$.

§ 7. Notation

As far as possible the notation used is in agreement with that recommended by the International Astronomical Union [1], and the International Union of Pure and Applied Physics [2]. The notation is usually described within each section, but a number of symbols are of such generality that it is not thought necessary to define them repeatedly. The notation in this section will be used without further definition when it is thought no ambiguity can arise. Sections (§§) 12, 22, and 93 also give notation in wide use.

Signs

$\simeq$	approximately equal	$\rightarrow$	leads to
$\propto$	varies as	∞	infinity
$\equiv$	equivalent to, means		

$\bar{x}$, $\bar{2}\cdot34$ mean value of x, $0\cdot34-2\cdot00$

$\int_{4\pi} \ldots d\omega$ integration in all directions over solid angle 4π

$\oint$ integration around a closed curve

Astronomical symbols

* Star

⊙	Sun	♂	⊕ Earth	♀	♅ Uranus
☾	Moon	♂	Mars	♆	Neptune
☿	Mercury	♃	Jupiter	♇	Pluto
♀	Venus	♄	Saturn	⚹	Comet

♈	Aries	0°	♌	Leo	120°	♐	Sagittarius	240°
♉	Taurus	30°	♍	Virgo	150°	♑	Capricornus	270°
♊	Gemini	60°	♎	Libra	180°	♒	Aquarius	300°
♋	Cancer	90°	♏	Scorpio	210°	♓	Pisces	330°

☌ Conjunction, having the same longitude or right ascension
▢ Quadrature, differing by 90° in longitude or right ascension
☍ Opposition, differing by 180° in longitude or right ascension
☊ Ascending node (longitude of)
☋ Descending node (longitude of)
♈ First point of Aries

Symbols in frequent use

Italic, Greek, and special type letters are used for symbols.

π	ratio circumference/diameter, parallax (in seconds of arc)
e	exponential base, electron charge (E.S.U. implied), eccentricity
ν, λ	frequency, wavelength
ω	solid angle, angular frequency ($= 2\pi\nu$)
c	velocity of light
t	time
$d\omega, dV, ds, dt$	element of solid angle, volume, length, time
T	temperature
m	mass of electron, apparent magnitude
m_{pv}, m_{pg}, m_{bol}	photovisual, photographic, and bolometric magnitudes

M	absolute magnitude (standardized to 10 pc). Subscripts often added
$\mathscr{M}, \mathscr{R}, \mathscr{L}$	mass, radius, and luminosity of an astronomical object
R	radius, Rydberg wave-number, gas constant, angle of refraction
k	Boltzmann constant, Gaussian gravitational constant
μ	microns, proper motion (in seconds of arc per year)
ρ	density
h	height, altitude, Planck constant ($= 2\pi\hbar$)
N	number of objects (usually per unit volume)
I_v, I_λ	spectral intensity
g	acceleration of gravity, statistical weight
α, δ	right ascension and declination
l, b	galactic longitude and latitude
σ	radiation constant ($\mathscr{F} = \sigma T^4$), standard deviation, cross-section

Units, operations, and dimensions

Roman type where possible.

log	logarithm to the base 10
ln	natural logarithm
dex	power of 10
exp	power of e
μ, cm, m, km	micron, centimetre, metre, kilometre
g	gram
s, h, d, y	second, hour, day, year
°, ′, ″	degree, minute of arc, second of arc
°C, °K	degree Centigrade, degree Kelvin
c, Mc	cycle, mega-cycle
AU	astronomical unit
Å (I.A.)	Angstrom unit (International Angstrom)
p.e.	probable error
s.e.	standard error, or root-mean-square error
s.d.	standard deviation ($= \sigma$)

Decimal multiples and sub-multiples

Factor					Prefix (to place before a unit)	Symbol
10^{12}	$=$	12 dex =	1 000 000 000 000		tera	T
10^{9}	$=$	9 dex =	1 000 000 000		giga	G
10^{6}	$=$	6 dex =	1 000 000		mega	M
10^{5}	$=$	5 dex =	100 000		hecto-kilo	hk
10^{4}	$=$	4 dex =	10 000		myria	ma
10^{3}	$=$	3 dex =	1 000		kilo	k
10^{2}	$=$	2 dex =	100		hecto	h
10	$=$	1 dex =	10		deca	da
1	$=$	0 dex =	1			
10^{-1}	$= -$	1 dex =	0·1		deci	d
10^{-2}	$= -$	2 dex =	0·01		centi	c
10^{-3}	$= -$	3 dex =	0·001	$= 0·0^21$	milli	m
10^{-4}	$= -$	4 dex =	0·000 1	$= 0·0^31$	decimilli or dimi	dm

				Prefix	Symbol
Factor				(to place before a unit)	
10^{-5}	$= -5$ dex $= 0 \cdot 000\ 01$		$= 0 \cdot 0^4 1$	centimilli	cm
10^{-6}	$= -6$ dex $= 0 \cdot 000\ 001$		$= 0 \cdot 0^5 1$	micro	μ
10^{-9}	$= -9$ dex $= 0 \cdot 000\ 000\ 001$		$= 0 \cdot 0^8 1$	nano	n
10^{-12}	$= -12$ dex $= 0 \cdot 000\ 000\ 000\ 001$		$= 0 \cdot 0^{11} 1$	pico	p

For writing large numbers the comma or stop should be reserved for the decimal point only; small intervals may be used to separate each three digits.

Throughout Europe: 1 million   = 6 dex
                      1 milliard   = 9 dex = 1 American billion
                      1 billion   = 12 dex
                      1 trillion   = 18 dex
                      1 quadrillion = 24 dex

[1] *Trans. I.A.U.*, **6**, 345, 1939.
[2] Report by Commission on Symbols, Units, and Nomenclature, Amsterdam, 1948.

CHAPTER 2

GENERAL CONSTANTS AND UNITS

§ 8. Mathematical Constants

Constant	Number	Log
π	3·14159 26536	0·49714 98727
2π	6·28318 53072	0·79817 98684
4π	12·56637 06144	1·09920 98640
π^2	9·86960 44011	0·99429 97454
$\sqrt{\pi}$	1·77245 38509	0·24857 49363
e	2·71828 18285	0·43429 44819
$M = \log e$	0·43429 44819	$\bar{1}$·63778 43113
$1/M = \ln 10$	2·30258 50930	0·36221 56887
2	2·00000 00000	0·30102 99957
$\sqrt{2}$	1·41421 35624	0·15051 49978
$\sqrt{3}$	1·73205 08076	0·23856 06274
$\sqrt{10}$	3·16227 76602	0·50000 00000
$\ln \pi$	1·14472 98858	
Euler constant γ	0·57721 56649	$\bar{1}$·76133 81088
1 radian r	57°·29577 95131	1·75812 26324
$=$	3437'·746 77078	3·53627 38828
$=$	206264"· 80625	5·31442 51332
1°	0^{r}·01745 32925	$\bar{2}$·24187 73676
1'	0^{r}·00029 08882	$\bar{4}$·46372 61172
1"	0^{r}·00000 48481	$\bar{6}$·68557 48668

Square degrees on a sphere $= 129600/\pi = 41252 \cdot 96124$

Square degrees in a steradian $= 32400/\pi^2 = 3282 \cdot 80635$

For Gaussian distribution $\dfrac{1}{\sigma\sqrt{2\pi}}\, e^{-\frac{x^2}{2\sigma^2}}$

Probable error/Standard deviation $= r/\sigma = 0 \cdot 67448\ 97502$

Probable error/Average error $\quad = r/\eta = 0 \cdot 84534\ 75394$

$$\sigma/\eta = 1 \cdot 25331\ 4137$$

[1] *A.Q.* **1**, § 7.
[2] L. J. COMRIE, *Chambers's Six-Figure Mathematical Tables*, 1949.

§ 9. Physical Constants

Fundamental constants

Velocity of light
$$c = (2 \cdot 997\ 929 \pm 0 \cdot 000\ 004) \times 10^{10} \text{ cm/s}$$
$$c^2 = 8 \cdot 987\ 58 \times 10^{20} \text{ cm}^2/\text{s}^2$$

Gravitation constant
$$G = (6 \cdot 668 \pm 0 \cdot 005) \times 10^{-8} \text{ dyn cm}^2 \text{ g}^{-2}$$

Planck constant
$$2\pi\hbar = h = (6 \cdot 625\ 2 \pm 0 \cdot 000\ 2) \times 10^{-27} \text{ erg s}$$

$\hbar \sim pg$ 15

Electron charge

$$e = (4.802\ 88 \pm 0.000\ 09) \times 10^{-10}\ \text{E.S.U.}$$
$$= (1.602\ 07 \pm 0.000\ 03) \times 10^{-20}\ \text{E.M.U.}$$
$$e^2 = 23.067\ 7 \times 10^{-20}\ \text{in E.S.U.}$$
$$e^4 = 5.321\ 17 \times 10^{-38}\ \text{in E.S.U.}$$

Mass of electron

$$m = (9.108\ 4 \pm 0.000\ 3) \times 10^{-28}\ \text{g}$$

Mass of unit atomic weight:

(Chem. scale) $M_0 = (1.660\ 26 \pm 0.000\ 05) \times 10^{-24}\ \text{g}$

Use this one → (Phys. scale) $M_{\text{ph}} = (1.659\ 81 \pm 0.000\ 05) \times 10^{-24}\ \text{g}$

(^{12}C = 12 scale) $= (1.660\ 33 \pm 0.000\ 05) \times 10^{-24}\ \text{g}$

Ratios (Chem./Phys.) $= 1.000\ 276 \pm 0.000\ 005$

(^{12}C/Chem.) [7] $= 1.000\ 037$

(^{12}C/Phys.) [7] $= 1.000\ 318$

Atomic weight ratios are reciprocal to these.

Both chemical and physical scales are in use and standardization awaits the introduction of the ^{12}C scale.

$\frac{3}{2}kT = 12.9\ T_8^{(\text{keV})}$

Boltzmann constant

$$k = (1.380\ 46 \pm 0.000\ 06) \times 10^{-16}\ \text{erg deg}^{-1}.$$
$$= (8.616\ 7 \pm 0.000\ 4) \times 10^{-5}\ \text{ev deg}^{-1}$$

Gas constant (Phys. scale)

$$R = (8.317\ 0 \pm 0.000\ 2) \times 10^7\ \text{erg deg}^{-1}\ \text{mole}^{-1}$$
$$= 1.987\ 1 \pm 0.000\ 2\ \text{cal deg}^{-1}\ \text{mole}^{-1}$$
$$= 82.082\ \text{cm}^3\ \text{atm deg}^{-1}\ \text{mole}^{-1}$$
$$= 62\ 382\ \text{cm}^3\ \text{mm-of-Hg deg}^{-1}\ \text{mole}^{-1}$$

Joule equivalent

$$J = 4.185\ 4 \pm 0.000\ 4\ \text{joule cal}^{-1}$$

Avogadro number:

(Chem. scale) $N_0 = (6.023\ 2 \pm 0.000\ 2) \times 10^{23}\ \text{mole}^{-1}$

(Phys. scale) $= (6.024\ 9 \pm 0.000\ 2) \times 10^{23}\ \text{mole}^{-1}$

Loschmidt number $n_0 = (2.687\ 14 \pm 0.000\ 09) \times 10^{19}\ \text{cm}^{-3}$

Volume of gram-molecule at S.T.P. $V_0 = (22.420\ 7 \pm 0.000\ 5) \times 10^3\ \text{cm}^3\ \text{mole}^{-1}$

Standard atmosphere $A_0 = 1\ 013\ 250\ \text{dyn cm}^{-2} = 760\ \text{mm-of-Hg}$

Ice point [3] $T_0 = 273.150\ ^\circ\text{K}$

Triple point of water $= 273.160\ ^\circ\text{K}$

Faraday constant (Phys.) $= 9652.0 \pm 0.2\ \text{E.M.U. g-equiv.}^{-1}$

Atomic constants

Rydberg constant for ^{1}H $R_\text{H} = 109\ 677.576 \pm 0.011\ \text{cm}^{-1}$ (I.A.)

$1/R_\text{H} = 911.763\ 40$ I.A. (vac.)

Rydberg constant for infinite mass $R_\infty = 2\pi^2 me^4/ch^3$

$$R_\infty = 109\ 737.31 \pm 0.01\ \text{cm}^{-1}$$
$$1/R_\infty = 911.267\ 10\ \text{I.A. (vac.)}$$
$$cR_\infty = 3.289\ 847 \times 10^{15}\ \text{s}^{-1}$$

Fine structure constant $\alpha = 2\pi e^2/hc$

$$\alpha = (7.297\ 29 \pm 0.000\ 03) \times 10^{-3}$$
$$1/\alpha = 137.037\ 3 \pm 0.000\ 6$$
$$\alpha^2 = 5.325\ 04 \times 10^{-5}$$

Radius of first Bohr orbit (infinite mass) $a_0 = h^2/4\pi^2 me^2$

$$a_0 = (0.529\ 172 \pm 0.000\ 002) \times 10^{-8}\ \text{cm}$$

Time for $(2\pi)^{-1}$ revolutions in first Bohr orbit $\tau_0 = m^{1/2}a^{3/2}e^{-1} = h^3/8\pi^3 me^4$

$$\tau_0 = 2\cdot418\ 8 \times 10^{-17}\,\text{s}$$

Frequency of first Bohr orbit $\quad = 6\cdot579\ 8 \times 10^{15}\,\text{s}^{-1}$

Atomic unit of energy (2 Rydbergs) $\ = e^2/a_0 = 2chR_\infty$

$$= 4\cdot359\ 2 \times 10^{-11}\,\text{erg} = 27\cdot21\,\text{ev}$$

Energy of 1 Rydberg (often adopted as atomic unit)

$$= 2\cdot179\ 58 \times 10^{-11}\,\text{erg} = 13\cdot604\ 8\,\text{ev}$$

Area of first Bohr orbit $\quad\quad \pi a_0^2 = 8\cdot797\ 2 \times 10^{-17}\,\text{cm}^2$

Classical electron radius $\quad\quad e^2/mc^2 = 2\cdot817\ 85 \times 10^{-13}\,\text{cm}$

Atomic unit of angular momentum $\hbar = h/2\pi$

$$\hbar = 1\cdot054\ 43 \times 10^{-27}\,\text{g cm}^2\,\text{s}^{-1}$$

Electron speed in first Bohr orbit $\quad = 6.582 \times 10^{-16}\,\text{ev-sec}$

$$a_0\tau_0^{-1} = 2\cdot187\ 7 \times 10^8\,\text{cm s}^{-1}$$

Schrödinger constant for fixed nucleus

$$8\pi^2 mh^{-2} = 1\cdot638\ 38 \times 10^{27}\,\text{erg}^{-1}\,\text{cm}^{-2}$$

Schrödinger constant for ^{1}H atom $\quad = 1\cdot637\ 5 \times 10^{27}\,\text{erg}^{-1}\,\text{cm}^{-2}$

Hyperfine structure splitting of ^{1}H ground state [6]

$$\nu_\text{H} = (1\ 420\cdot405\ 75 \pm 0\cdot000\ 08) \times 10^6\,\text{s}^{-1}$$

Doublet separation in ^{1}H $\quad (1/16)R_\text{H}\alpha^2[1+\alpha/\pi+(5/8-5\cdot946/\pi^2)\alpha^2]$

$$= 0\cdot365\ 871 \pm 0\cdot000\ 002\,\text{cm}^{-1}$$

Electron-proton distance in ground state of ^{1}H

$$a_0(1-\alpha^2)^{1/2}R_\infty/R_\text{H} = (0\cdot529\ 446 \pm 0\cdot000\ 002) \times 10^{-8}\,\text{cm}$$

Radius of electron orbit in ground state of ^{1}H (ref. centre of mass)

$$a_0(1-\alpha^2)^{1/2} = (0\cdot529\ 158 \pm 0\cdot000\ 002) \times 10^{-8}\,\text{cm}$$

Reduced mass of electron in ^{1}H atom

$$m(m_\text{p}/m_\text{H}) = (9\cdot103\ 4 \pm 0\cdot000\ 3) \times 10^{-28}\,\text{g}$$

Atomic specific heat constant $= c_2/c = h/k$

$$= (4\cdot799\ 3 \pm 0\cdot000\ 2) \times 10^{-11}\,\text{s deg}$$

Multiplier of (Curie constant)$^{1/2}$ to give magnetic moment per molecule

$$(3k/N)^{1/2} = (2\cdot621\ 78 \pm 0\cdot000\ 10)$$
$$\times 10^{-20}\,(\text{erg mole deg}^{-1})^{1/2}$$

Magnetic moment of 1 Bohr magneton $\mu_\text{B} = \tfrac{1}{2}\alpha m^{1/2}a_0^{5/2}\tau_0^{-1} = he/4\pi mc$

$$\mu_\text{B} = (0\cdot927\ 31 \pm 0\cdot000\ 02) \times 10^{-20}\,\text{erg gauss}^{-1}$$

Magnetic moment of 1 nuclear magneton $\mu_\text{K} = \mu_\text{B}(m/m_\text{p})$

$$\mu_\text{K} = 5\cdot050\ 4 \times 10^{-24}\,\text{erg gauss}^{-1}$$

Atomic unit of magnetic moment $\quad = m^{1/2}a_0^{5/2}\tau_0^{-1} = he/2\pi mc\alpha$

$$= 2\cdot541 \times 10^{-18}\,\text{erg gauss}^{-1}$$

Magnetic moment per mole of 1 Bohr magneton per molecule

$$= 5\ 587\,\text{erg gauss}^{-1}\,\text{mole}^{-1}$$

Zeeman displacement $= e/4\pi mc$ [e in E.M.U.]

$$= (4\cdot668\ 85 \pm 0\cdot000\ 06) \times 10^{-5}\,\text{cm}^{-1}\,\text{gauss}^{-1}$$

Mass energy of unit atomic mass (Phys. scale)

$$M_\text{ph}c^2 = 1\cdot491\ 77 \times 10^{-3}\,\text{erg}$$
$$= 931\cdot145\,\text{Mev}$$

Rest mass energy of electron $\quad\quad = 8 \cdot 186\ 2 \times 10^{-7}$ erg
$$= 0 \cdot 510\ 976 \text{ Mev}$$

Mass ratio proton/electron $\quad m_p/m = 1\ 836 \cdot 12 \pm 0 \cdot 02$

Mass of ^{1}H atom $\quad\quad\quad\quad\quad\quad = 1 \cdot 673\ 33 \times 10^{-24}$ g

Atomic weight of electron (Phys. scale)
$$= (5 \cdot 487\ 61 \pm 0 \cdot 000\ 04) \times 10^{-4}$$

Specific electron charge $\quad\quad e/m = 1 \cdot 758\ 88 \times 10^7$ E.M.U. g^{-1}
$$= 5 \cdot 273\ 02 \times 10^{17} \text{ E.S.U. g}^{-1}$$
$$h/e = 1 \cdot 379\ 43 \times 10^{-17} \text{ erg s E.S.U.}^{-1}$$
$$h/m = 7 \cdot 273\ 78 \text{ cm}^2 \text{ s}^{-1}$$

Compton wavelength $\quad\quad\quad h/mc = (2 \cdot 426\ 26 \pm 0 \cdot 000\ 03) \times 10^{-10}$ cm
$$h/2\pi mc = 3 \cdot 861\ 51 \times 10^{-11} \text{ cm}$$

Sakur-Tetrode constant (Phys. scale) $= -5 \cdot 573\ 24\ R$

Band spectrum constant (moment of inertia/wave number)
$$h/8\pi^2 c = 27 \cdot 989 \times 10^{-40} \text{ g cm}$$

The electron-volt and photons

Wavelength associated with 1 electron-volt (1 ev)
$$\lambda_0 = (12\ 397 \cdot 7 \pm 0 \cdot 2) \times 10^{-8} \text{ cm}$$

Wave number associated with 1 ev
$$s_0 = 8\ 066 \cdot 02 \pm 0 \cdot 14 \text{ cm}^{-1}$$

Frequency associated with 1 ev $= 10^8 e/hc$
$$\nu_0 = 2 \cdot 418\ 14 \times 10^{14} \text{ s}^{-1}$$

Energy of 1 ev $\quad\quad\quad\quad E_0 = (1 \cdot 602\ 07 \pm 0 \cdot 000\ 03) \times 10^{-12}$ erg

Photon energy associated with unit wave number
$$hc = 1 \cdot 986\ 20 \times 10^{-16} \text{ erg}$$

Photon energy associated with wavelength λ
$$= 1 \cdot 986\ 20 \times 10^{-8}/\lambda \text{ erg} \quad [\lambda \text{ in Å vac.}]$$

Speed of 1 ev electron $= \{2 \times 10^8 (e/mc)\}^{1/2}$
$$= 5 \cdot 931\ 1 \times 10^7 \text{ cm s}^{-1}$$
$$\text{velocity}^2 = 3 \cdot 517\ 8 \times 10^{15} \text{ cm}^2 \text{ s}^{-2}$$

Wavelength of electron of energy V in ev $= h(2mE_0)^{-1/2}V^{-1/2}$
$$= V^{-1/2}(12 \cdot 264 \times 10^{-8}) \text{ cm}$$

Energy associated with 1 °K $= k/E_0$
$$= 0 \cdot 861\ 67 \times 10^{-4} \text{ ev}$$

Temperature associated with 1 ev $= E_0/k$
$$= 11\ 605 \cdot 4 \text{ °K}$$

Temperature associated with 1 ev in common logs $= (E_0/k) \log e$
$$= 5\ 040 \cdot 2 \text{ °K} \quad (5040.13\ °K)$$

Energy of 1 ev per molecule (Chem. scale)
$$= 23\ 055 \text{ cal mole}^{-1}$$

Radiation constants

Radiation density constant $= 8\pi^5 k^4/15c^3 h^3$
$$a = (7 \cdot 564\ 1 \pm 0 \cdot 000\ 9) \times 10^{-15} \text{ erg cm}^{-3} \text{ deg}^{-4}$$

Stefan-Boltzmann constant $= ac/4$
$$\sigma = (5 \cdot 669\ 2 \pm 0 \cdot 000\ 7) \times 10^{-5} \text{ erg cm}^{-2} \text{ deg}^{-4} \text{ s}^{-1}$$

E w/ $10^8\ °K = 8.6167$ keV $\quad\quad\quad \frac{\sigma}{\pi} =$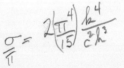

First radiation constant (emittance) $= 2\pi hc^2$
$$c_1 = (3\cdot741\ 2 \pm 0\cdot000\ 2) \times 10^{-5}\ \text{erg cm}^2\ \text{s}^{-1}$$
First radiation constant (radiation density) $= 8\pi hc$
$$c_1' = (4\cdot991\ 8 \pm 0\cdot000\ 2) \times 10^{-15}\ \text{erg cm}$$
Second radiation constant $= hc/k$
$$c_2 = 1\cdot438\ 79 \pm 0\cdot000\ 05\ \text{cm deg}$$
Wien displacement law constant $= c_2/4\cdot965\ 114\ 23$
$$= 0\cdot289\ 780\ \text{cm deg}$$
Mechanical equivalent of light at $\lambda = 5550\ \text{Å}$
$$= 0\cdot001\ 47 \pm 0\cdot000\ 05\ \text{watt/lumen}$$

Some general constants

Density of mercury (0 °C, 760 mm) [5]
$$= 13\cdot595\ 080\ \text{g cm}^{-3}$$

Ratio, grating to Siegbahn scale of x-ray wavelengths
$$\lambda_g/\lambda_s = 1\cdot002\ 03 \pm 0\cdot000\ 02$$

Grating space of calcite (20 °C) $= (3\cdot035\ 66 \pm 0\cdot000\ 05) \times 10^{-8}\ \text{cm}$

Density of calcite (20 °C) $= 2\cdot710\ 30 \pm 0\cdot000\ 03\ \text{g cm}^{-3}$

Maximum density of water $= 0\cdot999\ 972 \pm 0\cdot000\ 004\ \text{g cm}^{-3}$

Caesium resonator frequency $= 9\ 192\ 631\ 770 \pm 20\ \text{c/s}$

[1] *A.Q.* **1**, § 8.
[2] J. A. BEARDEN and J. S. THOMSEN, *Nuovo Cimento*, **5**, Suppl., 267, 1957; *American J. Phys.* **27**, 569, 1959.
[3] E. R. COHEN, CROWE, and DuMOND, *Fundamental Constants of Physics*, Interscience, 1957.
[4] E. R. COHEN and J. W. M. DuMOND, *Handb. der Phys.* **35**, 1, 1957.
[5] A. H. COOK and N. W. B. STONE, *Phil. Trans.*, A **250**, 279, 1957; **254**, 125, 1961.
[6] J. H. SANDERS, *The Fundamental Atomic Constants*, O.U.P., 1961.
[7] Private communication from National Bureau of Standards, U.S.A.

§ 10. General Astronomical Constants

Astronomical unit of distance = mean sun-earth distance = semi-major axis of earth orbit [1, 8], § 75 $\text{AU} = (1\cdot495\ 985 \pm 0\cdot000\ 005) \times 10^{13}\ \text{cm}$

Parsec pc $= 206\ 264\cdot8\ \text{AU}$ $\text{pc} = (3\cdot085\ 6 \pm 0\cdot000\ 1) \times 10^{18}\ \text{cm}$
$$= 3\cdot261\ 5\ \text{light year}$$

Light year $\text{ly} = 9\cdot460\ 5 \times 10^{17}\ \text{cm} = 6\cdot324 \times 10^4\ \text{AU}$

Light time for 1 AU $= 498\cdot99\ \text{s} = 0\cdot005\ 775\ 3\ \text{d}$

Solar mass $\mathcal{M}_\odot = (1\cdot989 \pm 0\cdot002) \times 10^{33}\ \text{g}$

Solar radius $\mathcal{R}_\odot = (6\cdot959\ 8 \pm 0\cdot000\ 7) \times 10^{10}\ \text{cm}$

Solar radiation $\mathcal{L}_\odot = (3\cdot90 \pm 0\cdot04) \times 10^{33}\ \text{erg/s}$

Earth mass $\mathcal{M}_\oplus = (5\cdot977 \pm 0\cdot004) \times 10^{27}\ \text{g}$

Earth mean density $\bar{\rho}_\oplus = 5\cdot517 \pm 0\cdot004\ \text{g cm}^{-3}$

Earth equatorial radius $= 6\ 378\cdot17 \pm 0\cdot04\ \text{km}$

Galactic pole $\alpha = 191°\cdot65$ $\delta = +27°\cdot67$ (1900)
in agreement with IAU coordinates [7]

Direction of galactic centre $\alpha = 264°\cdot83$ $\delta = -28°\cdot90$ (1900)

Solar motion   velocity $= 20{\cdot}0 \pm 0{\cdot}5$ km/s

$\qquad$ apex $\quad \alpha = 271^\circ \pm 2^\circ \qquad\qquad \delta = +30^\circ \pm {}^\circ1$

$\qquad\qquad l^{\mathrm{II}} = 57^\circ \qquad\qquad\qquad b^{\mathrm{II}} = +22^\circ$

Galactic rotation constants $P = +0''{\cdot}39 \pm 0''{\cdot}02$ per century

$\qquad\qquad\qquad\qquad\qquad\qquad Q = -0''{\cdot}15 \pm 0''{\cdot}03$ per century

Sun's equatorial horizontal parallax [1, 2, 8], § 75

$\qquad\qquad\qquad\qquad\qquad = 8''{\cdot}794\ 15 \pm 0''{\cdot}000\ 05$

$\qquad\qquad\qquad\qquad\qquad = 4{\cdot}263\ 52 \times 10^{-5}$ radians

Moon's equatorial horizontal parallax (see § 69)

$\qquad\qquad\qquad\qquad\qquad = 3\ 422''{\cdot}62$

Constant of nutation $= 9''{\cdot}207 \pm 0''{\cdot}001$

Constant of aberration $= \dfrac{2\pi \times 206\ 265 \times \mathrm{AU}}{ct(1-e^2)^{1/2}}$ [2, 4]

$\qquad\qquad\qquad\qquad\qquad = 20''{\cdot}49$

($t =$ sid. y, $e =$ earth orb. eccentricity)

Constant of precession [6] $= 5\ 493''{\cdot}6 - 0''{\cdot}003\ 6\ T$

$\qquad$ where T is epoch in tropical centuries from 1900$\cdot$0

Gaussian gravitational constant k in $a^3 n^2 = k^2(1+m)$, where $m =$ mass of planet in solar units, $n =$ mean daily motion, and $a =$ semi-major axis in AU [6]

$\qquad\qquad\qquad\qquad k = 0{\cdot}017\ 202\ 098\ 95$ radian

$\qquad\qquad\qquad\qquad\ \ = 3\ 548''{\cdot}187\ 607$

$\qquad\qquad\qquad\qquad\ \ = 0^\circ{\cdot}985\ 607\ 668\ 6$

Semi-major axis of earth orbit in terms of AU defined by gaussian constant [5]

$\qquad\qquad\qquad\qquad\qquad = 1{\cdot}000\ 000\ 23$ AU

Parallactic inequality [6] $= 125''{\cdot}05 \pm 0''{\cdot}01$

Constant of lunar inequality (observed)

$\qquad\qquad\qquad\qquad L = 6''{\cdot}438 \pm 0''{\cdot}002$

Lunar inequality in sun's longitude (observed)

$\qquad\qquad\qquad\qquad L_s = 6''{\cdot}467 \pm 0''{\cdot}002 = L \times 1{\cdot}004\ 5$

Mass ratios [1, 6] $\mathscr{M}_\oplus / \mathscr{M}_{\mathbb{C}} = 81{\cdot}33 \pm 0{\cdot}03$

$\qquad\qquad\qquad\qquad\quad \mathscr{M}_\odot / \mathscr{M}_\oplus = 332\ 700$

$\qquad\qquad\quad \mathscr{M}_\odot / (\mathscr{M}_\oplus + \mathscr{M}_{\mathbb{C}}) = 328\ 700$

Obliquity of ecliptic (instantaneous ecliptic)

$\qquad\qquad\qquad \epsilon = 23^\circ\ 27'\ 8''{\cdot}26 - 46''{\cdot}84\ T - 0''{\cdot}004\ T^2$

$\qquad\qquad\qquad\qquad\qquad + 0''{\cdot}001\ 8\ T^3$

Obliquity of ecliptic (fixed ecliptic of 1900$\cdot$0)

$\qquad\qquad\qquad \epsilon_1 = 23^\circ\ 27'\ 8''{\cdot}26 + 0''{\cdot}061\ T^2 - 0''{\cdot}007\ 7\ T^3$

$\qquad\qquad \sin \epsilon$ or ϵ_1 (1900) $= 0{\cdot}397\ 986$

$\qquad\qquad \cos \epsilon$ or ϵ_1 (1900) $= 0{\cdot}917\ 392$

[1] *A.Q.*1, § 9.
[2] E. RABE, *A.J.* 59, 409, 1954.
[3] J. V. EVANS, *Obs.* 80, 9, 1960.
[4] E. FICHERA and P. MELCHIOR, *Comm. Ob. R. Belg.* No. 135, 1958.
[5] R. M. BAKER and M. W. MAKEMSON, *Astrodynamics*, p. 83, Academic Press, 1960.
[6] D. BROUWER and G. M. CLEMENCE, *Planets and Satellites*, ed. Kuiper and Middlehurst, p. 31, Chicago, 1961.
[7] A. BLAAUW, C. S. GUM, et al., *M.N.* 121, 123, 1960.
[8] D. O. MUHLEMAN, HOLDRIDGE and BLOCK, *A.J.* 67, 191, 1962.

§ 11. Astronomical Constants involving Time

As a result of deceleration and unevenness of the earth's rotation, universal time t_U does not represent a constant rate. Consequently an ephemeris time t_E with a constant rate has been defined for physical and astronomical purposes [2]. The two measures of time are related by

$$t_E - t_U = 24^s \!\cdot\! 35 + 72^s \!\cdot\! 32 \ T + 29^s \!\cdot\! 95 \ T^2 + 1^s \!\cdot\! 821 \ B$$

where T is in Julian centuries of 36 525 days from 1900 Jan 0·5 u.t., and B is the fluctuation in the moon's longitude (unit $= 1''$). The term $1^s \!\cdot\! 821 \ B$ is attributable to the irregular fluctuation in the rate of the earth's rotation, $29^s \!\cdot\! 95 \ T^2$ represents the earth's deceleration, and the other two terms bring t_E and t_U into approximate agreement at the epoch 1900. The fluctuation B cannot be predicted with any certainty.

Mean solar second (smoothed)/ephemeris second
$$s_U/s_E = (1 - \Delta\nu/\nu) = 1 + 1 \!\cdot\! 90 \times 10^{-8} \ T$$

Difference between ephemeris and universal time and rate [4]

Epoch	$t_E - t_U$	$\Delta\nu/\nu$	Epoch	$t_E - t_U$	$\Delta\nu/\nu$	Epoch	$t_E - t_U$	$\Delta\nu/\nu$	Epoch	$t_E - t_U$	$\Delta\nu/\nu$
	s	10^{-8}		s	10^{-8}		s	10^{-8}		s	10^{-8}
1810·0	+4·4		1850·0	+2·2	−0·6	1890·0	− 7·6	+0·3	1930·0	+23·1	−0·4
1815	+3·6		1855	+3·4	−0·4	1895	− 7·3	−0·9	1935	+23·6	0·0
1820	+4·0	+1·7	1860	+3·7	+0·4	1900	− 4·5	−3·4	1940	+24·0	−1·0
1825	+2·9	+1·1	1865	+1·7	+1·3	1905	+ 2·6	−4·6	1945	+26·2	−1·6
1830	+1·7	+0·6	1870	−1·0	+3·5	1910	+ 9·6	−4·4	1950	+29·2	−1·6
1835	+0·2	+1·3	1875	−6·8	+2·1	1915	+15·8	−3·4	1955	+31·3	−1·6
1840	+0·3	−0·7	1880	−7·7	+0·2	1920	+20·1	−2·1	1960	+34	
1845	+1·0	−0·8	1885	−7·9	−0·3	1925	+22·5	−0·8	1965	+37	

Day

Period of rotation of earth (referred to fixed stars)
$$= (86 \ 164 \!\cdot\! 098 \ 92 + 0 \!\cdot\! 001 \ 64 \ T) \ s_E$$
$$= 23^h \ 56^m \ 04^s \!\cdot\! 098 \ 92 + 0 \!\cdot\! 001 \ 64 \ T \ s$$
$$= (0 \!\cdot\! 997 \ 269 \ 663 \ 4 + 1 \!\cdot\! 90 \times 10^{-8} \ T) \ d$$
$$= (1 \!\cdot\! 002 \ 737 \ 811 - 1 \!\cdot\! 90 \times 10^{-8} \ T)^{-1} \ d$$
$$= 1 \!\cdot\! 0 + (971 + 0 \!\cdot\! 59 \ T) \times 10^{-10} \text{ mean sid. d}$$

Sidereal day (referred to γ)
$$= (86 \ 164 \!\cdot\! 090 \ 56 + 0 \!\cdot\! 001 \ 6 \ T) \ s$$
$$= (1 \!\cdot\! 002 \ 737 \ 909 - 1 \!\cdot\! 90 \times 10^{-8} \ T)^{-1} \ d$$

Motion of mean sun in R.A., measured from a fixed equinox, in an ephemeris day
$$= 3 \ 548'' \!\cdot\! 204 \ 205$$

Sidereal mean motion of sun in longitude per ephemeris day [2]
$$= 3 \ 548'' \!\cdot\! 192 \ 782 \ 3 - 0'' \!\cdot\! 000 \ 001 \ T$$

Motion of mean sun in tropical longitude per ephemeris day
$$= 3 \ 548'' \!\cdot\! 330 \ 407 + 0'' \!\cdot\! 000 \ 060 \ T$$

Mean rotation of earth in an ephemeris day [2] ($= 86 \ 400 \ s_E$)
$$= 1 \ 299 \ 548'' \!\cdot\! 204 \ 205 - 0'' \!\cdot\! 024 \ 6 \ T$$

Mean solar day
$$= (86 \ 400 + 0 \!\cdot\! 001 \ 6 \ T) \ s_E$$
$$= 24^h \ 03^m \ 56^s \!\cdot\! 555 \text{ sidereal time}$$
$$= 1 \!\cdot\! 002 \ 737 \ 91 \text{ sidereal days}$$

Seasonal variation of earth rotation [5]

$$\text{earth rotation} = 21 \sin \frac{2\pi}{365} (d-17) + 10 \sin \frac{4\pi}{365} (d-93)$$

millisec slow

where d is day of the year

Year

Tropical year (equinox to equinox) [2]
$$= (365 \cdot 242\ 198\ 78 - 0 \cdot 000\ 006\ 16\ T) \text{ ephemeris days}$$
$$= (3 \cdot 155\ 692\ 597\ 47 \times 10^7 - 0 \cdot 530\ T) \text{ s}_\text{E}$$

Sidereal year (fixed stars) [2]
$$= (365 \cdot 256\ 365\ 56 + 0 \cdot 000\ 000\ 11\ T) \text{ ephemeris days}$$
$$= (3 \cdot 155\ 814\ 998\ 4 \times 10^7 + 0 \cdot 010\ T) \text{ s}_\text{E}$$

Time for 360° R.A. movement of mean sun measured from a fixed equinox
$$= 365 \cdot 255\ 189\ 7 \text{ ephemeris days}$$

Anomalistic year (perihelion to perihelion)
$$= (365 \cdot 259\ 641\ 34 + 0 \cdot 000\ 003\ 04\ T) \text{ ephemeris days}$$

Eclipse year
$$= (346 \cdot 620\ 031 + 0 \cdot 000\ 032\ T) \text{ ephemeris days}$$

Julian year
$$= 365 \cdot 25 \text{ days}$$

Gregorian calendar year
$$= 365 \cdot 242\ 5 \text{ days}$$

Commencement of Besselian year [1] (when mean sun R.A. $= 18^\text{h}\ 40^\text{m}$) $=$ Jan $0^\text{d} \cdot 813\ 516 + 0^\text{d} \cdot 242\ 198\ 78\ (x - 1900) - 0^\text{d} \cdot 000\ 308\ T^2 - n$ where $n =$ number of leap years between the year x and 1900 not counting x

Period of a comet or asteroid
$$= 1 \cdot 000\ 040\ 27\ a^{3/2} \text{ tropical years}$$
$$= 365 \cdot 265\ 898\ a^{3/2} \text{ d}$$

Moon (other data in § 69)

Synodical month (new moon to new moon)
$$= (29 \cdot 530\ 588\ 2 - 0 \cdot 000\ 000\ 2\ T) \text{ d}$$

Sidereal month (fixed stars)
$$= (27 \cdot 321\ 661\ 0 - 0 \cdot 000\ 000\ 2\ T) \text{ d}$$

Period of moon's node, nutation period
$$= 18 \cdot 61 \text{ tropical years}$$

Precession. The precessional constants from [2] have been reduced slightly. The epoch T is in tropical centuries from 1900·0. $N =$ Newcomb value.

Constant of precession $\qquad P = 5\ 493'' \cdot 6 - 0'' \cdot 003\ 6\ T \quad [= N + 2'' \cdot 9]$

Centennial luni-solar precession $\quad p_0 = 5\ 039'' \cdot 8 + 0'' \cdot 493\ T \quad [= N + 2'' \cdot 7]$

Geodetic precession (a relativity effect [6])
$$p_\text{g} = 1'' \cdot 92$$
$$p_1 = p_0 - p_\text{g} = 5\ 037'' \cdot 9 + 0'' \cdot 493\ T \quad [= N + 0'' \cdot 8]$$

Centennial precession in longitude $\quad p = 5\ 026'' \cdot 4 + 2'' \cdot 225\ T \quad [= N + 0'' \cdot 8]$

Planetary precession $\qquad \lambda = 12'' \cdot 47 - 1'' \cdot 889\ T$

Centennial precession in R.A. $\qquad m = 4\ 609 \cdot 2 + 2'' \cdot 797\ T \quad [= N + 0'' \cdot 7]$
$$= 307^\text{s} \cdot 28 + 0^\text{s} \cdot 186\ 5\ T$$

Centennial precession in dec $n = 2\ 005''{\cdot}0 - 0''{\cdot}854\ T$ $[\ = N + 0''{\cdot}4]$

Period of precession (fixed ecliptic) $= 25\ 725$ years
                    (moving ecliptic) $= 25\ 784$ years

Longitude of node of moving on fixed ecliptic [1]
$$\Pi = 173°\ 57'\ 10'' + 3\ 289''\ T$$

Speed of rotation of ecliptic per century [1]
$$d\pi/dT = 47''{\cdot}11 - 0''{\cdot}071\ T + 0''{\cdot}000\ 6\ T^2$$
$$\pi \sin \Pi = 4''{\cdot}96\ T + 0''{\cdot}194\ T^2 - 0''{\cdot}000\ 2\ T^3$$
$$\pi \cos \Pi = -\ 46''{\cdot}84\ T + 0''{\cdot}054\ T^2 + 0''{\cdot}000\ 3\ T^3$$

[1] A.Q. **1**, § 10.
[2] G. M. Clemence, A.J., **53**, 169, 1948; Sky and Tel., **19**, 148, 1960.
[3] D. Brouwer, A.J., **57**, 125, 1952.
[4] Explanatory Supplement to the Ephemeris.
[5] H. M. Smith and R. H. Tucker, M.N., **113**, 251, 1953.
[6] A. S. Eddington, Math. Theory of Relativity, p. 99, Cambridge, 1952.

§ 12. Units

Units are expressed in C.G.S. system: cm, g, and s

Length

Metre (M.K.S. unit)	$m = 100$ cm
Kilometre	$km = 10^5$ cm
X-ray unit (Siegbahn)	$x.u. = 1{\cdot}002\ 03 \times 10^{-11}$ cm
Angstrom unit	$Å = 10^{-8}$ cm $= 10^{-10}$ m
Micron	$\mu = 10^{-4}$ cm $= 10^{-6}$ m
Atomic unit	$a_0 = 0{\cdot}529\ 17 \times 10^{-8}$ cm
Astronomical unit	$AU = 1{\cdot}495\ 98 \times 10^{13}$ cm
Light year	$ly = 9{\cdot}460 \times 10^{17}$ cm $= 63\ 240$ AU
Parsec	$pc = 3{\cdot}085\ 6 \times 10^{18}$ cm
	$= 206\ 265$ AU $= 3{\cdot}262$ ly
Megaparsec	$Mpc = 1\ 000\ 000$ pc $= 1\ 000$ kpc
Foot	$ft = 30{\cdot}480\ 0$ cm $= 12 \times 2{\cdot}540\ 005\ 1$ cm (U.S.)
	$= 12 \times 2{\cdot}539\ 996\ 5$ cm (Brit.)
Inch (adopted here)	$= 2{\cdot}540\ 000$ cm
Mile	$= 1{\cdot}609\ 344$ km
Nautical mile (International) [2]	$= 6\ 076{\cdot}11$ ft $= 1{\cdot}852\ 0$ km
Solar radius	$\mathscr{R}_\odot = 6{\cdot}960 \times 10^{10}$ cm
Classical electron radius	$l = 2{\cdot}817\ 8 \times 10^{-13}$ cm

Area

Square foot	$ft^2 = 929{\cdot}03$ cm²
Acre	$= 4\ 046{\cdot}85$ m² $= 43\ 560$ ft²
Barn	$= 10^{-24}$ cm²
Area 1st Bohr orbit	$\pi a_0^2 = 8{\cdot}797\ 2 \times 10^{-17}$ cm²

3—A.Q.

Volume

Cubic foot	ft^3	$= 28\ 316 \cdot 9 \text{ cm}^3$
		$= 6 \cdot 229$ British gallons $= 7 \cdot 481$ U.S. gallons
Litre		$= 1\ 000 \cdot 027 \text{ cm}^3$
Fluid ounce $= 480$ minims (British)		$= 28 \cdot 413 \text{ cm}^3$
Fluid ounce $= 480$ minims (U.S.)		$= 29 \cdot 573\ 7 \text{ cm}^3 = 29 \cdot 572\ 9$ millilitres
Solar volume	$\frac{4}{3}\pi \mathscr{R}_\odot^3$	$= 1 \cdot 412\ 2 \times 10^{33} \text{ cm}^3$
Cubic parsec		$= 2 \cdot 937\ 8 \times 10^{55} \text{ cm}^3$

Time

Second	s	$= \text{C.G.S. unit} = \text{M.K.S. unit}$
Ephemeris second	s_E	$= 1/31\ 556\ 925 \cdot 974\ 7$ of a tropical year for 1900·0
Hour	h	$= 3\ 600\ s = 60$ min
Day	d	$= 86\ 400\ s$
Tropical year	y	$= 3 \cdot 155\ 692\ 6 \times 10^7\ s$
		$= 365 \cdot 242\ 20\ d$
Sidereal second		$= 0 \cdot 997\ 269\ 6\ s$
Sidereal year		$= 365 \cdot 256\ 36\ d$
Atomic unit (1st Bohr period/2π)	τ_0	$= 2 \cdot 418\ 8 \times 10^{-17}\ s$
Jordan's elementary time	l/c	$= 9 \cdot 399 \times 10^{-24}\ s$

Mass

Kilogram (M.K.S. unit)	kg	$= 1\ 000\ g$
Pound avoirdupois (British)	lb	$= 453 \cdot 592\ 37\ g = 7\ 000$ grains
„ „ (U.S.)		$= 453 \cdot 592\ 43\ g = 7\ 000$ grains
Pound troy and apothecary		$= 373 \cdot 242\ g = 5\ 760$ grains
Grain (all systems)		$= 0 \cdot 064\ 798\ 9\ g$
Carat		$= 0 \cdot 200\ 0\ g$
Ton $= 2\ 240\ lb$		$= 1 \cdot 016\ 047 \times 10^6\ g$
Solar mass	$\mathscr{M}_\odot$	$= 1 \cdot 989 \times 10^{33}\ g$
Atomic unit (electron)	m	$= 9 \cdot 108 \times 10^{-28}\ g$
Mass of unit atomic weight (chem. or ^{12}C scale)		
		$= 1 \cdot 660\ 3 \times 10^{-24}\ g$

Energy

Joule (M.K.S. unit)	J	$= 10^7$ erg
Calorie	cal	$= 4 \cdot 185\ 4 \times 10^7$ erg $= 4 \cdot 185\ 4$ J (absolute)
Kilowatt-hour (absolute)		$= 3 \cdot 600 \times 10^{13}$ erg $= 8 \cdot 601\ 3 \times 10^5$ cal
British thermal unit	B.T.U.	$= 1 \cdot 055 \times 10^{10}$ erg $= 252 \cdot 0$ cal
Therm		$= 100\ 000$ B.T.U.
Foot-pound		$= 1 \cdot 355\ 82 \times 10^7$ erg
Kiloton of TNT		$= 4 \cdot 2 \times 10^{19}$ erg

Joule ratio (international/absolute)
$$pq^2 = 1 \cdot 000 \ 17$$

Electron volt $E_0 = \text{ev} = 1 \cdot 602 \ 1 \times 10^{-12} \text{ erg} = 10^{-6} \text{ Mev}$
$$= 10^{-9} \text{ Gev, Bev or kMev}$$

Atomic unit (2 Rydbergs) $= 4 \cdot 359 \ 2 \times 10^{-11} \text{ erg}$

Rydberg energy $= 2 \cdot 179 \ 6 \times 10^{-11} \text{ erg}$

Energy of unit wave number $= 1 \cdot 986 \ 2 \times 10^{-16} \text{ erg}$

Mass energy of unit atomic weight $= 1 \cdot 491 \ 8 \times 10^{-3} \text{ erg} = 9 \cdot 311 \ 4 \times 10^8 \text{ ev}$

Energy associated with 1 °K $k = 1 \cdot 380 \ 5 \times 10^{-16} \text{ erg} = 0 \cdot 861 \ 67 \times 10^{-4} \text{ ev}$

Power

Watt (M.K.S. unit) $\text{W} = 10^7 \text{ erg/s} = \text{J/s}$

British horse-power $= 745 \cdot 7 \text{ watt} = 7 \cdot 457 \times 10^9 \text{ erg/s}$

Force de cheval $= 735 \cdot 5 \text{ watt}$

Watt ratio (international/absolute)
$$pq^2 = 1 \cdot 000 \ 17$$

Star, $M_{\text{bol}} = 0$, radiation $= 3 \cdot 02 \times 10^{28} \text{ watt}$

Solar luminosity $= 3 \cdot 90 \times 10^{26} \text{ watt}$

Force

Newton (M.K.S. unit) $\text{N} = 10^5 \text{ dyn}$

Poundal $= 1 \cdot 382 \ 5 \times 10^4 \text{ dyn}$

Pound weight $= 4 \cdot 448 \ 2 \times 10^5 \text{ dyn}$

Gramme weight $= 980 \cdot 665 \text{ dyn}$

Proton-electron attraction at distance a_0
$$= 8 \cdot 238 \times 10^{-3} \text{ dyn}$$

Acceleration

Gal $= 1 \text{ cm s}^{-2}$

Gravity (standard) $g = 980 \cdot 665 \text{ cm s}^{-2} = 32 \cdot 174 \text{ ft s}^{-2}$

Sun's surface $= 2 \cdot 740 \times 10^4 \text{ cm s}^{-2}$

At 1 AU from sun $= 0 \cdot 593 \ 0 \text{ cm s}^{-2}$

Velocity

Metre per sec (M.K.S. unit) $= 100 \text{ cm/s}$

Mile per hour $= 44 \cdot 704 \text{ cm/s} = 1 \cdot 466 \ 7 \text{ ft/s}$

Velocity of light $c = 2 \cdot 997 \ 93 \times 10^{10} \text{ cm/s}$

AU per year $= 4 \cdot 741 \text{ km/s}$

Parsec per year $= 9 \cdot 780 \times 10^{10} \text{ cm/s}$

Electron in 1st Bohr orbit $= 2 \cdot 188 \times 10^8 \text{ cm/s}$

Knot $= 51 \cdot 45 \text{ cm/s}$

Pressure

Pascal (M.K.S. unit) $= 10 \text{ dyn cm}^{-2} = 10 \ \mu\text{b}$

Barye (occasionally called Bar) $\mu\text{b} = 1 \cdot 000 \text{ dyn cm}^{-}$

Bar $\qquad$ bar $= 1 \cdot 000 \times 10^6$ dyn cm^{-2} $= 0 \cdot 986\ 927$ atm
$\qquad = 1 \cdot 019\ 7 \times 10^3$ g-weight cm^{-2}

Millibar $\qquad$ mb $= 10^{-3}$ bar $= 10^3\ \mu$b $= 10^3$ dyn cm^{-2}

Atmosphere (standard) $\qquad$ atm $= 1 \cdot 013\ 250 \times 10^6$ dyn cm^{-2}
$\qquad = 760$ mm-Hg $= 1\ 013 \cdot 250$ mb

Millimetre of mercury ($= 1$ Torr)
$\qquad$ mm-Hg $= 1\ 333 \cdot 22$ dyn cm^{-2} $= 0 \cdot 001\ 315\ 8$ atm

Inch of mercury $\qquad = 3 \cdot 386\ 38 \times 10^4$ dyn cm^{-2} $= 0 \cdot 033\ 421$ atm

Pound per sq. inch $\qquad = 6 \cdot 894\ 7 \times 10^4$ dyn cm^{-2} $= 0 \cdot 068\ 046$ atm

Density

Kilogram/cubic metre (M.K.S. unit) $\qquad = 1 \cdot 000 \times 10^{-3}$ g cm^{-3}

Density of water (4 °C) $\qquad = 0 \cdot 999\ 972$ g cm^{-3}

Density of mercury (0 °C) $\qquad = 13 \cdot 595\ 1$ g cm^{-3}

Solar mass/cubic parsec $\qquad = 6 \cdot 770 \times 10^{-23}$ g cm^{-3}

S.T.P. gas density $\qquad = 4 \cdot 461\ 4 \times 10^{-5}\ M_0$ g cm^{-3}
$\qquad$ where M_0 is molecular weight

Temperature

0 °C $= 32$° F $\qquad = 273 \cdot 155$ °K

100 °C $= 212$° F $\qquad = 373 \cdot 155$ °K

Elementary temperature $\qquad ch/lk = 8 \cdot 125 \times 10^{11}$ °K

Temperature associated with 1 ev
$\qquad E_0/k = 11\ 605$ °K

Fixed points at atm. pressure

Oxygen	B.P. $= -182 \cdot 970$ °C	Gold	M.P. $= 1\ 063 \cdot 0$ °C
Water	M.P. $= 0 \cdot 000$ °C	Platinum	M.P. $= 2\ 042$ °K
Sulphur	M.P. $= 444 \cdot 600$ °C	Rhodium	M.P. $= 2\ 233$ °K
Silver	M.P. $= 960 \cdot 8$ °C	Iridium	M.P. $= 2\ 716$ °K

Viscosity (dynamic)

Poise $\qquad$ P $= 1$ g cm^{-1} s^{-1}

Decapoise (M.K.S. unit) $\qquad = 10$ g cm^{-1} s^{-1}

Viscosity (kinematic)

Myriastokes (M.K.S. unit) $\qquad = 10\ 000$ cm^2 s^{-1}

Frequency

Hertz ($=$ cycle/s) $\qquad$ Hz $= 1$ c/s

Megacycle $\qquad$ Mc/s $= 10^6$ c/s

Rydberg frequency $\qquad cR_\infty = 3 \cdot 290 \times 10^{15}$ c/s

Frequency of 1st Bohr orbit $\qquad = 6 \cdot 580 \times 10^{15}$ c/s

Frequency of electron in magnetic field $\mathscr{H}$
$\qquad = 2 \cdot 800 \times 10^6\ \mathscr{H}$ c/s gauss^{-1}

Unit wave-number (in $cm^{-1} = $ kayser)
$$= 2 \cdot 997\ 93 \times 10^{10} \text{ c/s}$$

Angular velocity $(= 2\pi\ frequency)$

Unit angular velocity	$= 1 \text{ rad/s} \equiv (1/2\pi) \text{ c/s}$
$1''$ of arc per tropical year	$= 1 \cdot 536\ 314\ 68 \times 10^{-13} \text{ rad/s}$
$1''$ of arc per day	$= 5 \cdot 611\ 269\ 46 \times 10^{-11} \text{ rad/s}$
Angular velocity of earth on its axis	$= 7 \cdot 292\ 115\ 15 \times 10^{-5} \text{ rad/s}$

Mean angular velocity of earth in its orbit
$$= 1 \cdot 990\ 986\ 58 \times 10^{-7} \text{ rad/s}$$

Momentum

M.K.S. unit	$= 10^5 \text{ g cm s}^{-1}$
mc	$= 2 \cdot 730\ 6 \times 10^{-17} \text{ g cm s}^{-1}$
Electron momentum in 1st Bohr orbit	$= 1 \cdot 992\ 6 \times 10^{-19} \text{ g cm s}^{-1}$

Angular momentum

M.K.S. unit	$= 10^7 \text{ g cm}^2 \text{ s}^{-1}$
Quantum unit $(1/2\pi)h = \hbar$	$= 1 \cdot 054\ 4 \times 10^{-27} \text{ g cm}^2 \text{ s}^{-1}$

Homogeneous sphere, $R =$ radius, $\mathscr{M} =$ mass, $\omega =$ angular velocity
$$= \tfrac{2}{5}R^2 \mathscr{M} \omega$$

Luminous flux

Lumen (M.K.S. or C.G.S. unit) is defined as the luminous flux from an area of $\dfrac{1}{60\pi} \text{ cm}^2$
of a black body surface at the temperature of melting platinum (2 042 °K)

Lumen $lm = (1/4\pi)$ flux from 1 spherical candle

Lumen of maximum visibility radiation (5550 Å)
$$= 1 \cdot 47 \times 10^{-3} \text{ watt}$$

Luminous energy

Talbot (M.K.S. unit)	$= 1 \text{ lumerg (C.G.S. unit)}$
	$= 1 \text{ lumen second}$

Luminous intensity

Luminous intensity is defined as the luminous emission per unit solid angle

Candela (new candle)	$cd = 1 \text{ lumen radian}^{-2} = 1 \text{ lumen sterad}^{-1}$

1 projected cm^2 black body at temperature of melting platinum (2 042 °K)
$$= 60 \text{ cd}$$

International candle	$= 1 \cdot 019 \text{ cd}$
Hefner candle	$= 0 \cdot 903 \text{ cd}$

Star, $M_v = 0$ outside earth atmosphere
$$= 2 \cdot 5 \times 10^{29} \text{ cd}$$

Surface brightness (Luminance)

Stilb	$sb = 1 \text{ cd cm}^{-2} = \pi \text{ lambert}$
	$= 1 \text{ lumen cm}^{-2} \text{ sterad}^{-1}$
Lambert	$= (1/\pi) \text{ cd cm}^{-2} = 1\,000 \text{ millilambert}$
	$\equiv 1 \text{ lumen cm}^{-2} \text{ for perfectly diffusing surface}$
Apostilb	$= 1 \text{ lumen m}^{-2} \text{ for perfectly diffusing surface}$
Nit (M.K.S. unit)	$= 10^{-4} \text{ sb} = 10^{-4} \text{ cd cm}^{-2}$
Candle per sq. inch	$= 0.486\,95 \text{ lambert} = 0.155\,00 \text{ stilb}$
Foot-lambert	$= 1.076\,4 \times 10^{-3} \text{ lambert} = 3.426 \times 10^{-4} \text{ stilb}$

$1\ m_\mathrm{v} = 0$ star per sq. deg
    outside atmosphere $= 0.87 \times 10^{-6} \text{ stilb}$
    inside clear unit air mass $= 0.72 \times 10^{-6} \text{ stilb}$

Luminous emittance (of a surface)

Lumen per sq. metre (M.K.S. unit) $= 10^{-4} \text{ lumen cm}^{-2}$

Illuminance (light received per unit surface)

Phot (C.G.S. unit)	$= 1 \text{ lumen cm}^{-2}$
Lux (M.K.S. unit)	$lx = 1 \text{ lumen m}^{-2} = 10^{-4} \text{ phot}$
	$= 1 \text{ metre-candle}$
Foot-candle	$= 10.764 \text{ metre-candle} = 1.076\,4 \times 10^{-3} \text{ phot}$
	$= 10.764 \text{ lux} = 1 \text{ lumen ft}^{-2}$

Star, $m_\mathrm{v} = 0$, outside earth atmosphere
                     $= 2.65 \times 10^{-10} \text{ phot}$

Electric charge

The general inter-relations between electric and magnetic units are given in § 13.

Coulomb (M.K.S. unit) $C = 2.997\,93 \times 10^9 \text{ E.S.U.} = 0.10 \text{ E.M.U.}$

Coulomb ratio (international/absolute)
                     $q = 0.999\,84$

Electron charge $e = 4.802\,9 \times 10^{-10} \text{ E.S.U.} = 1.602\,1 \times 10^{-19} \text{ C}$

Electric potential

Volt (M.K.S. unit) $V = 3.335\,6 \times 10^{-3} \text{ E.S.U.} = 10^8 \text{ E.M.U.}$

Potential of electron in 1st Bohr orbit
                     $= 27.21 \text{ volt} = 0.090\,76 \text{ E.S.U.}$

H ionization potential $= 13.60 \text{ volt} = 0.045\,38 \text{ E.S.U.}$

Volt ratio (international/absolute) $pq = 1.000\,33$

Electric field

Volt per metre (M.K.S. unit) $= 3.335\,6 \times 10^{-5} \text{ E.S.U.} = 10^6 \text{ E.M.U.}$

Nuclear field at 1st Bohr orbit $= 5.140 \times 10^{11} \text{ volt/m} = 1.714\,5 \times 10^7 \text{ E.S.U.}$

Resistance

Ohm (M.K.S. unit) $\Omega = 1.112\,7 \times 10^{-12} \text{ E.S.U.} = 10^9 \text{ E.M.U.}$

Ohm ratio (international/absolute) $p = 1.000\,49$

Electric current

Ampere (M.K.S. unit) $A = 2.997\ 93 \times 10^9$ E.S.U.

Current in 1st Bohr orbit $= 1.054\ 0 \times 10^{-3}\ A = 3.160 \times 10^6$ E.S.U.

Ampere ratio (international/absolute)

$$q = 0.999\ 84$$

Electric dipole moment

Coulomb-metre (M.K.S. unit) $C\text{-}m = 2.997\ 9 \times 10^{11}$ E.S.U. $= 10$ E.M.U.

Dipole moment of nucleus and electron in 1st Bohr orbit

$$= 0.847\ 8 \times 10^{-29}\ C\text{-}m = 2.541\ 6 \times 10^{-18}\ \text{E.S.U.}$$

Magnetic field

Ampere-turn per metre (M.K.S. unit, rationalized)

$$= 4\pi \times 10^{-3} \text{ oersted} \quad [\text{oersted} = \text{E.M.U.}]$$
$$= 3.767 \times 10^8 \text{ E.S.U.}$$

Gauss (in free space) $= 1$ oersted $= 79.58$ amp-turn/m

Gamma $\gamma = 10^{-5}$ oersted

Atomic unit ($m^{1/2}a_0^{-1/2}\tau_0^{-1}$) $= 1.715 \times 10^7$ gauss

Field at nucleus due to electron in 1st Bohr orbit

$$(\alpha m^{1/2}a_0^{-1/2}\tau_0^{-1}) = 1.251 \times 10^5 \text{ oersted}$$

Magnetic moment

Weber-metre (M.K.S. unit, rationalized)

$$= (1/4\pi)10^{10} \text{ E.M.U.} = 0.026\ 54 \text{ E.S.U.}$$
$$[\text{E.M.U.} = \text{erg gauss}^{-1}]$$

Atomic unit ($m^{1/2}a_0^{5/2}\tau_0^{-1}$) $= 2.542 \times 10^{-18}$ erg gauss^{-1}

Bohr magneton, magnetic moment of electron in 1st Bohr orbit

$$\mu_B = (\tfrac{1}{2}\alpha m^{1/2}a_0^{5/2}\tau_0^{-1}) = 0.927\ 4 \times 10^{-20} \text{ erg gauss}^{-1}$$

Nuclear magneton $\mu_K = \mu_B(m/m_p) = 5.050 \times 10^{-24}$ erg gauss^{-1}

Earth magnetic moment $= 8.06 \times 10^{25}$ erg gauss^{-1}

[1] *A.Q.* **1**, § 11.
[2] *Sky and Tel.*, **13**, 427, 1954.

§ 13. Electric and Magnetic Unit Relations

In the table comparing electric and magnetic units the approximation $c = 3 \times 10^{10}$ cm/s has been adopted, but this can be readily converted into the more accurate $c = 2.997\ 93 \times 10^{10}$ cm/s if required. In the defining equations s = length, a = area, v = volume, t = time, E = energy, W = power, and r = radial distance.

For unrationalized M.K.S. units the second column should be introduced, and the names of the units may need to be changed. For rationalized units this column should be omitted.

Electric and

Quantity and symbol		M.K.S. Unit			E.S.U.
		unration-alized	rationalized	sym-bol	
Charge	Q	$1 \times$	1 coulomb	C	$= 3 \times 10^9$ E.S.U.
Current	I	$1 \times$	1 ampere	A	$= 3 \times 10^9$ E.S.U.
Potential, E.M.F.	V	$1 \times$	1 volt	V	$= \frac{1}{3} \times 10^{-2}$ E.S.U.
Electric Field	$\mathcal{E}$	$1 \times$	1 volt/m		$= \frac{1}{3} \times 10^{-4}$ E.S.U.
Resistance	R	$1 \times$	1 ohm	Ω	$= \frac{1}{9} \times 10^{-11}$ E.S.U.
Resistivity	ρ	$1 \times$	1 ohm m		$= \frac{1}{9} \times 10^{-9}$ E.S.U.
Conductance	G	$1 \times$	1 mho	$\mho$	$= 9 \times 10^{11}$ E.S.U.
Conductivity	σ	$1 \times$	1 mho/m		$= 9 \times 10^9$ E.S.U.
Capacitance	C	$1 \times$	1 farad	F	$= 9 \times 10^{11}$ cm
Electric flux	Ψ	$4\pi \times$	1 coulomb	C	$= 12\pi \times 10^9$ E.S.U.
Electric flux density, displacement	D	$4\pi \times$	1 coulomb/m^2		$= 12\pi \times 10^5$ E.S.U.
Polarization	P	$1 \times$	1 coulomb/m^2		$= 3 \times 10^5$ E.S.U.
Electric dipole moment	p	$1 \times$	1 coulomb m		$= 3 \times 10^{11}$ E.S.U.
Permittivity, dielectric const.	ϵ	$4\pi \times$	1 farad/m		$= 36\pi \times 10^9$ E.S.U.
Permittivity of free space	ϵ_0	$4\pi \times$	$\frac{1}{36\pi} \times 10^{-9}$ F/m		$= 1$ E.S.U.
Inductance	L	$1 \times$	1 henry	H	$= \frac{1}{9} \times 10^{-11}$ E.S.U.
Magnetic pole strength	m	$1/4\pi \times$	1 weber	Wb	$= \frac{1}{12\pi} \times 10^{-2}$ E.S.U.
Magnetic flux	Φ	$1 \times$	1 weber	Wb	$= \frac{1}{3} \times 10^{-2}$ E.S.U.
Magnetic field	$\mathcal{H}$	$4\pi \times$	1 ampere turn/m		$= 12\pi \times 10^7$ E.S.U.
Magnetomotive force, mag.-potential	$\mathcal{F}$	$4\pi \times$	1 ampere turn	AT	$= 12\pi \times 10^9$ E.S.U.
Magnetic moment	M	$1/4\pi \times$	1 weber m		$= \frac{1}{12\pi}$ E.S.U.
Magnetic flux density, mag.-induction	B	$1 \times$	1 weber/m^2		$= \frac{1}{3} \times 10^{-6}$ E.S.U.
Intensity of magnetization	J	$1/4\pi \times$	1 weber/m^2		$= \frac{1}{12\pi} \times 10^{-6}$ E.S.U.
Permeance	Λ	$1/4\pi \times$	1 henry		$= \frac{1}{36\pi} \times 10^{-11}$ E.S.U.
Reluctance	S	$4\pi \times$	1 AT/Wb		$= 36\pi \times 10^{11}$ E.S.U.
Permeability	μ	$1/4\pi \times$	1 henry/m		$= \frac{1}{36\pi} \times 10^{-13}$ E.S.U.
Permeability of free space	μ_0	$1/4\pi \times$	$4\pi \times 10^{-7}$ H/m		$= \frac{1}{9} \times 10^{-20}$ E.S.U.

Until 1930 the term oersted was used for the E.M.U. of reluctance. It is now used for the E.M.U. of magnetic field, but it is found sometimes applied to the M.K.S. unit. The E.M.U. of magnetic field was previously called gauss, but this term is now used for magnetic flux density or magnetic induction.

magnetic units

E.M.U.	Dimensions													M.K.S. rationalized, defining equation
	E.S.U.				E.M.U.				E.S.U./E.M.U.	M.K.S.				
	L	M	T	κ	L	M	T	μ		L	M	T	Q	
$=10^{-1}$ E.M.U.	$\frac{3}{2}$	$\frac{1}{2}$	-1	$\frac{1}{2}$	$\frac{1}{2}$	$\frac{1}{2}$	0	$-\frac{1}{2}$	$1/c$	0	0	0	1	Q
$=10^{-1}$ E.M.U.	$\frac{3}{2}$	$\frac{1}{2}$	-2	$\frac{1}{2}$	$\frac{1}{2}$	$\frac{1}{2}$	-1	$-\frac{1}{2}$	$1/c$	0	0	-1	1	$I = dQ/dt$
$=10^{8}$ E.M.U.	$\frac{1}{2}$	$\frac{1}{2}$	-1	$-\frac{1}{2}$	$\frac{3}{2}$	$\frac{1}{2}$	-2	$\frac{1}{2}$	c	2	1	-2	-1	$V = IR$
$=10^{6}$ E.M.U.	$-\frac{1}{2}$	$\frac{1}{2}$	-1	$-\frac{1}{2}$	$\frac{1}{2}$	$\frac{1}{2}$	-2	$\frac{1}{2}$	c	1	1	-2	-1	$\mathscr{E} = -\Delta V$
$=10^{9}$ E.M.U.	-1	0	1	-1	1	0	-1	1	c^2	2	1	-1	-2	$R = W/I^2$
$=10^{11}$ E.M.U.	0	0	1	-1	2	0	-1	1	c^2	3	1	-1	-2	$\rho = Ra/s$
$=10^{-9}$ E.M.U.	1	0	-1	1	-1	0	1	-1	$1/c^2$	-2	-1	1	2	$G = \sigma a/s$
$=10^{-11}$ E.M.U.	0	0	-1	1	-2	0	1	-1	$1/c^2$	-3	-1	1	2	$\sigma = 1/\rho$
$=10^{-9}$ E.M.U.	1	0	0	1	-1	0	2	-1	$1/c^2$	-2	-1	2	2	$C = Q/V$
$=4\pi \times 10^{-1}$ E.M.U.	$\frac{3}{2}$	$\frac{1}{2}$	-1	$\frac{1}{2}$	$\frac{1}{2}$	$\frac{1}{2}$	0	$-\frac{1}{2}$	$1/c$	0	0	0	1	$\Psi = Q$
$=4\pi \times 10^{-5}$ E.M.U.	$-\frac{1}{2}$	$\frac{1}{2}$	-1	$\frac{1}{2}$	$-\frac{3}{2}$	$\frac{1}{2}$	0	$-\frac{1}{2}$	$1/c$	-2	0	0	1	$D = Q/4\pi r^2$
$=10^{-5}$ E.M.U.	$-\frac{1}{2}$	$\frac{1}{2}$	-1	$\frac{1}{2}$	$-\frac{3}{2}$	$\frac{1}{2}$	0	$-\frac{1}{2}$	$1/c$	-2	0	0	1	$P = p/v$
$=10$ E.M.U.	$\frac{5}{2}$	$\frac{1}{2}$	-1	$\frac{1}{2}$	$\frac{3}{2}$	$\frac{1}{2}$	0	$-\frac{1}{2}$	$1/c$	1	0	0	1	$p = sQ$
$=4\pi \times 10^{-11}$ E.M.U.	0	0	0	1	-2	0	2	-1	$1/c^2$	-3	-1	2	2	$\epsilon = D/\mathscr{E}$
$=\frac{1}{9} \times 10^{-20}$ E.M.U.									$1/c^2$					
$=10^{9}$ cm	-1	0	2	-1	1	0	0	1	c^2	2	1	0	-2	$E = \frac{1}{2}LI^2$
$=\frac{1}{4\pi} \times 10^{8}$ E.M.U.	$\frac{1}{2}$	$\frac{1}{2}$	0	$-\frac{1}{2}$	$\frac{3}{2}$	$\frac{1}{2}$	-1	$\frac{1}{2}$	c	2	1	-1	-1	$m = \Phi$
$=10^{8}$ maxwell	$\frac{1}{2}$	$\frac{1}{2}$	0	$-\frac{1}{2}$	$\frac{3}{2}$	$\frac{1}{2}$	-1	$\frac{1}{2}$	c	2	1	-1	-1	$V = d\Phi/dt$
$=4\pi \times 10^{-3}$ oersted	$\frac{1}{2}$	$\frac{1}{2}$	-2	$\frac{1}{2}$	$-\frac{1}{2}$	$\frac{1}{2}$	-1	$-\frac{1}{2}$	$1/c$	-1	0	-1	1	$\oint \mathscr{H}\, ds = I$
$=4\pi \times 10^{-1}$ gilbert	$\frac{3}{2}$	$\frac{1}{2}$	-2	$\frac{1}{2}$	$\frac{1}{2}$	$\frac{1}{2}$	-1	$-\frac{1}{2}$	$1/c$	0	0	-1	1	$\mathscr{F} = \int \mathscr{H}\, ds$
$=\frac{1}{4\pi} \times 10^{10}$ E.M.U.	$\frac{3}{2}$	$\frac{1}{2}$	0	$-\frac{1}{2}$	$\frac{5}{2}$	$\frac{1}{2}$	-1	$\frac{1}{2}$	c	3	1	-1	-1	$M = sm$
$=10^{4}$ gauss	$-\frac{3}{2}$	$\frac{1}{2}$	0	$-\frac{1}{2}$	$-\frac{1}{2}$	$\frac{1}{2}$	-1	$\frac{1}{2}$	c	0	1	-1	-1	$B = \Phi/a$
$=\frac{1}{4\pi} \times 10^{4}$ E.M.U.	$-\frac{3}{2}$	$\frac{1}{2}$	0	$-\frac{1}{2}$	$-\frac{1}{2}$	$\frac{1}{2}$	-1	$\frac{1}{2}$	c	0	1	-1	-1	$J = M/v$
$=\frac{1}{4\pi} \times 10^{9}$ E.M.U.	-1	0	2	-1	1	0	0	1	c^2	2	1	0	-2	$\Lambda = 1/S$
$=4\pi \times 10^{-9}$ E.M.U.	1	0	-2	1	-1	0	0	-1	$1/c^2$	-2	-1	0	2	$S = \oint \dfrac{ds}{\mu a}$
$=\frac{1}{4\pi} \times 10^{7}$ E.M.U.	-2	0	2	-1	0	0	0	1	c^2	1	1	0	-2	$\mu = B/\mathscr{H}$
$=1$ E.M.U.									c^2					

[1] *A.Q.* **1**, § 12.
[2] R. K. Sas and F. B. Pidduck, *M.K.S. Units*, Methuen, 1947.
[3] T. McGreevy, *The M.K.S. System of Units*, Pitman, 1953.

CHAPTER 3

ATOMS

§ 14. Elements, Atomic Weights, Isotopes and Cosmic Abundance

ALTERNATIVE symbols for elements are quoted in parenthesis. Some alternative names are as follows: 1, ^{2}H = Deuterium; 1, ^{3}H = Tritium; 4, Be = Glucinium (Gl); 41, Nb = Columbium (Cb); 43, Tc = Masurium (Ma); 61, Pm = Illium (Il); 71, Lu = Cassiopium; 86, Rn = Niton, Thoron, Actinon (various emanations).

Atomic weights quoted are on the chemical scale; on the physical scale the values would be larger by a factor 1·000 28; on the ^{12}C scale they would be smaller by the factor 0·999 96.

Only stable isotopes are listed. They are in order of abundance and those less than 1% are in parenthesis.

The cosmic abundance is derived from the sun, stars, nebulae, meteorites, and the earth's crust. The absolute values are based on 12·00 dex for H.

Mean atomic weight for cosmic material = 1·40.

Composition of cosmic material by weight
$$X = \text{fraction of H} = 0·63$$
$$Y = \text{fraction of He} = 0·36$$
$$Z = \text{fraction of other atoms} = 0·014$$

Ratio of hydrogen to metals by number [2]
$$A = \text{H/metals} = 1·35 \times 10^4$$

Element	Symbol	Atomic number	Atomic weight (chem.) [1, 3]	Stable isotopes [1, 7]	Log cosmic abundance Number [1, 2, 3, 4, 5, 6]	Log cosmic abundance Weight
Hydrogen	H	1	1·008 01	1, (2)	12·00	12·00
Helium	He	2	4·002 8	4, (3)	11·16	11·76
Lithium	Li	3	6·939	7, 6	3	4
Beryllium	Be (Gl)	4	9·013	9	2·4	3·4
Boron	B	5	10·812	11, 10	2·8	3·8
Carbon	C	6	12·011 61	12, 13	8·48	9·56
Nitrogen	N	7	14·007 3	14, (15)	7·96	9·11
Oxygen	O	8	16·000 0	16, (18, 17)	8·83	10·03
Fluorine	F	9	18·999 2	19	5·4	6·7
Neon	Ne	10	20·184	20, 22, (21)	8·44	9·74
Sodium	Na	11	22·991	23	6·22	7·58
Magnesium	Mg	12	24·313	24, 26, 25	7·46	8·84
Aluminium	Al	13	26·982	27	6·28	7·71
Silicon	Si	14	28·09	28, 29, 30	7·47	8·92
Phosphorus	P	15	30·975	31	5·53	7·02

Element	Symbol	Atomic number	Atomic weight (chem.) [1, 3]	Stable isotopes [1, 7]	Log cosmic abundance Number [1, 2, 3, 4, 5, 6]	Log cosmic abundance Weight [1, 2, 3, 4, 5, 6]
Sulphur	S	16	32·066	32, 34, (33, 36)	7·22	8·72
Chlorine	Cl	17	35·454	35, 37	5·4	6·9
Argon	Ar (A)	18	39·949	40, (36, 38)	6·62	8·22
Potassium	K	19	39·103	39, (41, 40)	4·88	6·47
Calcium	Ca	20	40·08	40, 44, (42, 48, 43, 46)	6·22	7·82
Scandium	Sc	21	44·958	45	2·91	4·56
Titanium	Ti	22	47·90	48, 46, 47, 49, 50	4·82	6·50
Vanadium	V	23	50·944	51, (50)	3·78	5·48
Chromium	Cr	24	52·00	52, 53, 50, 54	5·38	7·09
Manganese	Mn	25	54·940	55	5·10	6·84
Iron	Fe	26	55·849	56, 54, 57, (58)	6·90	8·65
Cobalt	Co	27	58·935 6	59	4·72	6·49
Nickel	Ni	28	58·71	58, 60, 62, 61, 64	5·93	7·70
Copper	Cu	29	63·55	63, 65	4·65	6·45
Zinc	Zn	30	65·37	64, 66, 68, 67, (70)	4·28	6·09
Gallium	Ga	31	69·72	69, 71	2·45	4·29
Germanium	Ge	32	72·60	74, 72, 70, 76, 73	3·18	5·04
Arsenic	As	33	74·924 2	75	2·3	4·2
Selenium	Se	34	78·96	80, 78, 82, 76, 77, (74)	3·2	5·1
Bromine	Br	35	79·912	79, 81	2·6	4·5
Krypton	Kr	36	83·80	84, 86, 82, 83, 80, (78)	3·2	5·1
Rubidium	Rb	37	85·48	85, 87	2·35	4·28
Strontium	Sr	38	87·63	88, 86, 87, (84)	2·75	4·69
Yttrium	Y	39	88·908	89	2·40	4·34
Zirconium	Zr	40	91·22	90, 94, 92, 91, 96	2·4	4·4
Niobium	Nb (Cb)	41	92·91	93	1·7	3·7
Molybdenum	Mo	42	95·95	98, 96, 92, 95, 100, 97, 94	1·92	3·90
Technetium	Tc (Ma)	43	99		—	—
Ruthenium	Ru	44	101·07	102, 104, 101, 99, 100, 96, 98	1·52	3·52
Rhodium	Rh	45	102·91	103	0·78	2·79
Palladium	Pd	46	106·4	106, 108, 105, 110, 104, (102)	1·25	3·28
Silver	Ag	47	107·874	107, 109	0·7	2·7
Cadmium	Cd	48	112·41	114, 112, 111, 110, 113, 116, 106, (108)	1·50	3·55
Indium	In	49	114·82	115, 113	0·9	3·0
Tin	Sn	50	118·70	120, 118, 116, 119, 117, 124, 122, (112, 114, 115)	1·55	3·62

Element	Symbol	Atomic number	Atomic weight (chem.) [1, 3]	Stable isotopes [1, 7]	Log cosmic abundance	
					Number [1, 2, 3, 4, 5, 6]	Weight
Antimony	Sb	51	121·76	121, 123	1·6	3·7
Tellurium	Te	52	127·61	130, 128, 126, 125, 124, 122, (123, 120)	2·0	4·1
Iodine	I (J)	53	126·909	127	1·4	3·5
Xenon	Xe (X)	54	131·30	132, 129, 131, 134, 136, 130, 128, (124, 126)	2·0	4·1
Caesium	Cs	55	132·910	133	1·1	3·2
Barium	Ba	56	137·35	138, 137, 136, 135, 134, (130, 132)	2·11	4·25
Lanthanum	La	57	138·92	139, (138)	1·4	3·5
Cerium	Ce	58	140·13	140, 142, (138, 136)	1·6	3·7
Praseodymium	Pr	59	140·913	141	0·8	3·0
Neodymium	Nd	60	144·25	142, 144, 146, 143, 145, 148, 150	1·5	3·7
Promethium	Pm (Il)	61	147		—	—
Samarium	Sm (Sa)	62	150·36	152, 154, 147, 149, 148, 150, 144	1·0	3·2
Europium	Eu	63	151·96	153, 151	0·7	2·9
Gadolinium	Gd	64	157·25	158, 160, 156, 157, 155, 154, (152)	1·1	3·3
Terbium	Tb	65	158·930	159	0·4	2·6
Dysprosium	Dy (Ds)	66	162·50	164, 162, 163, 161, 160, (158, 156)	1·2	3·4
Holmium	Ho	67	164·937	165	0·5	2·7
Erbium	Er	68	167·27	166, 168, 167, 170, 164, (162)	0·9	3·2
Thulium	Tm (Tu)	69	168·941	169	0·1	2·3
Ytterbium	Yb	70	173·04	174, 172, 173, 171, 176, 170, (168)	1·1	3·3
Lutecium	Lu (Cp)	71	174·98	175, 176	0·3	2·5
Hafnium	Hf	72	178·50	180, 178, 177, 179, 176, (174)	0·6	2·8
Tantalum	Ta	73	180·955	181	0·3	2·6
Tungsten	W	74	183·86	184, 186, 182, 183, (180)	1·1	3·4
Rhenium	Re	75	186·3	187, 185	0·6	2·9
Osmium	Os	76	190·2	192, 190, 189, 188, 187, 186, (184)	1·3	3·6
Iridium	Ir	77	192·2	193, 191	1·2	3·5
Platinum	Pt	78	195·10	195, 194, 196, 198, (192)	1·6	3·9
Gold	Au	79	196·977	197	0·7	3·0
Mercury	Hg	80	200·60	202, 200, 199, 201, 198, 204, (196)	0·9	3·2

Element	Symbol	Atomic number	Atomic weight (chem.) [1, 3]	Stable isotopes [1, 7]	Log cosmic abundance	
					Number [1, 2, 3, 4, 5, 6]	Weight
Thallium	Tl	81	204·38	205, 203	0·5	2·8
Lead	Pb	82	207·20	208, 206, 207, 204	1·6	3·9
Bismuth	Bi	83	208·988	209	0·7	3·0
Polonium	Po	84	210		—	—
Astatine	At	85	211		—	—
Radon	Rn	86	222		—	—
Francium	Fr (Fa)	87	223		—	—
Radium	Ra	88	226·05		—	—
Actinium	Ac	89	227		—	—
Thorium	Th	90	232·047	232	0·3	2·7
Protactinium	Pa	91	231		—	—
Uranium	U (Ur)	92	238·04	238, (235, 234)	0·0	2·4
Neptunium	Np	93	237		—	—
Plutonium	Pu	94	239		—	—
Americium	Am	95	241		—	—
Curium	Cm	96	242		—	—
Berkelium	Bk	97	243		—	—
Californium	Cf	98	244		—	—
Einsteinium	Es	99	—		—	—
Fermium	Fm	100	—		—	—
Mendelevium	Md	101	—		—	—
Nobelium	No	102	—		—	—

[1] *A.Q.* 1, § 13.
[2] L. H. ALLER, *Steller Atmospheres*, ed. Greenstein, p. 232, Chicago, 1961; *Sky and Tel.*, 19, 338, 1960.
[3] *J. Chem. Soc.*, 5564, Dec. 1961.
[4] A. G. W. CAMERON, *Ap. J.*, 129, 676, 1959.
[5] H. E. SUESS and H. C. UREY, *Rev. Mod. Phys.*, 28, 53, 1956.
[6] L. GOLDBERG, MÜLLER, and ALLER, *Ap. J. Supp.*, 5, 1, 1960.
[7] D. STROMINGER, HOLLANDER, and SEABORG, *Rev. Mod. Phys.*, 30, 585, 1958.

§ 15. Excitation, Ionization and Partition Function

The number of atoms existing in various atomic levels 0, 1, 2, ... when in thermal equilibrium at temperature T is given by the Boltzmann distribution

$$N_2/N_1 = (g_2/g_1)\, e^{-\chi_{12}/kT}$$
$$N_2/N = (g_2/U)\, e^{-\chi_{02}/kT}.$$

Numerically $\log (N_2/N_1) = \log (g_2/g_1) - \chi_{12}(5\,040°/T)$ [χ_{12} in ev]

where N is the total number of atoms per cm^3, N_0, N_1, N_2 are the numbers of atoms per cm^3 in the zero and higher levels, g_0, g_1, g_2 are the corresponding statistical weights, χ_{12} the potential difference between levels 1 and 2, and U the partition function.

The degree of ionization in conditions of thermal equilibrium is given by the Saha equation

$$\frac{N_{r+1}}{N_r} P_e = \frac{U_{r+1}}{U_r} 2 \frac{(2\pi m)^{3/2}(kT)^{5/2}}{h^3} e^{-\chi_r/kT}$$

Numerically $\quad \log \frac{N_{r+1}}{N_r} P_e = -\chi_{r,r+1} \frac{5040}{T} + \frac{5}{2} \log T - 0{\cdot}477\ 2 + \log \frac{2 . U_{r+1}}{U_r}$

or $\qquad \log \frac{N_{r+1}}{N_r} N_e = -\chi_{r,r+1}\Theta - \frac{3}{2} \log \Theta + 20{\cdot}936\ 6 + \log \frac{2 . U_{r+1}}{U_r}$

where N_r and N_{r+1} are the numbers of atoms per cm^3 in the r and $r+1$ stages of ionization, N_e the number of electrons per cm^3, P_e the electron pressure in dyn cm^{-2}, $\chi_{r,r+1}$ the ionization potential in ev from the r to the $r+1$ stage of ionization, $\Theta = 5\,040\ ^{\circ}\mathrm{K}/T$, U_r and U_{r+1} the partition functions, and the factor 2 represents the statistical weight of an electron.

The degree of ionization when ionizations are caused by electron collisions and the recombinations are radiative is given by

$$N_{r+1}/N_r = S/\alpha$$

where S is the collision ionization coefficient (such that $SN_eN_r = $ rate of collisional ionization), and α the recombination coefficient (such that $\alpha N_e N_{r+1} = $ rate of recombination). Using approximate rate coefficients (§§ 18, 37, 38) the degree of ionization in these conditions becomes [2].

$$\log (N_{r+1}/N_r) \simeq 4{\cdot}0 + \log T - 3 \log \chi_{r,r+1} - \chi_{r,r+1}\Theta + \log (\zeta_r/n_r)$$

where ζ_r is the number of electrons in the outer shell and n_r the ground level total quantum number of the r ion or atom.

The partition function may be regarded as the effective statistical weight of the atom or ion under existing conditions of excitation. Except in extreme conditions it is approximately equal to the weight of the lowest or ground term. The ground term weight g_0 is therefore given and this can normally be extrapolated along the iso-electronic sequences to give the approximate partition function for any ion. The partition functions, tabulated in the form $\log U$ for $\Theta = 1{\cdot}0$ and $0{\cdot}5$, are *not* intended to include the concentration of terms close to each series limit [3]. The part of the partition function associated with these high n terms is dependent on both T and P_e [4]. This part is usually negligible unless the atom concerned is mainly ionized in which case the high n terms can be counted statistically with the ion.

Lowering of $\chi_{r,r+1}$ in Saha equation to allow for merging of high level spectrum lines [5, 6]

$$\Delta\chi_{r,r+1} = 7{\cdot}0 \times 10^{-7} N^{1/3} Z^{2/3}$$

with $\Delta\chi$ in ev, N_e in cm^{-3}, and Z is the charge on the $r+1$ ion.

Partition function [3, 7, 9]

Element		Ion						
		I			II			III
		g_0	log U		g_0	log U		g_0
			$\Theta = 1$	$\Theta = 0.5$		$\Theta = 1$	$\Theta = 0.5$	
1	H	2	0·30	0·30	1	0·00	0·00	——
2	He	1	0·00	0·00	2	0·30	0·30	1
3	Li	2	0·32	0·49	1	0·00	0·00	2
4	Be	1	0·01	0·13	2	0·30	0·30	1
5	B	6	0·78	0·78	1	0·00	0·00	2
6	C	9	0·97	1·00	6	0·78	0·78	1
7	N	4	0·61	0·66	9	0·95	0·97	6
8	O	9	0·94	0·97	4	0·60	0·61	9
9	F	6	0·75	0·77	9	0·92	0·94	4
10	Ne	1	0·00	0·00	6	0·73	0·75	9
11	Na	2	0·31	0·46	1	0·00	0·00	6
12	Mg	1	0·01	0·14	2	0·31	0·31	1
13	Al	6	0·77	0·79	1	0·00	0·00	2
14	Si	9	0·98	1·04	6	0·76	0·77	1
15	P	4	0·65	0·79	9	0·91	0·94	6
16	S	9	0·91	0·94	4	0·62	0·72	9
17	Cl	6	0·72	0·75	9	0·89	0·92	4
18	Ar	1	0·00	0·00	6	0·69	0·71	9
19	K	2	0·34	0·60	1	0·00	0·00	6
20	Ca	1	0·07	0·48	2	0·34	0·54	1
21	Sc	10	1·08	1·46	15	1·36	1·50	10
22	Ti	21	1·48	1·83	28	1·75	1·91	21
23	V	28	1·69	2·01	25	1·64	1·83	28
24	Cr	7	1·01	1·38	6	0·86	1·07	25
25	Mn	6	0·81	1·07	7	0·89	1·02	6
26	Fe	25	1·42	1·65	30	1·61	1·73	25
27	Co	28	1·50	1·73	21	1·44	1·63	28
28	Ni	21	1·46	1·58	10	1·00	1·27	21
29	Cu	2	0·36	0·58	1	0·01	0·18	10
30	Zn	1	0·00	0·01	2	0·30	0·30	1
31	Ga	6	0·73	0·77	1	0·00	0·00	2
32	Ge	9	0·91	1·01	6	0·64	0·70	1
34	Se	9	0·83	0·89	4	——	——	9
36	Kr	1	0·00	0·00	6	0·62	0·66	9
37	Rb	2	0·36	0·7	1	0·00	0·00	6
38	Sr	1	0·09	0·55	2	0·34	0·52	1
39	Y	10	1·09	1·40	1	1·15	1·34	10
48	Cd	1	0·00	0·02	2	0·30	0·30	1
50	Sn	9	0·73	0·88	6	0·52	0·61	1
56	Ba	1	0·36	0·92	2	0·62	0·85	1
70	Yb	1	0·02	0·21	2	0·30	0·31	——
82	Pb	9	0·26	0·54	6	0·32	0·40	1

The degree of ionization in the material of stellar atmospheres is given by the following table relating gas pressure P_g, electron pressure P_e, and temperature T [7, 8].

$$\log P_g$$

$\log P_e$ Θ: T:	Θ and T							
	0·1 50 400	0·2 25 200	0·4 12 600	0·6 8 400	0·8 6 300	1·0 5 040	1·2 4 200	1·4 3 600
-2	$-1·9$	$-1·8$	$-1·70$	$-1·67$	$-1·54$	$+0·78$	$+2·0$	$+2·4$
-1	$-0·8$	$-0·74$	$-0·70$	$-0·66$	$-0·01$	$2·57$	$3·1$	$3·9$
0	$+0·27$	$+0·29$	$+0·31$	$+0·35$	$+1·90$	$3·9$	$4·5$	$5·3$
1	$1·27$	$1·30$	$1·33$	$1·47$	$3·87$	$5·2$	$6·0$	$6·7$
2	$2·27$	$2·30$	$2·34$	$2·98$	$5·65$	$6·7$	$7·7$	$8·5$
3	$3·28$	$3·30$	$3·35$	$4·87$	$7·0$	$8·3$	$9·4$	$10·4$
4	$4·28$	$4·31$	$4·43$	$6·84$	$8·7$	$10·0$	$11·2$	$12·4$
5	$5·29$	$5·30$	$5·87$	$8·66$	$10·4$	$11·8$	$13·2$	$14·4$

[1] *A.Q.* **1**, § 15.
[2] C. W. ALLEN, Liège Symp., *Spectra in Far Ultra-violet*, p. 241, 1961.
[3] W. J. CLAAS, *K. Ned. Akad. Wet.*, **52**, 518, 1949; *Rech. Astron. Ob. Utrecht*, **12**, 1, 1951.
[4] C. DE JAGER and L. NEVEN, *Rech. Astron. Ob. Utrecht*, **13**, No. 4, 30, 1957; *B.A.N.*, **15**, 55, 1960.
[5] A. UNSÖLD, *Z. Ap.*, **24**, 355, 1948.
[6] W. LOCHTE-HOLTGREVEN, *Rep. Prog. Phys.*, **21**, 312, 1958.
[7] L. H. ALLER, *Stellar Atmospheres*, ed. Greenstein, p. 232, Chicago, 1961.
[8] A. ROSA, *Z. Ap.*, **25**, 1, 1948.
[9] C. H. CORLISS, *N.B.S. J. of R.*, **66A** 169, 1962.

§ 16. Ionization Potentials

The table gives the energy in volts required to ionize each element to the next stage of ionization. I = neutral atom, II = first ion, etc. Dividing lines between the shells and sub-shells are added to assist interpolation. Ions above XII are detached from the main table for convenience of display.

Ionization potentials

Atom	I (ev)	II (ev)	III (ev)	IV (ev)	V (ev)	VI (ev)	VII (ev)	VIII (ev)	IX (ev)	X (ev)	XI (ev)	XII (ev)
1 H	13·595											
2 He	24·581	54·403										
3 Li	5·390	75·619	122·419									
4 Be	9·320	18·206	153·850	217·657								
5 B	8·296	25·149	37·920	259·298	340·127							
6 C	11·256	24·376	47·871	64·476	391·986	489·84						
7 N	14·53	29·593	47·426	77·450	97·863	551·925	666·83					
8 O	13·614	35·108	54·886	77·394	113·873	138·080	739·114	871·12				
9 F	17·418	34·98	62·646	87·14	114·214	157·117	185·139	953·60	1 102·0			
10 Ne	21·559	41·07	63·5	97·02	126·3	157·91	207·2	239·1	1 195·6	1 360·4		
11 Na	5·138	47·29	71·65	98·88	138·37	172·09	208·444	264·155	299·78	1 464·8	1 646·1	
12 Mg	7·644	15·031	80·12	109·29	141·23	186·49	224·90	265·957	327·90	367·36	1 761·2	1 646·1
13 Al	5·984	18·823	28·44	119·96	153·77	190·42	241·38	284·53	330·1	398·5	441·9	1 761·2
14 Si	8·149	16·34	33·46	45·13	166·73	205·11	246·41	303·07	350·96	401·3	476·0	441·9
15 P	10·484	19·72	30·156	51·354	65·007	220·414	263·31	309·26	371·6	424·3	479·4	476·0
16 S	10·357	23·4	35·0	47·29	72·5	88·029	280·99	328·80	378·95	447	505·8	479·4
17 Cl	13·01	23·80	39·90	53·5	67·80	96·7	114·27	348·3	400·7	455·3	530·9	505·8
18 Ar	15·755	27·62	40·90	59·79	75·0	91·3	124·0	143·46	422·6	479·4	538·9	530·9
19 K	4·339	31·81	46	60·90	82·6	99·7	118	155	175·94	503·8	564	538·9
20 Ca	6·111	11·868	51·21	67	84·39	109	128	143·3	188	211·3	591·8	564
21 Sc	6·54	12·80	24·75	73·9	92	111	139	159	180	226	250	591·8
22 Ti	6·82	13·57	27·47	43·24	99·8	120	141	172	193	217	266	250
23 V	6·74	14·65	29·31	48	65	129	151	174	206	230·5	258	266
24 Cr	6·764	16·49	30·95	50	73	91	161	185	210	249	272	258
25 Mn	7·432	15·636	33·69	53	76	100	119	196	222	248	288	272
26 Fe	7·87	16·18	30·643	57	79	103	130	151	235	262	290	288
27 Co	7·86	17·05	33·49	53	83	108	134	164	190	290	305	290
28 Ni	7·633	18·15	35·16	56	79	112	140	169	202	230	321	305
29 Cu	7·724	20·29	36·83	59	82	110	140	170	206	241		321
30 Zn	9·391	17·96	39·70	62	86	115	145	180	210	250	265	265

Ionization potentials

Atom	I	II	III	IV	V	VI	VII	VIII	IX	X	XI	XII
	ev	ev	ev	ev	ev	ev	ev	ev	ev	ev	ev	ev
31 Ga	6·00	20·51	30·70	64·2	90	118	144	174	218	255		
32 Ge	7·88	15·93	34·21	45·7	93·4	113	148	177	212	262		
33 As	9·81	18·63	28·34	50·1	62·6	127·5	150	182	218	253		
34 Se	9·75	21·5	32	43	68	82	155	187	223	260		
35 Br	11·84	21·6	35·9	47·3	59·7	88·6	103	193	228	266		
36 Kr	13·996	24·56	36·9	52	65	79	110	126	234	270		
37 Rb	4·176	27·5	40	52	71	85	100	135	151	277	324	
38 Sr	5·692	11·027	43	57	72	92	107	124	162	179	206	
39 Y	6·38	12·23	20·5	62	77	93	116	131	148	191	222	
40 Zr	6·84	13·13	22·98	34·33	82	99	117	141	157	176	203	
41 Nb	6·88	14·32	25·04	38·3	50	103	125	143	167	185	210	
42 Mo	7·10	16·15	27·13	46·4	61·2	68	126	153	169	197	224	
43 Tc	7·28	15·26	31	43	59	76	94	161	183	199	225	
44 Ru	7·364	16·76	28·46	46	63	81	100	119	193	216	250	
45 Rh	7·46	18·07	31·05	46	67	85	105	126	147	226	261	
46 Pd	8·33	19·42	32·92	49	66	90	110	132	155	178		
47 Ag	7·574	21·48	34·82	52	70	89	116	139	162	187		
48 Cd	8·991	16·904	37·47	55	73	94	115	146	170	195		
49 In	5·785	18·86	28·03	54·4	77	98	120	144	178	204		
50 Sn	7·342	14·628	30·49	40·72	72·3	103	126	150	176	213		
51 Sb	8·639	16·5	25·3	44·1	56	108	132	157	184	211		
52 Te	9·01	18·6	31	38	60	72	137	164	192	220		
53 I	10·454	19·09	32	42	66	81	99	170	200	229		
54 Xe	12·127	21·2	32·1	46	57	82	100	121	213	238		
55 Cs	3·893	25·1	35	46	62	74	101	120	144	253		
56 Ba	5·210	10·001	36	49	62	80	93	120	143	157		
57 La	5·61	11·43	19·17	52	66	80	100	114	144	165		
58 Ce	6·9	12·3	20	35	70	85	100	122	137	165	204	
59 Pr	5·8					89	106	122	146	162	189	
60 Nd	6·3						110	128	147	171	197	
61 Pm								135	154	173		
62 Sm	5·6	11·3							161	181		

Stage of ionization

Stage of ionization

Atom	I	II	III	IV	V	VI	VII	VIII	IX	X	XI	XII
	ev	ev	ev	ev	ev	ev	ev	ev	ev	ev	ev	ev
63 Eu	5·67	11·2									187	
64 Gd	6·16	12										
65 Tb	6·7											
66 Dy	6·8											
67 Ho	6											
68 Er	6											
69 Tm	6											
70 Yb	6·2	12·1	19									
71 Lu	6·1	15	21									
72 Hf	7	14·9	22									
73 Ta	7·88	16·2	24									
74 W	7·98	17·7	26	31								
75 Re	7·87	16·6	25	33	45	61	79					
76 Os	8·7	17	27	35	48	64	83	99				
77 Ir	9	17	28	38	51	68	88	104	121			
78 Pt	9·0	18·56	30	40	54	72	92	109	127	146		
79 Au	9·22	20·5	34·2	39	57	75	96	114	133	153		
80 Hg	10·43	18·751	29·8	41	55	73	94	120	139	159		
81 Tl	6·106	20·42	31·93	44	58	77	98	116	145	166		
82 Pb	7·415	15·028	25·56	46	61	81	103	122	142	173		
83 Bi	7·287	16·68	27	50·7	64	84	107	127	148	169		
84 Po	8·43	19	29	42·31	68·8	88·3	112	132	154	176		
85 At	9·3	20	29	45·3	56·0	73	91	138	160	183		
86 Rn	10·746	21	33	38	61	78	97	111	166	190		
87 Fa	4·0	22	34	41	51	67	84	117	133	197		
88 Ra	5·277	10·144	20	44	55	71	89	103	140	156		
89 Ac	6·9	12·1	20	43	59	76	95	109	123	164		
90 Th	6	12		46	58	76	94	115	130	145		
91 Pa				49	62	80	100	115	138	154		
92 U	6			29·2	65	84	104	121	137	162		

Ionization potentials (Ions above XII)

Atom	Stage of ionization								
	XII	XIII	XIV	XV	XVI	XVII	XVIII	XIX	XX
	ev	ev	ev	ev	ev	ev	ev	ev	
12 Mg	1 959								
13 Al	2 085·5	2 299							
14 Si	523·2	2 436	2 666						
15 P	560·3	611·4	2 815	3 061					
16 S	566	651	706	3 220	3 482				
17 Cl	593	663	749	807	3 654	3 931			
18 Ar	621	687	755	854	916	4 115	4 407		
19 K	629	717	788	870	966	1 031	4 603	4 910	
20 Ca	655	727	820	896	990	1 084	1 153	5 119	
21 Sc	687	758	830	930	1 010	1 115	1 210	1 282	
22 Ti	291	788	864	941	1 046	1 132	1 245	1 341	
23 V	309	336	897	976	1 057	1 170	1 260	1 380	
24 Cr	299	355	384	1 013	1 095	1 182	1 301	1 395	
25 Mn	315	350	404	435	1 136	1 222	1 313	1 438	
26 Fe	330	355	390	457	489	1 266	1 354	1 450	
27 Co	337	380	412	444	512	547	1 403	1 495	
28 Ni	350	385	430	455	500	530	607	1 541	
29 Cu	370	400	440	480	520	560	630	671	
30 Zn	311	420	450	490	540	580	620	700	

[1] *A.Q.* **1**, § 16.
[2] C. E. MOORE, *Atomic Energy Levels*, **3**, Circ. N.B.S., 467, 1958.
[3] W. FINKELNBURG and W. HUMBACH, *Naturwiss.*, **42**, 35, 1955.
[4] A. UNSÖLD, *Sternatmosphären*, p. 90, Springer, 1955.

§ 17. Electron Affinities

Electron affinities are positive for those atoms or molecules that form stable negative ions. A second stable state of H⁻ has been found [2].

Atom	Electron affinity		Atom	Electron affinity		Atom	Electron affinity		Molecule	Electron affinity
	ev			ev			ev			ev
H	+0·754		O	+1·465		S	+2·5		OH	+1·8
H [2]	+0·29		F	+3·61		Cl	+3·7		CN	+3·1
He	−0·5		Ne	−0·8		Ar	−1		C₂	+3·3
Li	+0·6		Na	+0·4		K	+1		O₂	+0·7
Be	−0·6		Mg	−0·4		Br	+3·6		CH	+1·6
B	+0·4		Al	+1·0		I	+3·3			
C	+1·13		Si	+1·8		Hg	+2			
N	−0·1		P	+1·1						

[1] *A.Q.* **1**, § 17.
[2] E. HYLLERAAS, *Ap. J.*, **111**, 209, 1950.
[3] L. M. BRANSCOMB and B. E. J. PAGEL, *M.N.*, **118**, 258, 1958.
[4] H. R. JOHNSON and F. ROHLICH, *J. Chem. Phys.*, **30**, 1608, 1959.
[5] B. L. MOISEIWITSCH, *Proc. Phys. Soc.*, **67A**, 25, 1954.
[6] L. M. BRANSCOMB, *Adv. Electronic and El. Phys.*, **9**, 1957.
[7] J. W. EDIE, Thesis, Iowa, 1961.

§ 18. Atomic Cross-sections for Electronic Collisions

Atomic unit cross-section $\qquad \pi a_0^2 = 8 \cdot 797 \times 10^{-17}$ cm

Atomic cross-section Q and collision probability P_c

$$Q = 2 \cdot 828\ 3 \times 10^{-17} P_c = 0 \cdot 321\ 5\ \pi a_0^2 P_c$$

where P_c collisions are encountered by an electron per cm at 0 °C and 1 mm-Hg pressure.

Ionization cross-section

Classical cross-section of atom for ionization by electrons [1, 2]

$$= 4n\pi a_0^2 \frac{1}{\chi\epsilon} \left(1 - \frac{\chi}{\epsilon} \right)$$

where χ = ionization energy in Rydbergs, ϵ = electronic energy before collision in Rydbergs, and n = number of optical electrons.

General formula for cross-section of atoms for ionization by electrons [2]

$$Q_i = n\pi a_0^2 \frac{1}{\chi\epsilon} F(Z, \epsilon/\chi) = \frac{nq}{\chi^2} \pi a_0^2$$

$$= 1 \cdot 63 \times 10^{-14} n \frac{1}{\chi_{ev}^2} \frac{\chi}{\epsilon} F(Z, \epsilon/\chi)$$

where Z = charge on ionized atom, and χ_{ev} is the ionization energy in electron volts. The function $F(Z, \epsilon/\chi)$ is tabulated and also $q = (\chi/\epsilon) F(Z, \epsilon/\chi)$ which is sometimes called the reduced cross section. The $Z = 1$ and $Z = 2$ values are from experiment and $Z = \infty$ from calculation. About 10% accuracy may be expected in each case.

ϵ/χ	1·0	1·2	1·5	2·0	3	5	10
F(classical) $= 4(1 - \chi/\epsilon)$	0·00	0·67	1·33	2·00	2·67	3·20	3·60
$F(1, \epsilon/\chi)$	0·00	0·22	0·54	1·12	2·2	4·0	6·4
$F(2, \epsilon/\chi)$	0·00	0·31	0·75	1·48	2·7	4·2	6·4
$F(\infty, \epsilon/\chi)$	0·00	0·49	1·20	2·20	3·7	4·7	6·4
q(classical) $= 4(\chi/\epsilon)(1 - \chi/\epsilon)$	0·00	0·56	0·89	1·00	0·89	0·64	0·36
$q(1, \epsilon/\chi)$	0·00	0·18	0·36	0·56	0·75	0·80	0·64
$q(2, \epsilon/\chi)$	0·00	0·26	0·50	0·74	0·89	0·83	0·64
$q(\infty, \epsilon/\chi)$	0·00	0·41	0·80	1·10	1·21	0·93	0·64

Maximum ionization cross-section [1, 2].

    Classical case: $\qquad\qquad Q_{\max} = n\pi a_0^2 \chi^{-2}$ at $\epsilon = 2\chi$

The value of $Q_{\max}$ is approximately the same in actual cases but the maximum occurs near $\epsilon = 4\chi$ [ϵ and χ in Rydbergs].

Rate of ionization by electrons $S = \overline{vQ_1}$, where v = electron velocity before collision.

    Neutral atoms (and kT < ionization energy)

$$S = 1{\cdot}1 \times 10^{-8} n T^{1/2} \chi_{ev}^{-2} 10^{-5\,040\chi_{ev}/T} \quad \text{cm}^3\,\text{s}^{-1}$$

    Coronal ions (kT < ionization energy)

$$S = 2{\cdot}3 \times 10^{-8} n T^{1/2} \chi_{ev}^{-2} 10^{-5\,040\chi_{ev}/T} \quad \text{cm}^3\,\text{s}^{-1}$$

$$[\chi_{ev} \text{ in ev}]$$

Excitation cross-section (*permitted transitions*)

General formula for Q_{ex}, the excitation cross-section of an atom [2]

$$Q_{ex} = \frac{8\pi}{\sqrt{3}}\, \pi a_0^2\, \frac{f}{\epsilon W}\, b$$

$$= 1740\, \pi a_0^2\, \lambda^2 (W/\epsilon) f b$$

$$= 1{\cdot}28 \times 10^{-15} (f/\epsilon W) b \quad \text{cm}^2$$

where f = oscillator strength, W = excitation energy in Rydbergs ($= 0{\cdot}091\,2/\lambda$ with λ in μ), ϵ = electron energy before collision also in Rydbergs.

Variations of the numerical factors b and bW/ϵ.

ϵ/W	1·0	1·2	1·5	2·0	3	5	10	30	100
b, neutral atoms	0·00	0·032	0·064	0·11	0·21	0·33	0·56	0·98	1·33
b, ions	0·20	0·20	0·20	0·20	0·24	0·33	0·56	0·98	1·33
bW/ϵ, neutral atoms	0·00	0·027	0·043	0·055	0·070	0·066	0·056	0·033	0·013
bW/ϵ, ions	0·20	0·17	0·13	0·10	0·080	0·066	0·056	0·033	0·013

The trend of these values from [2] for low ϵ/χ in neutral atoms is to be smaller than earlier estimates [1, 5].

Maximum excitation cross-section

    Neutral atom: $\qquad\qquad Q_{\max} \simeq 125\, \pi a_0^2\, \lambda^2 f$ near $\epsilon = 3W$

    Ion: $\qquad\qquad\qquad Q_{\max} \simeq 350\, \pi a_0^2\, \lambda^2 f$ near $\epsilon = W$ [λ in μ]

Rate of excitation $\qquad\qquad L = \overline{vQ_{ex}}$

$$L = 17{\cdot}0 \times 10^{-4} \frac{f}{T^{1/2} W_{ev}}\, 10^{-5\,040 W_{ev}/T} \cdot P(W/kT)$$

where W_{ev} and W are excitation energy in ev and ergs (hence $11\,600\,W_{ev}/T = W/kT$), and $P(W/kT)$ is tabulated

W/kT	$P(W/kT)$ [8]	
	Neutral atoms	Ions
< 0·01	0·29 $E_1(W/kT)$	
0·01	1·16	1·16
0·02	0·96	0·98
0·05	0·70	0·74
0·1	0·49	0·55
0·2	0·33	0·40
0·5	0·17	0·26
1	0·10	0·22
2	0·063	0·21
5	0·035	0·20
10	0·023	0·20
> 10	$0·066/(W/kT)^{1/2}$	0·20

$E_1(\ )$ is the first exponential integral.

De-excitation cross-section

De-excitation cross-sections Q_{21} are related to excitation cross-sections Q_{12} (2 being the upper level) through

$$g_2\epsilon_2 Q_{21} = g_1\epsilon_1 Q_{12}$$

where $\epsilon_2 = \epsilon_1 + W$ and g_2 and g_1 are statistical weights.

De-excitation rate S_{21} and excitation rate S_{12}

$$g_2 S_{21} = g_1 S_{12} e^{W/kT}$$

Excitation cross-section (forbidden transitions)

Collision strength Ω for each line defined [4] by

$$Q_f = \pi\Omega/g_1 k_v^2 = \pi a_0^2 \Omega/g_1 \epsilon$$

$$= \frac{h}{4\pi m^2} \frac{\Omega}{g_1 v^2} = 4·21\ \Omega/g_1 v^2$$

where $k_v/2\pi$ is the wave number of the incident electron and ϵ its energy in Rydbergs (then k_v^2 in atomic units $= \epsilon$ in Rydbergs), g_1 is the statistical weight of the initial (lower) level, and Q_f is the forbidden-line cross-section for atoms in this level. Then Ω_{12} (excitation) $= \Omega_{21}$ (de-excitation).

The values of Ω for cases of interest in astrophysics are, (a) of the order of unity for ions, and (b) varying from 0 at threshold ($\epsilon = W$) to order of unity at $\epsilon - W \simeq$ 1 Rydberg, for atoms.

Values of Ω [4, 6]

Atom or ion	λ	g_1	Ω
	Å		
N II	6548–83	9	2·17
O I ($\epsilon - W \simeq 1$)	5577	5	0·35
	6300–63	9	1·77
O II	3726–9	4	1·28
O III	4959–5007	9	1·59
Fe XIV	5303	2	0·23

In an isoelectronic sequence (approximately)

$$\Omega \propto Z^{-2}.$$

Total atomic cross-section (elastic and inelastic collisions)

An approximate expression for total cross-section [1]

$$Q \simeq 180\pi a_0^2 \lambda/\epsilon^{1/2} \quad [\epsilon \text{ in Rydbergs}]$$

where λ is wavelength in μ of the strongest low-level spectrum lines.

Ionic collision cross-section [7]

Cross-section for collision deflection of at least a right-angle

$$Q_\perp = \pi(Ze^2/mv^2)^2 = \pi(Ze^2/2\epsilon hcR)^2$$
$$= \pi a_0^2 Z^2/\epsilon^2 \quad [\epsilon \text{ in Rydbergs}]$$

where Z is the ionic charge.

The effective ionic collision cross-section is usually concerned with the more distant collisions involving deflections much less than a right-angle. These increase the effective Q by a factor (depending logarithmically on the most distant collisions that enter the integration) which varies with circumstances but is usually between 10 and 50. We may write an approximate generalization

$$Q \text{ (effective)} \simeq 30\pi a_0^2 Z^2/\epsilon^2$$

[1] *A.Q.* **1**, § 18.
[2] M. J. Seaton, *Atomic and Molecular Processes*, ed. Bates, Ch. 11, Academic Press, 1962; *J. Indian Nat. Ac. Sci.*, 1963; and private communications.
[3] C. W. Allen, *Spectra in Far Ultra-violet*, p. 241, Liège Symp., 1961.
[4] M. J. Seaton, *Airglow and Aurorae*, ed. Armstrong and Dalgarno, p. 289, Pergamon, 1956; *Rev. Mod. Phys.*, **30**, 979, 1958.
[5] S. N. Milford (and J. H. Scanlon), *Ap. J.*, **131**, 407, 1960; **134**, 724, 1961.
[6] M. Blaha, *B.A. Czech*, **9**, 160, 1958 (revised later).
[7] L. Spitzer, *Physics of fully ionized Gases*, Interscience, 1956.
[8] H. van Regemorter, private communication, 1962.

§ 19. Atomic Radii

Atomic radii are defined through the closeness of approach of atoms in the formation of molecules and crystals. The radius r so derived is approximately that of maximum radial density in the charge distribution of neutral atoms [2]. For ions the appropriate radius measures to the point where the radial density falls to 10% of its maximum value. The atomic mass divided by the atomic volume $4\pi r^3/3$ gives the density of the more compact solids. $2r$ is approximately the gas-kinetic diameter of monatomic molecules.

om	Radius	Ion	Radius	Atom	Radius	Ion	Radius	Atom	Radius	Ion	Radius
	Å		Å		Å		Å		Å		Å
	0·53	H^-	2·02	S	0·95	S^{--}	1·96	Br	1·05	Br^-	1·97
	1·05			Cl	0·89	Cl^-	1·79	Kr	1·77		
	1·61	Li^+	0·68	Ar	1·56			Rb	3·1	Rb^+	1·51
	1·09	Be^{++}	0·42	K	2·8	K^+	1·32	Sr	2·5	Sr^{++}	1·28
	0·84	B^{+++}	0·32	Ca	2·3	Ca^{++}	1·08	Ag	1·8	Ag^+	1·22
	0·69	C^{++++}	0·27	Sc	2·0	Sc^{+++}	0·93	Cd	1·7	Cd^{++}	1·05
	0·63	N^{---}	2·07	Ti	1·9	Ti^{++++}	0·78	Sn	1·49	Sn^{++++}	0·80
	0·56	O^{--}	1·46	V	1·8	V^{++++}	0·60	I	1·24	I^-	2·21
	0·53	F^-	1·29	Cr	1·7			Xe	1·99		
	1·1			Mn	1·7	Mn^{++}	0·86	Cs	3·4	Cs^+	1·75
	2·05	Na^+	0·94	Fe	1·6	Fe^{++}	0·79	Ba	2·8	Ba^{++}	1·47
	1·61	Mg^{++}	0·77	Co	1·5	Co^{++}	0·77	Pt	1·8		
	1·39	Al^{+++}	0·62	Ni	1·4	Ni^{++}	0·74	Au	1·8	Au^+	1·37
	1·18	Si^{++++}	0·51	Cu	1·4	Cu^+	0·96	Hg	1·8	Hg^{++}	1·16
	1·02	P^{---}	2·48	Zn	1·5	Zn^{++}	0·78				

[1] *A.Q.* **1**, § 19.
[2] J. C. SLATER, *Phys. Rev.* **36**, 57, 1930.
[3] J. D'ANS and E. LAX, *Taschenbuch für Chem. und Phys.*, p. 183, 1949.
[4] *Handbook of Chemistry and Physics*, p. 2680, 31st ed., 1949.

§ 20. Particles of Modern Physics

I_z = component of isospin, S = strangeness, and 'Life' means mean life in free space. The decay products are given in certain cases in the 'Decay' column. The symbol ⊟ is used for the Xi-hyperon.

For conversion to mass units in terms of Mev/c^2 use

$$M_{ph}c^2 = 931 \cdot 145 \ Mev$$

[1] *A.Q.* **1**, § 20.
[2] A. SALAM, *Endeavour*, **17**, 97, 1958.
[3] P. E. HODGSON, *Science News*, **52** (Penguin), 95, 1959.
[4] R. H. DALITZ, *Rep. Prog. Phys.*, **20**, 163, 1957.
[5] E. H. S. BURHOP, 1961 Inaugural Lecture and private communications.

Particles of modern physics

Classification	Name and symbol		Charge	Mass (electron)	Mass atomic weight M_{ph} (phys)	Spin	I_z	S	Life (s)	Decay
Bosons — Mesons	Photon	γ	0	0	0·0	1	—	—	∞	stable
	π-meson (pion)	π^+, π^-	$+1, -1$	273·2	0·149 9	0	$+1, -1$	0	$2\cdot55\times10^{-8}$	$\mu+\nu$
		π^0	0	264·3	0·145 0	0	0	0	$2\cdot2\times10^{-16}$	$\gamma+\gamma$
	K-meson (kayon)	K^+, K^-	$+1, -1$	966·8	0·530 5	0	$+\frac{1}{2}, -\frac{1}{2}$	$+1, -1$	$1\cdot22\times10^{-8}$	several modes
		$K^0, \bar{K}^0$	0	974	0·534 6	0	$-\frac{1}{2}, +\frac{1}{2}$	$+1, -1$	$\begin{cases}1\cdot0\times10^{-10}\ K_1^0\\ 6\times10^{-8}\ K_2^0\end{cases}$	$\pi^++\pi^-, \pi^0+\pi^0$
Fermions — Leptons	Neutrino	$\nu, \bar{\nu}$	0	0	0·0	$\frac{1}{2}$	—	—	∞	stable
	Electron, positron	e^-, e^+	$-1, +1$	1	0·000 548 761	$\frac{1}{2}$			∞	stable
	μ-meson (muon)	μ^-, μ^+	$-1, +1$	206·79	0·113 48	$\frac{1}{2}$	—	—	$2\cdot212\times10^{-6}$	$e^-+\nu+\bar{\nu}$
Fermions — Baryons (Nucleons)	Proton	$p, \bar{p}$	$+1, -1$	1 836·12	1·007 593	$\frac{1}{2}$	$+\frac{1}{2}, -\frac{1}{2}$	0	∞	stable, $\bar{p}+e^++\nu$
	Neutron	$n, \bar{n}$	0	1 838·65	1·008 985	$\frac{1}{2}$	$-\frac{1}{2}, +\frac{1}{2}$	0	$1\cdot13\times10^{3}$	$p+e^-+\bar{\nu},\ \bar{p}+e^+, n+\pi^0$
Fermions — Baryons	Λ^0-hyperon	$\Lambda^0, \bar{\Lambda}^0$	0	2 182·0	1·197 6	$\frac{1}{2}$	0	$-1, +1$	$2\cdot51\times10^{-10}$	$p+\pi^-, n+\pi^0$
	Σ^+-hyperon	$\Sigma^+, \bar{\Sigma}^+$	$+1, -1$	2 327·8	1·277 4	$\frac{1}{2}$	$+1, -1$	$-1, +1$	$0\cdot81\times10^{-10}$	$p+\pi^0, n+\pi^+$
	Σ^0-hyperon	$\Sigma^0, \bar{\Sigma}^0$	0	2 332	1·280	$\frac{1}{2}$	0	$-1, +1$	10^{-13}	$\Lambda^0+\gamma$
	Σ^--hyperon	$\Sigma^-, \bar{\Sigma}^-$	$-1, +1$	2 341·7	1·284 7	$\frac{1}{2}?$	$-1, +1$	$-1, +1$	$1\cdot6\times10^{-10}$	$n+\pi^-$
	Ξ^0-hyperon	$\Xi^0, \bar{\Xi}^0$	0	2 570	1·409	$\frac{1}{2}?$	$+\frac{1}{2}, -\frac{1}{2}$	$-2, +2$	$1\cdot5\times10^{-10}$	$\Lambda^0+\pi^0$
	Ξ^--hyperon	$\Xi^-, \bar{\Xi}^-$	$-1, +1$	2 581	1·416 2	$\frac{1}{2}?$	$-\frac{1}{2}, +\frac{1}{2}$	$-2, +2$	$1\cdot3\times10^{-10}$	$\Lambda^0+\pi^-$
Atomic particles	Hydrogen ($^2S_{\frac{1}{2}}$)	^{1}H	0	1 837·13	1·008 144				∞	
	Deuterium ($^2S_{\frac{1}{2}}$)	^{2}H	0	3 671·43	2·014 738				∞	
	Deuteron	D	1	3 670·43	2·014 191				∞	
	α-particle	α	2	7 294·0	4·002 67				∞	

§ 21. Molecules

$\mu_A = M_1 M_2/(M_1 + M_2)$ where M_1 and M_2 are the atomic weights (physical scale) of atoms in a diatomic molecule, r = internuclear distance.

Molecule	Dissociation energy	Reduced mass μ_A	r Ground state	Ionization potential	Molecular diameter
	ev		Å	ev	Å
H_2	4·477 3	0·504 1	0·741 6	15·422	2·5
H_2^+	2·648	0·503 9	1·06		
He_2	2·6?	2·001 9	1·041	4·251	
BH	< 3·5	0·923 6	1·232 5		
BO	8	6·523 0	1·204 9		
C_2	5	6·001 9	1·311 7		
CH	3·47	0·930 0	1·119 8	11·1	
CH^+	3·6	0·930 0	1·130 8		
CO	11·090	6·858 4	1·209 3	14·01	3·3
CO^+	8	6·858 2	1·115 0	43	
CN	8·2	6·464 3	1·171 8		
N_2	9·758	7·003 8	1·094	15·576	3·5
N_2^+	6·34 or 8·72	7·003 6	1·116	50	
NH	3·76	0·940 4	1·038		
NO	6·503	7·468 8	1·150 8	9·25	3·4
O_2	5·115	8·000 0	1·207 4	12·07	3·2
O_2^+	6·5	7·999 9	1·122 7	50	
OH	4·40	0·948 4	0·970 6	13·2	
OH^+	> 4·4	0·948 4	1·028 9		
MgH	2	0·967 5	1·730 6		
AlH	2·9	0·971 8	1·645 9		
AlO	3·7	10·045 2	1·617 6		
SiH	3·2	0·973 1	1·520		
SiO	8	10·180 1	1·510		
SiN	4·5	9·335 3	1·572		
SO	5·36	10·664 7	1·493 3		
CaH	< 1·7	0·983 3	2·002 0		
CaO	3·9	11·426 5			
ScO	7	11·801 2			
TiO	6	11·997 9	1·620		
VO	7	12·176 8	1·890		
CrO	5·3	12·236 6			
FeO	4·3	12·437 8			
YO	8	13·560 6			
ZrO	7	13·583 6	1·42		
LaO	8	14·347 9			
H_2O				12·6	3·5
N_2O				12·9	4·0
CO_2				13·73	3·8
NH_3				11·2	3·0
CH_4					3·5

[1] *A.Q.* **1**, § 21.
[2] C. DE JAGER and L. NEVEN, *Molecules*, Liège Symp., 357, 1957.
[3] J. C. PECKER and M. PEUCHOT, *Molecules*, Liège Symp., 352, 1957.
[4] M. NICOLET, *Far ultra-violet spectra*, Liège Symp., 319, 1961.
[5] G. R. SOMAYAJULU, *J. Chem. Phys.*, **33**, 1541, 1960.

CHAPTER 4

SPECTRA

§ 22. Terminology for Atomic States, Levels, Terms, etc.

SPECTROSCOPIC levels are normally described by quantum numbers based on LS (Russell-Saunders) coupling.

Orbital angular momentum (or azimuthal quantum number) L = vector sum of orbital angular momenta l of individual electrons. The unit is $h/2\pi = \hbar$, and the designation

L (or l)	0	1	2	3	4	5	6	7	8	9	10	11	12	13	14	15
Designation (L)	S	P	D	F	G	H	I	K	L	M	N	O	Q	R	T	U
Designation (l)	s	p	d	f	g	h	i	k	l	m	n	o	q	r	t	u

Spin angular momentum S = vector sum of s for individual electrons. The multiplicity of terms = $(2S+1)$.

Total angular momentum (or inner quantum number) J = vector sum $L+S$ (in LS coupling). In jj coupling j = vector $l+s$ for each electron, and $J = \Sigma j$.

Total quantum number for each electron $n = 1 + \text{orbital} + \text{radial quantum numbers}$. Total quantum number is closely related to energy and defines electron shells as follows:

n	1	2	3	4	5	6	7
Shell designation	K	L	M	N	O	P	Q

Magnetic quantum numbers M_L, M_S, M express the components of L, S, and J in the direction of the magnetic field.

Maximum values of various quantum numbers are limited as follows:

$$l \leqslant n-1; \quad s = \tfrac{1}{2}; \quad J \leqslant S+L; \quad M_L \leqslant L; \quad M_S \leqslant S; \quad M \leqslant J;$$
$$S \leqslant \tfrac{1}{2}n_a; \quad L \leqslant n_a l$$

where there are n_a electrons not in closed shells.

Interpretation of a typical symbol for an atomic level

$$2p^3 \, {}^4S^0_{1\frac{1}{2}}$$

2   total quantum number of outer electrons = 2; i.e., L shell

p^3 3 outer electrons in $l = 1$ condition

4   multiplicity = 4, whence $S = 1\frac{1}{2}$

S   orbital momentum $L = 0$

$1\frac{1}{2}$ $J = 1\frac{1}{2}$, whence statistical weight $g = 2J+1 = 4$

0   the level is odd (0 omitted when even)

The magnetic quantum numbers do not appear unless the level is split by a magnetic field.

Spectrum lines are obtained by transitions between atomic levels in accordance with the following scheme.

Atomic division	Specification	Statistical weight g	Transition
State	Specified by L, S, J, M or $L, S, M_\mathrm{L}, M_\mathrm{S}$	1	Component of line
Level	Specified by L, S, J, e.g. $^4\mathrm{S}_{1\frac{1}{2}}$	$2J+1$	Spectrum line
Term	Group of levels specified by L, S	$(2S+1)(2L+1)$	Multiplet
Polyad	Group of terms from one parent term and with same multi-plicity or S		Super-multiplet
Configuration	Specified by n and l of all electrons	see § 23	Transition array

Possible levels:

Singlets	$^1\mathrm{S}_0$, $^1\mathrm{P}_1$, $^1\mathrm{D}_2$, $^1\mathrm{F}_3$, $^1\mathrm{G}_4$, $^1\mathrm{H}_5$, ...
Doublets	$^2\mathrm{S}_{\frac{1}{2}}$, $^2\mathrm{P}_{\frac{1}{2}, 1\frac{1}{2}}$, $^2\mathrm{D}_{1\frac{1}{2}, 2\frac{1}{2}}$, $^2\mathrm{F}_{2\frac{1}{2}, 3\frac{1}{2}}$, $^2\mathrm{G}_{3\frac{1}{2}, 4\frac{1}{2}}$, ...
Triplets	$^3\mathrm{S}_1$, $^3\mathrm{P}_{0, 1, 2}$, $^3\mathrm{D}_{1, 2, 3}$, $^3\mathrm{F}_{2, 3, 4}$, $^3\mathrm{G}_{3, 4, 5}$, ...
Quartets	$^4\mathrm{S}_{1\frac{1}{2}}$, $^4\mathrm{P}_{\frac{1}{2}, 1\frac{1}{2}, 2\frac{1}{2}}$, $^4\mathrm{D}_{\frac{1}{2}, 1\frac{1}{2}, 2\frac{1}{2}, 3\frac{1}{2}}$, $^4\mathrm{F}_{1\frac{1}{2}, 2\frac{1}{2}, 3\frac{1}{2}, 4\frac{1}{2}}$, ...
Quintets	$^5\mathrm{S}_2$, $^5\mathrm{P}_{1, 2, 3}$, $^5\mathrm{D}_{0, 1, 2, 3, 4}$, $^5\mathrm{F}_{1, 2, 3, 4, 5}$, $^5\mathrm{G}_{2, 3, 4, 5, 6}$, ...
Sextets	$^6\mathrm{S}_{2\frac{1}{2}}$, $^6\mathrm{P}_{1\frac{1}{2}, 2\frac{1}{2}, 3\frac{1}{2}}$, $^6\mathrm{D}_{\frac{1}{2}, 1\frac{1}{2}, 2\frac{1}{2}, 3\frac{1}{2}, 4\frac{1}{2}}$, $^6\mathrm{F}_{\frac{1}{2}, 1\frac{1}{2}, 2\frac{1}{2}, 3\frac{1}{2}, 4\frac{1}{2}, 5\frac{1}{2}}$, $^6\mathrm{G}_{1\frac{1}{2}, 2\frac{1}{2}, 3\frac{1}{2}, 4\frac{1}{2}, 5\frac{1}{2}, 6\frac{1}{2}}$, ...
Septets	$^7\mathrm{S}_3$, $^7\mathrm{P}_{2, 3, 4}$, $^7\mathrm{D}_{1, 2, 3, 4, 5}$, $^7\mathrm{F}_{0, 1, 2, 3, 4, 5, 6}$, $^7\mathrm{G}_{1, 2, 3, 4, 5, 6, 7}$, ...

[1] *A.Q.* **1**, § 22.

§ 23. Terms from Various Configurations

The table gives the multiplicities and orbital angular momenta of the various terms arising in LS coupling from the configurations listed. When a term can appear more than once the number of possible terms is written below the symbol.

Any complete shell s^2, p^6, d^{10}, f^{14}, etc. gives rise to only one $^1\mathrm{S}$ term. Complete shells need not be considered for possible terms of outer electrons.

Electrons with the same n and l are said to be equivalent. Non-equivalent electrons are separated by a point, thus $p.p$. Terms arising from complementary numbers of equivalent electrons are the same; e.g. terms from p^2 and p^4 are the same since 6 electrons complete the p shell.

Configuration	Terms	Total weight
Equivalent s electrons		
s	^{2}S	2
s^2	^{1}S	1
Equivalent p electrons		
p p^5	^{2}P^0	6
p^2 p^4	^{1}SD ^{3}P	15
p^3	^{2}PD^0 ^{4}S^0	20
Equivalent d electrons		
d d^9	^{2}D	10
d^2 d^8	^{1}SDG ^{3}PF	45
d^3 d^7	^{2}PDFGH ^{4}PF 2	120
d^4 d^6	^{1}SDFGI ^{3}PDFGH ^{5}D 2 2 2 2 2	210
d^5	^{2}SPDFGHI ^{4}PDFG ^{6}S 3 2 2	252
Equivalent f electrons		
f f^{13}	^{2}F^0	14
f^2 f^{12}	^{1}SDGI ^{3}PFH	91
f^3 f^{11}	^{2}PDFGHIKL^0 ^{4}SDFGI^0 2 2 2 2	364
f^4 f^{10}	^{1}SDFGHIKLN ^{3}PDFGHIKLM ^{5}SPFGI 2 4 4 2 3 2 3 2 4 3 4 2 2	1 001
f^5 f^9	^{2}PDFGHIKLMNO^0 ^{4}SPDFGHIKLM^0 ^{6}PFH^0 4 5 7 6 7 5 5 3 2 2 3 4 4 3 3 2	2 002
f^6 f^8	^{1}SPDFGHIKLMNQ ^{3}PDFGHIKLMNO ^{5}SPDFGHIKL ^{7}F 4 6 4 8 4 7 3 4 2 2 6 5 9 7 9 6 6 3 3 3 2 3 2 2	3 003
f^7	^{2}SPDFGHIKLMNOQ^0 ^{4}SPDFGHIKLMN^0 ^{6}PDFGHI^0 ^{8}S^0 2 5 7 10 10 9 9 7 5 4 2 2 2 6 5 7 5 5 3 3	3 432
2-electron systems		
$s.s$	^{1}S ^{3}S	4
sp	^{1}P^0 ^{3}P^0	12
sd	^{1}D ^{3}D	20
sf	^{1}F^0 ^{3}F^0	28
sg	^{1}G ^{3}G	36
$p.p$	^{1}SPD ^{3}SPD	36
pd	^{1}PDF^0 ^{3}PDF^0	60
pf	^{1}DFG ^{3}DFG	84
pg	^{1}FGH^0 ^{3}FGH^0	108
$d.d$	^{1}SPDFG ^{3}SPDFG	100
df	^{1}PDFGH^0 ^{3}PDFGH^0	140
$f.f$	^{1}SPDFGHI ^{3}SPDFGHI	196

Configuration	Terms			Total weight
Equivalent electrons and 1 s electron				
sp^2	^2SPD	^4P		30
sp^3	$^1PD^0$	$^3SPD^0$	$^5S^0$	40
sd^2	^2SPDFG	^4PF		90
sd^3	^1PDFGH $\;\;2$	^3PDFGH $\;\;2\,2\,2$	^5PF	240
sd^4	$^2SPDFGHI$ $\;\;2\,2\,3\,3\,3$	^4PDFGH $\;\;2\,2\,2$	^6D	420
sd^5	$^1SPDFGHI$ $\;\;3\,2\,2$	$^3SPDFGHI$ $\;\;2\,4\,3\,3$	$^5SPDFG \quad {}^7S$	504
sf^2	$^2SPDFGHI$	^4PFH		182
sf^3	$^1PDFGHIKL^0$ $\;\;2\,2\,2\,2$	$^3SPDFGHIKL^0$ $\;\;3\,3\,3\,2\,2$	$^5SDFGI^0$	728
3-electrons, 2 equivalent and no s electrons				
$p^2.p$	$^2SPDF^0$ $\;\;3\,2$	$^4SPD^0$		90
p^2d	^2SPDFG $\;\;2\,3\,2$	^4PDF		150
p^2f	$^2PDFGH^0$ $\;\;2\,3\,2$	$^4DFG^0$		210
pd^2	$^2SPDFGH^0$ $\;\;3\,3\,3\,2$	$^4SPDFG^0$ $\;\;2$		270
$d^2.d$	$^2SPDFGHI$ $\;\;3\,5\,4\,3\,2$	^4PDFGH $\;\;2\,2\,2$		450
3 non-equivalent electrons				
$s.sp$	$^2P^0$ $\;\;2$	$^4P^0$		24
$s.sd$	^2D $\;\;2$	^4D		40
$sp.p$	^2SPD $\;\;2\,2\,2$	^4SPD		72
spd	$^2PDF^0$ $\;\;2\,2\,2$	$^4PDF^0$		120
spf	^2DFG $\;\;2\,2\,2$	^4DFG		168
$sd.d$	^2SPDFG $\;\;2\,2\,2\,2\,2$	^4SPDFG		200

[1] *A.Q.* **1**, § 23.

§ 24. Electronic Configurations

The table gives the electron configurations for ground-level neutral atoms. Complete tabulations of energy levels are available in [2, 3].

Atom	K 1s	L 2s 2p	M 3s 3p 3d	N 4s 4p 4d	O 5s	Ground level
H 1	1					$^2S_{\frac12}$
He 2	2					$^1S_0$
Li 3	2	1				$^2S_{\frac12}$
Be 4	2	2				$^1S_0$
B 5	2	2 1				$^2P^0_{\frac12}$
C 6	2	2 2				$^3P_0$
N 7	2	2 3				$^4S^0_{1\frac12}$
O 8	2	2 4				$^3P_2$
F 9	2	2 5				$^2P^0_{1\frac12}$
Ne 10	2	2 6				$^1S_0$
Na 11	2	2 6	1			$^2S_{\frac12}$
Mg 12			2			$^1S_0$
Al 13			2 1			$^2P^0_{\frac12}$
Si 14		10	2 2			$^3P_0$
P 15			2 3			$^4S^0_{1\frac12}$
S 16		Ne core	2 4			$^3P_2$
Cl 17			2 5			$^2P^0_{1\frac12}$
A 18			2 6			$^1S_0$
K 19	2	2 6	2 6	1		$^2S_{\frac12}$
Ca 20				2		$^1S_0$
Sc 21			1	2		$^2D_{1\frac12}$
Ti 22			2	2		$^3F_2$
V 23		18	3	2		$^4F_{1\frac12}$
Cr 24			5	1		$^7S_3$
Mn 25		A core	5	2		$^6S_{2\frac12}$
Fe 26			6	2		$^5D_4$
Co 27			7	2		$^4F_{4\frac12}$
Ni 28			8	2		$^3F_4$
Cu 29	2	2 6	2 6 10	1		$^2S_{\frac12}$
Zn 30				2		$^1S_0$
Ga 31				2 1		$^2P^0_{\frac12}$
Ge 32				2 2		$^3P_0$
As 33		28		2 3		$^4S_{1\frac12}$
Se 34				2 4		$^3P_2$
Br 35				2 5		$^2P_{1\frac12}$
Kr 36				2 6		$^1S_0$
Rb 37	2	2 6	2 6 10	2 6	1	$^2S_{\frac12}$
Sr 38					2	$^1S_0$
Y 39				1	2	$^2D_{1\frac12}$
Zr 40				2	2	$^3F_2$
Nb 41			36	4	1	$^6D_{\frac12}$
Mo 42				5	1	$^7S_3$
Tc 43			Kr core	5	2	$^6S_{2\frac12}$
Ru 44				7	1	$^5F_5$
Rh 45				8	1	$^4F_{4\frac12}$
Pd 46				10		$^1S_0$

Atom	K L M N	N 4f	O 5s 5p 5d 5f	P 6s 6p 6d	Q 7s	Ground level
Ag 47			1			$^2S_{\frac12}$
Cd 48			2			^1S
In 49			2 1			$^2P^0_{\frac12}$
Sn 50			2 2			^3P
Sb 51			2 3			$^4S^0_{1\frac12}$
Te 52			2 4			^3P
I 53			2 5			$^2P^0_{1\frac12}$
Xe 54			2 6			^1S
Cs 55			2 6	1		$^2S_{\frac12}$
Ba 56			8	2		^1S
La 57	N 4s 4p 4d)		1	2		$^2D_{1\frac12}$
Ce 58		1	2 6 1	2		^3H
Pr 59		3		2		$^4I_{4\frac12}$
Nd 60		4		2		^5I
Pm 61		5		2		$^6H^0_{2\frac12}$
Sm 62	M 3s 3p 3d,	6		2		^7F
Eu 63		7		2		$^8S^0_{3\frac12}$
Gd 64		7	1	2		^9D
Tb 65		9	8	2		$^6H^0_{7\frac12}$
Dy 66		10		2		^5I
Ho 67		11		2		$^4I^0_{7\frac12}$
Er 68		12		2		^3H
Tm 69	L 2s 2p,	13		2		$^2F^0_{3\frac12}$
Yb 70		14		2		^1S
Lu 71		14	1	2		$^2D_{2\frac12}$
Hf 72	(K 1s,	14	2 6 2	2		^3F
Ta 73			3	2		$^4F_{1\frac12}$
W 74			4	2		^5D
Re 75	46 + 22		5	2		$^6S_{2\frac12}$
Os 76			6	2		^5D
Ir 77			7	2		$^4F_{1\frac12}$
Pt 78			9	1		^3D
Au 79	Pd core	14	2 6 10	1		$^2S_{\frac12}$
Hg 80				2		^1S
Tl 81				2 1		$^2P^0_{\frac12}$
Pb 82				2 2		^3P
Bi 83	46 + 32			2 3		$^4S^0_{1\frac12}$
Po 84	46			2 4		^3P
At 85				2 5		$^2P^0_{1\frac12}$
Rn 86				2 6		^1S
Fr 87		14	2 6 10	2 6	1	$^2S_{\frac12}$
Ra 88					2	^1S
Ac 89				1	2	$^2D_{1\frac12}$
Th 90	46 + 32		8	2	2	^3F
Pa 91			2	1	2	$^4K_{5\frac12}?$
U 92			3	1	2	^5L

New elements [2]

| Atom | O
5f | P | | | Q | Ground
level |
		6s	6p	7d	7s	
Np 93	4	2	6	1	2	$^6L_{5\frac{1}{2}}$
Pu 94	6	2	6		2	$^7F_0$
Am 95	7	2	6		2	$^8S^0_{3\frac{1}{2}}$
Cm 96	7	2	6	1	2	$^9D^0_2$

[1] *A.Q.* 1, § 24.
[2] C. E. MOORE, *Atomic Energy Levels*, N.B.S. Circ. No. 467, 1949, 1952, 1958; and private
  communications.
[3] R. F. BACHER and S. GOUDSMIT, *Atomic Energy States*, McGraw-Hill, 1932.

§ 25. Spectrum Line Intensities

Quantities

f = oscillator strength, or effective number of electrons in an atom. Unless
  otherwise stated the absorption oscillator strength f_{abs} will be understood. This is related to the emission oscillator strength f_{em} (which
  is negative) by
$$g_1 f_{abs} = -g_2 f_{em}$$
  where 1 is the lower and 2 the upper state. Then $f_{12} = f_{abs}$ and
  $f_{21} = f_{em}$

g = statistical weight; subscripts denote level, term, etc.
$$g(\text{level}) = 2J+1; \qquad g(\text{term}) = (2S+1)(2L+1)$$

gf = weighted oscillator strength = $g_1 f_{12} = -g_2 f_{21}$. gf is symmetrical
  between emission and absorption and is additive for lines, multiplets,
  etc.

A = spontaneous transition probability (for a downward transition)
 = reciprocal mean life in simple cases.

B_{12} and B_{21} = induced transition probability upward and downward. $B\,u(\nu)$ = probability of transition when $u(\nu)$ is the radiation density at the frequency ν of the transition. The B coefficients are sometimes defined
  in relation to radiation intensity instead of density.

S = line strength (electric dipole $e^2|x|^2$ unless otherwise stated). $S_{12} = S_{21}$

γ_{cl} = classical damping constant. $\gamma_{cl}/2\pi$ = classical whole-$\frac{1}{2}$-width of line in
  frequency units.

γ_2 = reciprocal mean life of level 2
$$= \sum_1 A_{21} + \sum_1 B_{21} u(\nu_{21}) + \sum_3 B_{23} u(\nu_{23}) + \text{collision terms}$$
  where levels 1 are below and levels 3 are above 2.

γ = damping constant = $\gamma_1 + \gamma_2$ for transition $1 \to 2$.

σ_2 = atomic scattering coefficient near an absorption line.

ν_0 = frequency at line centre.

σ_1 = integrated atomic scattering coefficient for a spectrum line = $\int \sigma_\nu \, d\nu$

R_1 and R_f. R_1/r and R_f/r are initial and final radial wave functions of the active electron normalized in atomic units. r = radius.

σ, ρ = Quantities related to radial wave functions (not connected with σ_v or σ_1).

$\mathscr{S}$ = relative multiplet strength, scale of § 26.

$\mathscr{S}(\mathscr{M})$ = relative multiplet strength, scale of § 27.

$S(\mathscr{M})$ = total absolute multiplet strength = $\sigma^2 \mathscr{S}(\mathscr{M})$.

N_1 = number of atoms per unit volume in level 1 (the lower level).

E = energy emitted by a line in all directions per unit volume and time.

Relations

$$g_2 A_{21} = g_2 \frac{8\pi h\nu^3}{c^3} B_{21} = g_1 \frac{8\pi h\nu^3}{c^3} B_{12} = \frac{64\pi^4}{3h\lambda^3} S_{12 \text{ or } 21}$$

$$= 3\gamma_{\rm cl} g_1 f_{12} = -3\gamma_{\rm cl} g_2 f_{21} = \frac{8\pi^2 e^2 \nu^2}{mc^3} g_1 f_{12}$$

$$\gamma_{\rm cl} = \frac{8\pi^2 e^2 \nu^2}{3mc^3} = \frac{8\pi^2 e^2}{3mc\lambda^2}$$

$$gf = g_1 f_{12} = -g_2 f_{21} = \frac{mh\nu}{\pi e^2} g_1 B_{12} = \frac{8\pi^2 m\nu}{3he^2} S_{12}$$

$$g_1 B_{12} = g_2 B_{21} = \frac{8\pi^3}{3h^2} S_{12}$$

$$E = N_2 A_{21} h\nu = \frac{N_2}{g_2} \frac{8\pi^2 e^2 h\nu^3}{mc^3} g_1 f_{12} = N_2 \frac{8\pi^2 e^2 h\nu^3}{mc^3} (-f_{21})$$

$$= N_2 \frac{8\pi^2 e^2 h}{m\lambda^3} (-f_{21})$$

$$\sigma^2 = \frac{\rho^2}{4l^2 - 1} = \frac{1}{4l^2 - 1} \left(\int_0^\infty R_1 R_f \, r \, dr \right)^2$$

l being the greater of the two orbital quantum numbers involved in the transition.

$$\sigma_1 = \int \sigma_v \, d\nu = \frac{\pi e^2}{mc} f_{\rm abs} N_1$$

$$\sigma_v = \frac{\pi e^2}{mc} f_{\rm abs} \frac{\gamma}{4\pi^2} \frac{N_1}{(\nu - \nu_0)^2 + (\gamma/4\pi)^2}$$

$$\sigma_{\nu_0} = \frac{4}{\gamma} \frac{\pi e^2}{mc} f_{\rm abs} N_1$$

Numerical relations

$$gf = 0.030\ 38\ S/\lambda$$

$$= 1.499 \times 10^{-8} g_2 A \lambda^2 \quad [S \text{ in atomic units, } \lambda \text{ in } \mu,\ A \text{ in s}^{-1}]$$

$$S = |x|^2/a_0^2 = 32.92 gf\lambda$$

$$= 4.94 \times 10^{-7} g_2 A \lambda^3 \quad [\text{same units}]$$

$$A = 2 \cdot 026 \times 10^6 \, S/g_2 \lambda^3 = 2 \cdot 677 \times 10^9 i^3 S/g_2$$

$$= 0 \cdot 667 \, 0 \times 10^8 gf/g_2 \lambda^2 \quad \text{[same units, and } i = \text{wave number in Rydbergs]}$$

$$\sigma_1 = \int \sigma_\nu \, d\nu = \frac{\pi e^2}{mc} f_{\text{abs}} N_1$$

$$= 0 \cdot 026 \, 54 f_{\text{abs}} N_1 \quad [\sigma \text{ in cm}^{-1}, \, \nu \text{ in s}^{-1}, \, N_1 \text{ in cm}^{-3}]$$

$$f = 4 \cdot 318 \times 10^{-9} \int \epsilon_\nu \, d(1/\lambda)$$

where ϵ_ν is the molar extinction coefficient such that $\epsilon_\nu l C = -\log (I/I_0)$ with l = path length in cm, C = concentration in moles/litre, and $d(1/\lambda)$ in cm^{-1}.

$$\gamma_{\text{cl}} = 0 \cdot 222 \, 3 \times 10^8 / \lambda^2 \text{ s}^{-1} \quad [\lambda \text{ in } \mu]$$

$$8 \pi h \nu^3 / c^3 = 8 \pi h / \lambda^3 = 1 \cdot 665 \times 10^{-13} / \lambda^3 \quad [\lambda \text{ in } \mu]$$

Atomic unit for S (electric dipole)

$$a_0^2 e^2 = 6 \cdot 459 \times 10^{-36} \text{ cm}^2 \text{ E.S.U.}^2$$

Electric quadrupole and magnetic dipole

$$g_2 A_{21} = \frac{32 \pi^6 \nu^5}{5 h c^5} S_{\text{q}} = 2 \, 674 \, i^5 S_{\text{q}} \quad \text{s}^{-1} \quad [i \text{ in Rydbergs, } S_{\text{q}} \text{ in atomic units}]$$

where the atomic unit for the electric quadrupole strength S_{q} is $a_0^4 e^2 = 1 \cdot 808 \, 8 \times 10^{-52} \text{ cm}^4 \text{ E.S.U.}^2$

$$g_2 A_{21} = \frac{64 \pi^4 \nu^3}{3 h c^3} S_{\text{m}} = 35 \, 660 \, i^3 S_{\text{m}} \quad \text{s}^{-1} \quad [i \text{ in Rydbergs, } S_{\text{m}} \text{ in atomic units}]$$

where the atomic unit for magnetic dipole strength S_{m} is $e^2 h^2 / 16 \pi^2 m^2 c^2 = 0 \cdot 859 \, 9 \times 10^{-40} \text{ erg}^2 \text{ gauss}^{-2}$

Absolute intensities

Absolute values of f, A, B, and S may be determined by (a) evaluating σ^2, (b) using an f-summation rule, or (c) absolute measurements.

A general method [2] for evaluating σ gives

$$\sigma = \frac{1}{Z} \mathscr{F}(n_l^*, l) \mathscr{I}(n_{l-1}^*, n_l^*, l)$$

where Z is degree of ionization (1 for neutral, 2 for singly ionized, etc.), l is the higher of the two orbital quantum numbers (which differ by 1), and n^* the effective principal quantum number $= Z/(\chi - W)^{1/2}$ with χ and W the ionization and excitation energy in Rydbergs. The functions $\mathscr{F}$ and $\mathscr{I}$ have been tabulated [2].

Kuhn-Thomas-Reiche f-sum rule

$$\sum_1 f_{21} + \sum_3 f_{23} = z$$

where the summations are for levels 1 below the selected level 2, and 3 above that level (including the continuum). z = number of optical electrons, f_{21} is negative and hence for upward transitions $\sum_3 f_{23} \geqslant z$. The rule may be applied to alkali metals and earths.

Application of the f-sum rule in more complex spectra where the lines concerned are mainly the lowest members of their series and therefore contain most of the total oscillator strength [3]

$$\sum_a g_t f = b r g_t - \sum_1 g_t f$$

where g_t represents the weight of the term and $g_t f$ is the weighted oscillator strength for the multiplet. r is the number of electrons involved in the transition. The summation on the left is to upper arrays (usually only one or two) and the emission component $-\sum_1 g_t f$ summed to lower l terms, is often zero but otherwise positive. $b \simeq 0.7$.

Wigner-Kirkwood rule for 1 electron jump [1]

$$\text{for } l \to l-1 \quad \sum f = -\frac{1}{3}\frac{l(2l-1)}{2l+1}$$

$$\text{for } l \to l+1 \quad \sum f = \frac{1}{3}\frac{(l+1)(2l+3)}{2l+1} \quad [l = \text{orbital quantum number}]$$

• for example

$$p \to ns \quad \sum f = -1/9 \qquad s \to np \quad \sum f = 1$$
$$d \to np \quad \sum f = -2/5 \qquad p \to nd \quad \sum f = 10/9$$

This rule may sometimes be used for complicated spectra; it applies precisely for hydrogen.

[1] *A.Q.* **1**, § 26.
[2] D. R. BATES and A. DAMGAARD, *Phil. Trans.*, **242**, 101, 1949.
[3] C. W. ALLEN, *M.N.*, **121**, 299, 1960.

§ 26. Relative Strengths Within Multiplets

The tables of relative strengths of lines in multiplets are based on LS coupling. The total strength $\mathscr{S}$ for each multiplet is made an integral number by selecting

$$\mathscr{S} = g_1 g_2/(2S_m+1) = (2S_m+1)(2L_1+1)(2L_2+1)$$

where g_1 and g_2 are the total weights of the initial and final terms, $(2S_m+1)$ is the multiplicity and S_m the spin, and L_1 and L_2 are the orbital quanta. It should be noted that $\mathscr{S}$ is not in general the same as $\mathscr{S}(\mathscr{M})$ of § 27. The strengths of the main diagonal are $x_1, x_2, \ldots$; the first satellites $y_1, y_2, \ldots$; and the second satellites $z_1, z_2, \ldots$. The multiplet arrangements are

Normal multiplets SP, PD, DF, etc.   *Symmetrical multiplets PP, DD, etc.*

	J_m	J_m-1	J_m-2	J_m-3	J_m-4
J_m-1	x_1	y_1	z_1		
J_m-2		x_2	y_2	z_2	
J_m-3			x_3	y_3	z_3
J_m-4				x_4	y_4

	J_m	J_m-1	J_m-2	J_m-3
J_m	x_1	y_1		
J_m-1	y_1	x_2	y_2	
J_m-2		y_2	x_3	y_3
J_m-3			y_3	x_4

The maximum inner quantum number J_m is S_m+L_m, where L_m is the orbital quantum number (the greater of the two in the case of normal multiplets). With the selected $\mathscr{S}$ the summed strengths of rows and columns of multiplets (in the above arrangement) are whole numbers. Since the total strength $\mathscr{S}$ is tabulated it is easy to determine the strength of a line relative to its multiplet.

Logarithmic tabulations of multiplet intensities are available [2], and also tabulations in which the first line of the leading diagonal x_1 is fixed at 100 [3, 4].

	Multiplicity										
	1	2	3	4	5	6	7	8	9	10	11
SP											
$\mathscr{S}$	3	6	9	12	15	18	21	24	27	30	33
x_1	3·0	4·0	5·0	6·0	7·0	8·0	9·0	10·0	11·0	12·0	13·0
y_1		2·0	3·0	4·0	5·0	6·0	7·0	8·0	9·0	10·0	11·0
z_1			1·0	2·0	3·0	4·0	5·0	6·0	7·0	8·0	9·0
PP											
$\mathscr{S}$	9	18	27	36	45	54	63	72	81	90	99
x_1	9·0	10·0	11·25	12·6	14·0	15·4	16·9	18·3	19·8	21·3	22·8
x_2		4·0	2·25	1·60	1·25	1·04	0·88	0·75	0·68	0·61	0·55
x_3			0·00	1·00	2·25	3·6	5·0	6·4	7·9	9·3	10·80
y_1		2·0	3·75	5·40	7·00	8·6	10·1	11·65	13·2	14·7	16·2
y_2			3·00	5·00	6·75	8·4	10·0	11·6	13·1	14·7	16·2
PD											
$\mathscr{S}$	15	30	45	60	75	90	105	120	135	150	165
x_1	15·0	18·0	21·0	24·0	27·0	30·0	33·0	36·0	39·0	42·0	45·0
x_2		10·0	11·25	12·6	14·0	15·4	16·9	18·3	19·8	21·3	22·8
x_3			5·0	5·0	5·25	5·6	6·0	6·4	6·9	7·3	7·8
y_1		2·0	3·75	5·40	7·00	8·6	10·1	11·65	13·2	14·7	16·2
y_2			3·75	6·40	8·75	11·0	13·1	15·2	17·3	19·3	21·4
y_3				5·00	6·75	8·4	10·0	11·6	13·1	14·7	16·2
z_1			0·25	0·60	1·00	1·43	1·88	2·33	2·80	3·27	3·75
z_2				1·00	2·25	3·60	5·0	6·4	7·86	9·3	10·8
z_3					3·00	6·0	9·0	12·0	15·0	18·0	21·0
DD											
$\mathscr{S}$	25	50	75	100	125	150	175	200	225	250	275
x_1	25·0	28·0	31·1	34·3	37·5	40·7	44·0	47·3	50·6	53·8	57·2
x_2		18·0	17·4	17·2	17·5	17·9	18·3	19·0	19·6	20·1	20·9
x_3			11·25	8·0	6·25	5·14	4·37	3·81	3·37	3·03	2·75
x_4				5·0	1·25	0·22	0·00	0·14	0·48	0·95	1·50
x_5					0·0	2·23	5·00	8·0	11·1	14·3	17·5
y_1		2·0	3·9	5·7	7·5	9·25	11·0	12·75	14·4	16·1	17·8
y_2			3·75	7·0	10·0	12·85	15·6	18·4	21·0	23·6	26·3
y_3				5·0	8·75	12·0	15·0	17·8	20·6	23·4	26·0
y_4					5·0	7·8	10·0	12·0	13·9	15·7	17·5

	Multiplicity										
	1	2	3	4	5	6	7	8	9	10	11
DF											
$\mathscr{S}$	35	70	105	140	175	210	245	280	315	350	385
x_1	35·0	40·0	45·0	50·0	55·0	60·0	65·0	70·0	75·0	80·0	85·0
x_2		28·0	31·1	34·3	37·5	40·7	44·0	47·3	50·6	53·8	57·2
x_3			21·0	22·5	24·0	25·8	27·5	29·4	31·2	33·1	35·0
x_4				14·0	14·0	14·4	15·0	15·7	16·5	17·4	18·2
x_5					7·0	6·2	6·0	6·0	6·1	6·3	6·5
y_1		2·0	3·9	5·7	7·5	9·2	11·0	12·8	14·4	16·1	17·8
y_2			3·9	7·3	10·5	13·6	16·5	19·4	22·2	25·1	27·8
y_3				5·6	10·0	13·9	17·5	21·0	24·4	27·5	30·8
y_4					7·0	11·4	15·0	18·3	21·4	24·4	27·3
y_5						7·8	10·0	12·0	13·9	15·7	17·5
z_1			0·11	0·29	0·50	0·74	1·00	1·28	1·56	1·84	2·14
z_2				0·40	1·00	1·71	2·50	3·33	4·20	5·10	6·0
z_3					1·00	2·40	4·0	5·7	7·5	9·3	11·2
z_4						2·22	5·0	8·0	11·1	14·3	17·5
z_5							5·0	10·0	15·0	20·0	25·0
FF											
$\mathscr{S}$	49	98	147	196	245	294	343	392	441	490	539
x_1	49·0	54·0	59·0	64·1	69·3	74·4	79·6	84·8	90·0	95·2	100·4
x_2		40·0	41·2	42·7	44·5	46·2	48·2	50·1	52·2	54·2	56·4
x_3			31·1	28·9	27·6	26·7	26·3	25·9	25·9	25·9	26·0
x_4				22·4	17·5	14·4	12·3	10·7	9·5	8·5	7·7
x_5					14·0	7·6	4·38	2·50	1·36	0·67	0·26
x_6						6·2	0·89	0·00	0·49	1·60	3·06
x_7							0·00	3·50	7·89	12·6	17·5
y_1		2·0	3·94	5·8	7·7	9·5	11·4	13·2	15·0	16·8	18·6
y_2			3·88	7·5	11·0	14·2	17·5	20·7	23·9	26·9	30·0
y_3				5·6	10·5	15·0	19·2	23·3	27·4	31·1	35·0
y_4					7·0	12·6	17·5	22·0	26·3	30·3	34·2
y_5						7·7	13·1	17·5	21·4	25·0	28·5
y_6							7·0	10·5	13·1	15·4	17·5

	Multiplicity										
	1	2	3	4	5	6	7	8	9	10	11
FG											
$\mathscr{S}$	63	126	189	252	315	378	441	504	567	630	693
x_1	63·0	70·0	77·0	84·0	91·0	98·0	105·0	112·0	119·0	126·0	133·0
x_2		54·0	59·0	64·1	69·3	74·4	79·6	84·8	90·0	95·2	100·4
x_3			45·0	48·2	51·5	55·0	58·4	62·0	65·8	69·3	73·0
x_4				36·0	37·5	39·3	41·2	43·4	45·5	47·8	49·9
x_5					27·0	27·0	27·5	28·3	29·3	30·4	31·5
x_6						18·0	16·9	16·5	16·5	16·8	17·0
x_7							9·0	7·5	6·9	6·6	6·5
y_1		2·0	3·94	5·8	7·7	9·5	11·4	13·2	15·0	16·8	18·6
y_2			3·94	7·6	11·2	14·5	17·9	21·2	24·4	27·6	30·7
y_3				5·8	11·0	15·7	20·2	24·6	28·9	33·0	37·1
y_4					7·5	13·7	19·2	24·5	29·3	34·0	38·5
y_5						9·0	15·6	21·2	26·3	31·0	35·5
y_6							10·1	16·0	20·6	24·6	28·5
y_7								10·5	13·2	15·4	17·5
z_1			0·06	0·17	0·30	0·46	0·62	0·81	1·00	1·20	1·41
z_2				0·21	0·56	1·00	1·50	2·05	2·63	3·23	3·85
z_3					0·50	1·29	2·25	3·34	4·51	5·7	7·0
z_4						1·00	2·50	4·29	6·25	8·3	10·5
z_5							1·88	4·50	7·5	10·7	14·0
z_6								3·50	7·9	12·6	17·5
z_7									7·0	14·0	21·0
GG											
$\mathscr{S}$	81	162	243	324	405	486	567	648	729		
x_1	81·0	88·0	95·0	102·1	109·2	116·4	123·4	130·6	137·7		
x_2		70·0	73·0	76·1	79·9	83·5	87·0	90·9	94·2		
x_3			59·0	58·4	58·4	59·0	59·6	60·4	61·3		
x_4				48·2	44·5	41·8	39·7	38·2	37·1		
x_5					37·5	30·9	26·3	22·8	20·2		
x_6						27·0	18·4	13·0	9·4		
x_7							16·9	7·7	3·36		
x_8								7·5	0·67		
x_9									0·00		
y_1		2·0	3·96	5·9	7·8	9·7	11·6	13·4	15·3		
y_2			3·94	7·7	11·4	14·9	18·4	21·8	25·1		
y_3				5·8	11·2	16·2	21·1	25·7	30·4		
y_4					7·5	14·2	20·2	26·0	31·5		
y_5						9·0	16·5	23·2	29·2		
y_6							10·1	17·8	24·3		
y_7								10·5	17·3		
y_8									9·0		

	Multiplicity							Multiplicity				
	1	2	3	4	5	6	7	1	2	3	4	5
	GH							HI				
$\mathscr{S}$	99	198	297	396	495	594	693	143	286	429	572	715
x_1	99·0	108·0	117·0	126·0	135·0	144·0	153·0	143·0	154·0	165·0	176·0	187·0
x_2		88·0	95·0	102·1	109·2	116·3	123·4		130·0	139·0	148·1	157·2
x_3			77·0	82·0	87·4	92·6	97·9			117·0	124·0	131·0
x_4				66·0	69·1	72·9	76·5				104·0	109·0
x_5					55·0	56·6	58·4					91·0
x_6						44·0	44·0					
x_7							33·0					
y_1		2·0	3·96	5·9	7·8	9·7	11·6		2·0	3·97	5·9	7·8
y_2			3·96	7·8	11·4	15·1	18·6			3·97	7·8	11·6
y_3				5·9	11·3	16·5	21·6				5·9	11·6
y_4					7·7	14·6	21·1					7·8
y_5						9·4	17·5					
y_6							11·0					
z_1			0·04	0·11	0·20	0·31	0·43			0·03	0·08	0·14
z_2				0·13	0·36	0·65	1·00				0·09	0·25
z_3					0·30	0·80	1·44					0·20
z_4						0·57	1·50					
z_5							1·00					

	HH						
$\mathscr{S}$	121	242	363	484	605	726	847
x_1	121·0	130·0	139·0	148·1	157·2	166·2	175·3
x_2		108·0	113·0	118·0	123·7	129·2	134·7
x_3			95·0	96·3	98·1	100·0	102·0
x_4				82·3	79·9	78·3	77·3
x_5					69·2	63·7	59·5
x_6						56·6	48·2
x_7							44·1
y_1		2·0	3·97	5·9	7·8	9·8	11·7
y_2			3·97	7·8	11·6	15·2	19·8
y_3				5·9	11·4	16·8	22·0
y_4					7·7	14·8	21·6
y_5						9·4	17·8
y_6							11·0

[1] *A.Q.* **1**, § 27.
[2] H. N. RUSSELL, *Ap. J.*, **83**, 129, 1936.
[3] H. E. WHITE and A. Y. ELIASON, *Phys. Rev.*, **44**, 753, 1933.
[4] E. U. CONDON and G. H. SHORTLEY, *Theory of Atomic Spectra*, p. 241, 1935.

§ 27. **Strengths of Multiplets**

The tables give the values of the sums of the angular matrices or relative multiplet strengths $\mathscr{S}(\mathscr{M})$ from which the absolute total multiplet strength $S(\mathscr{M}) = \sigma^2 \mathscr{S}(\mathscr{M})$ may be determined. Larger tabulations are available in [2], to be adjusted by the factors in [3]. Then the total weighted oscillator strength for a multiplet is

$$g_t f = \sum_{\text{mult}} gf = 0 \cdot 030\ 38\ \sigma^2 \mathscr{S}(\mathscr{M})/\lambda \quad [\lambda \text{ in } \mu]$$

$$= 0 \cdot 030\ 38\ S(\mathscr{M})/\lambda \quad [\lambda \text{ in } \mu]$$

The tables are arranged in the order $s, p, d, \ldots$. The orbital quantum number l of the jumping electron always changes by 1 and the *lower* value is on the left. When the total strength for two or more terms is known, but they are not known individually, then the known total strength is given and the number of terms involved is placed in front of the term symbol. For example $3\,^2D$ in the $p^3 - p^2d$ transition gives the combined strength of the three ^2D transitions.

The summation of rows and columns $\sum \mathscr{S}(\mathscr{M})$ is seen to obey the following rules.

Summation of terms with lower l (i.e. row summation)

$$\sum \mathscr{S}(\mathscr{M}) = k(2S+1)(2L+1)(l+1)(2l+3)$$

where k is the number of equivalent electrons (e.g. $k = 1$ for p, 2 for p^2, etc.). Although the jumping electron may be equivalent for the term being summed the rule will not apply if the jumping electron is equivalent in the configuration to (or from) which the transition is made.

Summation of terms with higher l (i.e. column summation)

$$\sum \mathscr{S}(\mathscr{M}) = k(2S+1)(2L+1)l(2l-1)$$

where k is the number of equivalent electrons. Again the rule will not apply for transitions connecting a configuration in which the jumping electron is equivalent.

Summation for whole transition array [4]

$$\sum \mathscr{S}(\mathscr{M}) = \tfrac{1}{2} l g_r [2(2l-1)+1-k_1][2(2l+1)+1-k_h]$$

where l is the *higher* orbital moment, g_r is the weight of the parent configuration (i.e. product of the incomplete shell weights, § 23), and k_1 and k_h the number of equivalent electrons involved in the low (l) and high (h) configurations respectively ($k = 1$ if electrons not equivalent, 2 for p^2, etc.).

Within a transition array

$$\sum f_{12} = \frac{0 \cdot 030\ 4}{\lambda} \frac{\sum \mathscr{S}(\mathscr{M})\sigma^2}{(2S+1)(2L+1)} \quad [\text{atomic units, } \lambda \text{ in } \mu]$$

$$= 0 \cdot 030\ 4\ \lambda^{-1} k(l+1)(2l+3)\sigma^2 \quad \text{for row summation}$$

or

$$= 0 \cdot 304 \lambda^{-1} kl(2l-1)\sigma^2 \quad \text{for column summation}$$

with the above restrictions on equivalent electrons.

Some of the ambiguities still remaining in the tables may be resolved by more recent analysis [5] but tabular information is not available.

[1] *A.Q.* 1, § 28.
[2] L. GOLDBERG, *Ap. J.*, **82**, 1, 1935.
[3] L. GOLDBERG, *Ap. J.*, **84**, 11, 1936.
[4] D. H. MENZEL, *Ap. J.*, **105**, 126, 1947.
[5] F. ROHRLICH, *Ap. J.*, **129**, 441, 449, 1959.

1 *electron*

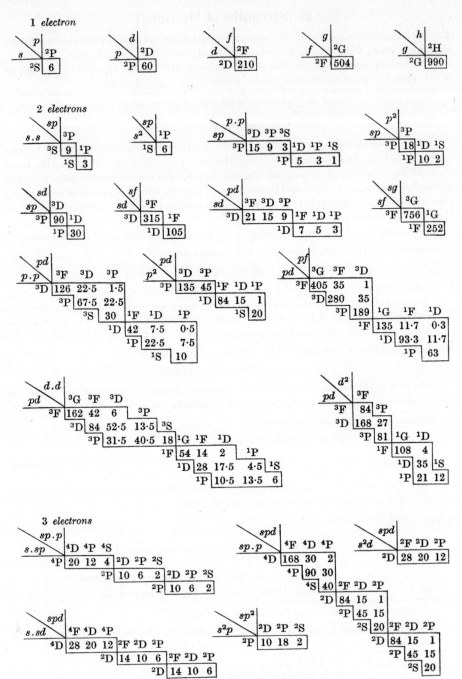

2 *electrons*

3 *electrons*

3 *electrons* [*contd.*]

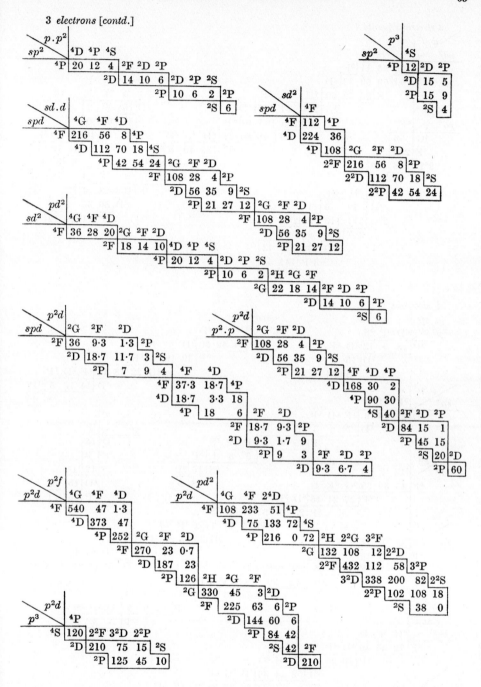

p.p² / sp²

	⁴D	⁴P	⁴S			
⁴P	20	12	4	²F	²D	²P
²D		14	10	6	²D	²P	²S
²P			10	6	2	²P
²S				6

p³ / sp²

	⁴S		
⁴P	12	²D	²P
²D		15	5
²P		15	9
²S		4

sd.d / spd

	⁴G	⁴F	⁴D			
⁴F	216	56	8	⁴P
⁴D	112	70	18	⁴S
⁴P	42	54	24	²G	²F	²D
²F	108	28	4	²P
²D	56	35	9	²S
²P	21	27	12	²G	²F	²D
²F	108	28	4	²P
²D	56	35	9	²S
²P	21	27	12

sd² / pd²

	⁴G	⁴F	⁴D			
⁴F	36	28	20	²G	²F	²D
²F	18	14	10	⁴D	⁴P	⁴S
⁴P	20	12	4	²D	²P	²S
²P	10	6	2	²H	²G	²F
²G	22	18	14	²F	²D	²P
²D	14	10	6	²P
²S	6

sd² / spd

	⁴F		
⁴F	112	⁴P
⁴D	224	36
⁴P	108	²G	²F	²D
2²F	216	56	8	²P
2²D	112	70	18	²S
2²P	42	54	24
²F	108	28	4	²P
²D	56	35	9	²S
²P	21	27	12
²G	22	18	14	²F	²D	²P
²D	14	10	6	²P
²S	6

p²d / spd

	²G	²F	²D		
²F	36	9·3	1·3	²P
²D	18·7	11·7	3	²S
²P	7	9	4	⁴F	⁴D
⁴F	37·3	18·7	⁴P
⁴D	18·7	3·3	18
⁴P	18	6	²F	²D
²F	18·7	9·3	²P
²D	9·3	1·7	9
²P	9	3	²F	²D	²P
²D	9·3	6·7	4

p²d / p².p

	²G	²F	²D			
²F	108	28	4	²P
²D	56	35	9	²S
²P	21	27	12	⁴F	⁴D	⁴P
⁴D	168	30	2
⁴P	90	30
⁴S	40	²F	²D	²P
²D	84	15	1
²P	45	15
²S	20	²D
²P	60

p²f / p²d

	⁴G	⁴F	⁴D			
⁴F	540	47	1·3
⁴D	373	47
⁴P	252	²G	²F	²D
²F	270	23	0·7
²D	187	23
²P	126	²H	²G	²F
²G	330	45	3	²D
²F	225	63	6	²P
²D	144	60	6
²P	84	42
²S	42	²F
²D	210

pd² / p²d

	⁴G	⁴F	2⁴D			
⁴F	108	233	51	⁴P
⁴D	75	133	72	⁴S
⁴P	216	0	72	²H	2²G	3²F
²G	132	108	12	2²D
2²F	432	112	58	3²P
3²D	338	200	82	2²S
2²P	102	108	18
²S	38	0

p²d / p³

	⁴P			
⁴S	120	2²F	3²D	2²P
²D	210	75	15	²S
²P	125	45	10

3 electrons [contd.]

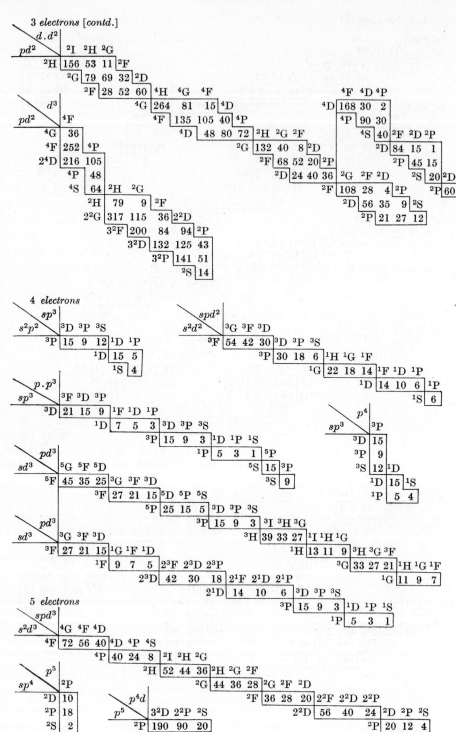

```
        d.d²
pd²           ²I   ²H   ²G
²H    | 156   53   11 | ²F
²G    |  79   69   32 | ²D
²F    |  28   52   60 |    ⁴H   ⁴G   ⁴F
                ⁴G | 264   81   15 | ⁴D
                ⁴F | 135  105   40 | ⁴P
                ⁴D |  48   80   72 |   ²H   ²G   ²F
                              ²G | 132   40    8 | ²D
                              ²F |  68   52   20 | ²P
                              ²D |  24   40   36 |   ²G   ²F   ²D
                                            ²F | 108   28    4 | ²P
                                            ²D |  56   35    9 | ²S
                                            ²P |  21   27   12

                                                    ⁴F   ⁴D   ⁴P
                                            ⁴D | 168   30    2
                                            ⁴P |  90   30
                                            ⁴S |  40 | ²F   ²D   ²P
                                                  ²D |  84   15    1
                                                  ²P |  45   15
                                                        ²S |  20 | ²D
                                                        ²P | 60

        d³
pd²     ⁴F
⁴G  |  36
⁴F  | 252 | ⁴P
2⁴D | 216  105
⁴P  |  48
⁴S  |  64 |  ²H   ²G
      ²H  |  79    9 | ²F
      2²G | 317  115   36 | 2²D
      3²F | 200   84   94 | ²P
      3²D | 132  125   43
      3²P | 141   51
            ²S  |  14
```

4 electrons

```
        sp³                               spd²
s²p²          ³D   ³P   ³S      s²d²          ³G   ³F   ³D
³P | 15    9   12 | ¹D  ¹P      ³F | 54   42   30 | ³D  ³P  ³S
      ¹D | 15    5              ³P | 30   18    6 | ¹H  ¹G  ¹F
      ¹S |  4                         ¹G | 22   18   14 | ¹F  ¹D  ¹P
                                            ¹D | 14   10    6 | ¹P
                                            ¹S |  6

        p.p³
sp³        ³F   ³D   ³P
³D | 21   15    9 | ¹F  ¹D  ¹P
      ¹D |  7    5    3 | ³D  ³P  ³S
            ³P | 15    9    3 | ¹D  ¹P  ¹S
                  ¹P |  5    3    1 | ⁵P
                              ⁵S | 15 | ³P                    p⁴
                                    ³S |  9          sp³        ³P
        pd³                                          ³D | 15
sd³        ⁵G   ⁵F   ⁵D                               ³P |  9
⁵F | 45   35   25 | ³G  ³F  ³D                        ³S | 12 | ¹D
      ³F | 27   21   15 | ⁵D  ⁵P  ⁵S                        ¹D | 15 | ¹S
            ⁵P | 25   15    5 | ³D  ³P  ³S                        ¹P |  5    4
                  ³P | 15    9    3 | ³I  ³H  ³G
                        ³H | 39   33   27 | ¹I  ¹H  ¹G
        pd³                   ¹H | 13   11    9 | ³H  ³G  ³F
sd³        ³G   ³F   ³D              ³G | 33   27   21 | ¹H  ¹G  ¹F
³F | 27   21   15 | ¹G  ¹F  ¹D             ¹G | 11    9    7
      ¹F |  9    7    5 | 2³F 2³D 2³P
            2³D | 42   30   18 | 2¹F 2¹D 2¹P
                  2¹D | 14   10    6 | ³D  ³P  ³S
                              ³P | 15    9    3 | ¹D  ¹P  ¹S
                                    ¹P |  5    3    1
```

5 electrons

```
        spd³
s²d³         ⁴G   ⁴F   ⁴D
⁴F | 72   56   40 | ⁴D  ⁴P  ⁴S
      ⁴P | 40   24    8 | ²I  ²H  ²G
            ²H | 52   44   36 | ²H  ²G  ²F
        p⁵        ²G | 44   36   28 | ²G  ²F  ²D
sp⁴     ²P              ²F | 36   28   20 | 2²F 2²D 2²P
²D | 10                       2²D | 56   40   24 | ²D  ²P  ²S
²P | 18         p⁴d                        ²P | 20   12    4
²S |  2    p⁵         3²D 2²P  ²S
           ²P | 190   90   20
```

§ 28. Permitted Atomic Oscillator Strengths

The notation used for the table of permitted atomic oscillator strengths is from § 25. The units used for expressing the multiplet or line intensities are weighted oscillator strengths; $g_t f$ for multiplets, and gf for lines. Strengths, transition probabilities, emission rates, etc. may be derived from these by use of the relations in § 25.

In order that the tabulation may cover as wide a field of spectra as possible the intensity data is restricted to $g_t f$ for the whole multiplet and gf for the leading line only. Either of these may be used for deriving the gf for other lines if the rules of § 26 are satisfied, otherwise the leading gf and measured relative intensity (from the original sources) should be used. Note particularly that the gf column refers only to the line defined by the two preceding columns even if other lines are not resolved from it in normal practice.

The multiplet numbers are from [2, 3], and are labeled u when the ultra-violet table [3] is used. In the last column C indicates that a Coulomb approximation has been used for computing the gf values (usually by the use of the Bates-Damgaard tables [4]), f indicates that absolute values have been determined by an f-sum rule (§ 25).

Permitted atomic oscillator strengths

Atom	Transition		Multiplet			Line			Notes
		No.	Desig.	$g_t f$	J	λ	gf		
H I	Lα　$1s$–$2p$	1u	^{2}S–^{2}P^0	0·832 4	$\frac{1}{2}$–$1\frac{1}{2}$	Å 1215	0·554 9		C [1, 16]
Lyman	Lβ　$1s$–$3p$	2u	^{2}S–^{2}P^0	0·158 2	$\frac{1}{2}$–$1\frac{1}{2}$	1025	0·105 5		,,
series	Lγ　$1s$–$4p$	3u	^{2}S–^{2}P^0	0·058 0	$\frac{1}{2}$–$1\frac{1}{2}$	972	0·038 7		,,
	Lδ　$1s$–$5p$	4u	^{2}S–^{2}P^0	0·027 9	$\frac{1}{2}$–$1\frac{1}{2}$	949	0·018 6		,,
	Lϵ　$1s$–$6p$	5u	^{2}S–^{2}P^0	0·015 6	$\frac{1}{2}$–$1\frac{1}{2}$	937	0·010 4		,,
	Lζ　$1s$–$7p$	6u	^{2}S–^{2}P^0	0·009 6	$\frac{1}{2}$–$1\frac{1}{2}$	930	0·006 4		,,
	Lη　$1s$–$8p$	7u	^{2}S–^{2}P^0	0·006 4	$\frac{1}{2}$–$1\frac{1}{2}$	926	0·004 3		,,
	Lθ　$1s$–$9p$	8u	^{2}S–^{2}P^0	0·004 4	$\frac{1}{2}$–$1\frac{1}{2}$	923	0·002 9		,,
	Lι　$1s$–$10p$	9u	^{2}S–^{2}P^0	0·003 2	$\frac{1}{2}$–$1\frac{1}{2}$	920	0·002 1		,,
	Lκ　$1s$–$11p$	10u	^{2}S–^{2}P^0	0·002 4	$\frac{1}{2}$–$1\frac{1}{2}$	919	0·001 6		,,
	Lλ　$1s$–$12p$	11u	^{2}S–^{2}P^0	0·001 8	$\frac{1}{2}$–$1\frac{1}{2}$	918	0·001 2		,,
	limiting $1s$–np			$3·2n^{-3}$	$\frac{1}{2}$–$1\frac{1}{2}$	912	$2·1n^{-3}$		,,
	Lyman total			1·128 2					
	$1s$ continuum			0·817 8					
Balmer	$2s$–$3p$			^{2}S–^{2}P^0	0·869 7	$\frac{1}{2}$–$1\frac{1}{2}$	6562	0·579 8	,,
series	$2p$–$3s$			^{2}P^0–^{2}S	0·081 5	$1\frac{1}{2}$–$\frac{1}{2}$	,,	0·054 3	
	$2p$–$3d$			^{2}P^0–^{2}D	4·174 7	$1\frac{1}{2}$–$2\frac{1}{2}$	,,	2·504 8	
	Hα	1		5·126 0		6562			
	$2s$–$4p$			^{2}S–^{2}P^0	0·205 5	$\frac{1}{2}$–$1\frac{1}{2}$	4861	0·137 0	,,
	$2p$–$4s$			^{2}P^0–^{2}S	0·018 3	$1\frac{1}{2}$–$\frac{1}{2}$	,,	0·012 2	
	$2p$–$4d$			^{2}P^0–^{2}D	0·730 8	$1\frac{1}{2}$–$2\frac{1}{2}$	,,	0·438 5	
	Hβ	1		0·954 6		4861			
	$2s$–$5p$			^{2}S–^{2}P^0	0·083 9	$\frac{1}{2}$–$1\frac{1}{2}$	4340	0·055 9	,,
	$2p$–$5s$			^{2}P^0–^{2}S	0·007 3	$1\frac{1}{2}$–$\frac{1}{2}$	,,	0·004 9	
	$2p$–$5d$			^{2}P^0–^{2}D	0·266 2	$1\frac{1}{2}$–$2\frac{1}{2}$	,,	0·159 7	
	Hγ	1		0·357 3		4340			

Atom	Transition	Multiplet			Line			Notes
		No.	Desig.	$g_t f$	J	λ	gf	
						Å		
H I Balmer series (contd.)	$2s-6p$		$^2S-^2P^0$	0·043 2	$\frac{1}{2}-1\frac{1}{2}$	4101	0·028 8	[C 1, 16]
	$2p-6s$		$^2P^0-^2S$	0·003 7	$1\frac{1}{2}-\frac{1}{2}$	,,	0·002 5	
	$2p-6d$		$^2P^0-^2D$	0·129 8	$1\frac{1}{2}-2\frac{1}{2}$	,,	0·077 8	
	Hδ	1		0·176 7		4101		
	$2s-7p$		$^2S-^2P^0$	0·025 5	$\frac{1}{2}-1\frac{1}{2}$	3970	0·017 0	,,
	$2p-7s$		$^2P^0-^2S$	0·002 2	$1\frac{1}{2}-\frac{1}{2}$	,,	0·001 5	
	$2p-7d$		$^2P^0-^2D$	0·074 0	$1\frac{1}{2}-2\frac{1}{2}$	,,	0·044 4	
	Hϵ	1		0·101 6		3970		
	$2s-8p$		$^2S-^2P^0$	0·016 4	$\frac{1}{2}-1\frac{1}{2}$	3889	0·010 8	,,
	$2p-8s$		$^2P^0-^2S$	0·001 4	$1\frac{1}{2}-\frac{1}{2}$	,,	0·000 9	
	$2p-8d$		$^2P^0-^2D$	0·046 5	$1\frac{1}{2}-2\frac{1}{2}$	,,	0·027 9	
	Hζ	2		0·064 3		3889		
	Hη	2		0·043 4		3835		,,
	Hθ	2		0·030 8		3797		
	Hι	2		0·022 7		3770		
	Hκ	2		0·017 2		3750		
	limiting $2s-np$		$^2S-^2P^0$	$7·4n^{-3}$	$\frac{1}{2}-1\frac{1}{2}$	3646	$4·9n^{-3}$	,,
	$2p-ns$		$^2P^0-^2S$	$0·7n^{-3}$	$1\frac{1}{2}-\frac{1}{2}$	,,	$0·5n^{-3}$	
	$2p-nd$		$^2P^0-^2D$	$19·8n^{-3}$	$1\frac{1}{2}-2\frac{1}{2}$	,,	$11·8n^{-3}$	
	H(n)			$28\ n^{-3}$		3646		
	total $2s-np$		$^2S-^2P^0$	1·27	$\frac{1}{2}-1\frac{1}{2}$		0·85	,,
	$2p-ns$		$^2P^0-^2S$	0·12	$1\frac{1}{2}-\frac{1}{2}$		0·08	
	$2p-nd$		$^2P^0-^2D$	5·54	$1\frac{1}{2}-2\frac{1}{2}$		3·35	
	Balmer total			6·93				
	$2s-p$ continuum			0·724				
	$2p-s$,,			0·048				
	$2p-d$,,			1·128				
	Balmer ,,			1·900				
Paschen series	$3s-4p$		$^2S-^2P^0$	0·970	$\frac{1}{2}-1\frac{1}{2}$	18751	0·647	,,
	$3p-4s$		$^2P^0-^2S$	0·19	$1\frac{1}{2}-\frac{1}{2}$	,,	0·128	
	$3p-4d$		$^2P^0-^2D$	3·72	$1\frac{1}{2}-2\frac{1}{2}$	,,	2·23	
	$3d-4p$		$^2D-^2P^0$	0·110	$2\frac{1}{2}-1\frac{1}{2}$	,,	0·066	
	$3d-4f$		$^2D-^2F^0$	10·16	$2\frac{1}{2}-3\frac{1}{2}$	,,	5·80	
	Pα	8		15·158		18751		
	$3s-5p$		$^2S-^2P^0$	0·242	$\frac{1}{2}-1\frac{1}{2}$	12818	0·161	,,
	$3p-5s$		$^2P^0-^2S$	0·043	$1\frac{1}{2}-\frac{1}{2}$	,,	0·029	
	$3p-5d$		$^2P^0-^2D$	0·835	$1\frac{1}{2}-2\frac{1}{2}$	,,	0·500	
	$3d-5p$		$^2D-^2P^0$	0·022	$2\frac{1}{2}-1\frac{1}{2}$	,,	0·013	
	$3d-5f$		$^2D-^2F^0$	1·565	$2\frac{1}{2}-3\frac{1}{2}$	,,	0·894	
	Pβ	8		2·710		12818		
	Pγ	8		1·005		10938		,,
	Pδ	8		0·498		10049		
	Pϵ	8		0·289		9545		
	Pζ	8		0·184		9229		
	Pη	9		0·126		9014		
	Pθ	9		0·090		8862		

Atom	Transition	Multiplet			Line			Notes
		No.	Desig.	$g_t f$	J	λ	gf	
						Å		
H I	$4s$–$5p$		^{2}S–^{2}P^0	1·09	$\frac{1}{2}$–$1\frac{1}{2}$	40512	0·73	C [1, 16]
Brackett	$4p$–$5s$		^{2}P^0–^{2}S	0·318	$1\frac{1}{2}$–$\frac{1}{2}$	,,	0·212	
series	$4p$–$5d$		^{2}P^0–^{2}D	3·66	$1\frac{1}{2}$–$2\frac{1}{2}$	,,	2·20	
	$4d$–$5p$		^{2}D–^{2}P^0	0·273	$2\frac{1}{2}$–$1\frac{1}{2}$	,,	0·164	
	$4d$–$5f$		^{2}D–^{2}F^0	8·90	$2\frac{1}{2}$–$3\frac{1}{2}$	,,	5·09	
	$4f$–$5d$		^{2}F^0–^{2}D	0·124	$3\frac{1}{2}$–$2\frac{1}{2}$	,,	0·071	
	$4f$–$5g$		^{2}F^0–^{2}G	18·83	$3\frac{1}{2}$–$4\frac{1}{2}$	,,	10·45	
	Bα			33·21		40512		
	Bβ			5·74		26252		,,
	Bγ			2·10		21656		
	Bδ			1·03		19445		
He II								
Li III		Hydrogen-like ions have values of $g_t f$ and gf as for analogous hydrogen lines.						
Be IV								
B V								
He I	$1s^2$–$1s2p$	2u	^{1}S–^{1}P^0	0·35	0–1	584	0·35	[1, 6, 17]
	$1s^2$–$1s3p$	3u	^{1}S–^{1}P^0	0·071	0–1	537	0·071	,,
	$1s^2$–$1s4p$	4u	^{1}S–^{1}P^0	0·028	0–1	522	0·028	,,
	$1s2s$–$1s2p$	1	^{3}S–^{3}P^0	1·75	1–2	10830	0·97	,,
			^{1}S–^{1}P^0	0·375	0–1	20582	0·375	,,
	$1s2s$–$1s3p$	2	^{3}S–^{3}P^0	0·19	1–2	3888	0·11	[18]
		4	^{1}S–^{1}P^0	0·17	0–1	5015	0·17	[1, 6, 17]
	$1s2s$–$1s4p$	3	^{3}S–^{3}P^0	0·08	1–2	3187	0·04	,,
		5	^{1}S–^{1}P^0	0·058	0–1	3964	0·058	,,
	$1s2p$–$1s3s$	10	^{3}P^0–^{3}S	0·64	2–1	7065	0·36	,,
		45	^{1}P^0–^{1}S	0·140	1–0	7281	0·140	,,
	$1s2p$–$1s4s$	12	^{3}P^0–^{3}S	0·10	2–1	4713	0·06	,,
		47	^{1}P^0–^{1}S	0·022	1–0	5047	0·022	,,
	$1s2p$–$1s3d$	11	^{3}P^0–^{3}D	5·61	2–3	5875	2·62	,,
		46	^{1}P^0–^{1}D	2·18	1–2	6678	2·18	,,
	$1s2p$–$1s4d$	14	^{3}P^0–^{3}D	1·10	2–3	4471	0·51	,,
		48	^{1}P^0–^{1}D	0·36	1–2	4921	0·36	,,
	$1s2p$–$1s5d$	18	^{3}P^0–^{3}D	0·42	2–3	4026	0·20	,,
		51	^{1}P^0–^{1}D	0·129	1–2	4387	0·129	,,
Li I	$2s$–$2p$	1	^{2}S–^{2}P^0	1·59	$\frac{1}{2}$–$1\frac{1}{2}$	6707	1·06	[1, 5, 22]
Be I	$2s2p$–$2s3s$	1	^{3}P^0–^{3}S	0·31	2–1	3321	0·17	C [5]
Be II	$2s$–$2p$	1	^{2}S–^{2}P^0	1·05	$\frac{1}{2}$–$1\frac{1}{2}$	3130	0·70	C, f [22]
C I	$2p^2$–$2p3s$	2u	^{3}P–^{3}P^0	0·8	2–2	1656	0·3	f
		60u	^{1}S–^{3}P^0	0·0^{4}11	0–1	2582	0·0^{4}11	
	$2p^2$–$2p3d$	7u	^{3}P–^{3}D^0	6	2–3	1277	3	f
	$2s^22p^2$–$2s2p^3$	3u	^{3}P–^{3}D^0	4·6	2–3	1561	2	[22]
	$2p3s$–$2p3p$	1	^{3}P^0–^{3}D	4·5	2–3	10691	2·1	[5]
		10	^{1}P^0–^{1}S	0·36	1–0	8335	0·36	,,
	$2p3s$–$2p4p$	4	^{3}P^0–^{3}D	0·011	2–3	5041	0·005	[9, 10, 11]
		6	^{3}P^0–^{3}P	0·030	2–2	4771	0·013	,,
		11	^{1}P^0–^{1}P	0·014	1–1	5380	0·014 0	,,
		12	^{1}P^0–^{1}D	0·024 3	1–2	5052	0·024 3	,,
		13	^{1}P^0–^{1}S	0·012 0	1–0	4932	0·012 0	,,

Atom	Transition	Multiplet			Lines			Notes
		No.	Desig.	$g_t f$	J	λ	gf	
						Å		
C II	$2p$–$3s$	4u	$^2P^0$–^2S	1·3	$1\frac{1}{2}$–$\frac{1}{2}$	858	0·9	C [15]
	$2p$–$3d$	5u	$^2P^0$–^2D	0·9	$1\frac{1}{2}$–$2\frac{1}{2}$	687	0·5	C [15]
	$2s^22p$–$2s2p^2$	1u	$^2P^0$–^2D	2·3	$1\frac{1}{2}$–$2\frac{1}{2}$	1335	1·4	[22]
	$2s2p^2$–$2s^23p$	13u	^2S–$^2P^0$	0·26	$\frac{1}{2}$–$1\frac{1}{2}$	2836	0·17	[9]
	$2s2p^2$–$2p^3$	14u	^2P–$^2D^0$	0·98	$1\frac{1}{2}$–$2\frac{1}{2}$	2512	0·58	[9]
	$3s$–$3p$	2	^2S–$^2P^0$	1·7	$\frac{1}{2}$–$1\frac{1}{2}$	6578	1·1	C [15]
	$3p$–$4s$	4	$^2P^0$–^2S	1·0	$1\frac{1}{2}$–$\frac{1}{2}$	3920	0·7	C [1]
	$3d$–$4f$	6	^2D–$^2F^0$	9·4	$2\frac{1}{2}$–$3\frac{1}{2}$	4267	5·4	C [15]
C III	$2s^2$–$2s2p$	1u	^1S–$^1P^0$	1·3	0–1	977	1·3	C, f [22]
	$2s^2$–$2s3p$	2u	^1S–$^1P^0$	0·2	0–1	386	0·2	C
	$2s3s$–$2s3p$	1	^3S–$^3P^0$	2·3	1–2	4647	1·3	C
C IV	$2s$–$2p$	1u	^2S–$^2P^0$	0·6	$\frac{1}{2}$–$1\frac{1}{2}$	1548	0·4	C [22]
	$2s$–$3p$	2u	^2S–$^2P^0$	0·4	$\frac{1}{2}$–$1\frac{1}{2}$	312	0·3	C [15]
	$3s$–$3p$	1	^2S–$^2P^0$	0·88	$\frac{1}{2}$–$1\frac{1}{2}$	5801	0·58	C [15]
N I	$2p^3$–$2p^23s$	1u	$^4S^0$–^4P	0·5	$1\frac{1}{2}$–$2\frac{1}{2}$	1199	0·3	f
	$2p^3$–$2p^23d$		$^4S^0$–^4P	6	$1\frac{1}{2}$–$2\frac{1}{2}$	952	3	f
	$2s^22p^3$–$2s2p^4$	2u	$^4S^0$–^4P	3	$1\frac{1}{2}$–$2\frac{1}{2}$	1134	1·5	C [22]
	$2p^23s$–$2p^23p$	1	^4P–$^4D^0$	6	$2\frac{1}{2}$–$3\frac{1}{2}$	8680	2·4	C [5, 20]
		8	^2P–$^2P^0$	1·9	$1\frac{1}{2}$–$1\frac{1}{2}$	8629	1·1	C [5, 20]
	$2p^23s$–$2p^24p$	6	^4P–$^4S^0$	0·017	$2\frac{1}{2}$–$1\frac{1}{2}$	4151	0·010	[23]
N II	$2p^2$–$2p3s$	3u	^3P–$^3P^0$	0·8	2–2	671	0·3	f
	$2p^2$–$2p3d$	5u	^3P–$^3D^0$	6	2–3	533	3	f
	$2s^22p^2$–$2s2p^3$	1u	^3P–$^3D^0$	3·4	2–3	1085	1·6	[22]
	$2p3s$–$2p3p$	3	$^3P^0$–^3D	4·7	2–3	5679	2·2	f [21]
		12	$^1P^0$–^1D	1·5	1–2	3994	1·5	f
	$2p3p$–$2p3d$	19	^3D–$^3F^0$	9·5	3–4	5005	4·1	f [21]
N III	$2p$–$3s$	4u	$^2P^0$–^2S	1·6	$1\frac{1}{2}$–$\frac{1}{2}$	452	1·1	C [15]
	$2p$–$3d$	5u	$^2P^0$–^2D	1·2	$1\frac{1}{2}$–$2\frac{1}{2}$	374	0·7	C [15]
	$2s^22p$–$2s2p^2$	1u	$^2P^0$–^2D	1·7	$1\frac{1}{2}$–$2\frac{1}{2}$	991	1·0	[22]
	$3s$–$3p$	1	^2S–$^2P^0$	1·4	$\frac{1}{2}$–$1\frac{1}{2}$	4097	0·9	C [15]
	$3p$–$3d$	2	$^2P^0$–^2D	2·6	$1\frac{1}{2}$–$2\frac{1}{2}$	4640	1·6	C [15]
	$2s2p3s$–$2s2p3p$	3	$^4P^0$–^4D	2·1	$2\frac{1}{2}$–$3\frac{1}{2}$	4514	0·84	C
N IV	$2s^2$–$2s2p$	1u	^1S–$^1P^0$	1·1	0–1	765	1·1	C, f [22]
	$2s^2$–$2s3p$	2u	^1S–$^1P^0$	0·3	0–1	247	0·3	C
	$2s3s$–$2s3p$	1	^3S–$^3P^0$	2·0	1–2	3478	1·1	C f
	$2s3p$–$2s3d$	3	$^1P^0$–^1D	1·5	1–2	4057	1·5	C f
N V	$2s$–$2p$	1u	^2S–$^2P^0$	0·49	$\frac{1}{2}$–$1\frac{1}{2}$	1238	0·33	C [22]
	$2s$–$3p$	2u	^2S–$^2P^0$	0·22	$\frac{1}{2}$–$1\frac{1}{2}$	209	0·15	C [15]
	$3s$–$3p$	1	^2S–$^2P^0$	0·75	$\frac{1}{2}$–$1\frac{1}{2}$	4603	0·50	C [15]
O I	$2p^4$–$2p^33s$	2u	^3P–$^3S^0$	0·42	2–1	1302	0·23	[12]
		5u	^3P–$^3D^0$	0·71	2–3	988	0·33	[12]
	$2p^33s$–$2p^33p$	1	$^5S^0$–^5P	7·7	2–3	7771	3·6	[5, 19]
		4	$^3S^0$–^3P	3·0	1–2	8446	1·7	[5, 20]
	$2p^33s$–$2p^34p$	3	$^5S^0$–^5P	0·012	2–3	3947	0·006	[11, 19, 20]
		5	$^3S^0$–^3P	0·022	1–2	4368	0·012	[11, 19, 20]
	$2p^33p$–$2p^35s$	9	^5P–$^5S^0$	0·24	3–2	6456	0·11	[19, 20]
	$2p^33p$–$2p^34d$	10	^5P–$^5D^0$	0·99	3–4	6158	0·37	C [20, 29]
	$2p^33p$–$2p^35d$	12	^5P–$^5D^0$	0·21	3–4	5330	0·08	[11]
O II	$2p^3$–$2p^23s$	2u	$^4S^0$–^4P	0·3?	$1\frac{1}{2}$–$2\frac{1}{2}$	539	0·2?	C, f
	$2p^3$–$2p^23d$	3u	$^4S^0$–^4P	5	$1\frac{1}{2}$–$2\frac{1}{2}$	430	2·5	C, f
	$2s^22p^3$–$2s2p^4$	1u	$^4S^0$–^4P	3·1	$1\frac{1}{2}$–$2\frac{1}{2}$	834	1·5	[22]
	$2p^23s$–$2p^23p$	1	^4P–$^4D^0$	6·3	$2\frac{1}{2}$–$3\frac{1}{2}$	4649	2·4	C[12, 20, 21]
		3	^4P–$^4S^0$	1·6	$2\frac{1}{2}$–$1\frac{1}{2}$	3749	0·7	C [12, 20]
	$2p^23p$–$2p^23d$	20	$^4P^0$–^4D	7·6	$2\frac{1}{2}$–$3\frac{1}{2}$	4119	3·0	C [12, 20]

Atom	Transition	Multiplet			Line			Notes
		No.	Desig.	$g_t f$	J	λ	gf	
						Å		
O III	$2p^2$–$2p3s$	4u	^3P–$^3P^0$	0·8	2–2	374	0·3	f
	$2p^2$–$2p3d$	5u	^3P–$^3D^0$	6	2–3	305	3	f
	$2s^2 2p^2$–$2s2p^3$	1u	^3P–$^3D^0$	2·6	2–3	835	1·2	[22]
	$2p3s$–$2p3p$	2	$^3P^0$–^3D	3·6	2–3	3759	1·7	C,f
		5	$^1P^0$–^1P	0·6	1–1	5592	0·6	C,f
	$2p3p$–$2p3d$	14	^3P–$^3P^0$	4	2–3	3715	1·8	C,f
		17	^1D–$^1F^0$	2·0	2–3	3961	2·0	C,f
O IV	$2p$–$3s$	4u	$^2P^0$–^2S	1·9	$1\frac{1}{2}$–$\frac{1}{2}$	279	1·3	C [15]
	$2p$–$3d$	5u	$^2P^0$–^2D	2·2	$1\frac{1}{2}$–$2\frac{1}{2}$	238	1·0	C [15]
	$2s^2 2p$–$2s2p^2$	1u	$^2P^0$–^2D	1·4	$1\frac{1}{2}$–$2\frac{1}{2}$	790	0·7	[22]
	$3p$–$3d$	2	$^2P^0$–^2D	2·0	$1\frac{1}{2}$–$2\frac{1}{2}$	3411	1·2	C [15]
	$2s2p3s$–$2s2p3p$	3	$^4P^0$–^4D	6	$2\frac{1}{2}$–$3\frac{1}{2}$	3385	2·4	C,f
	$2s2p3p$–$2s2p3d$	6	^4D–$^4F^0$	13	$3\frac{1}{2}$–$4\frac{1}{2}$	3736	5	C,f
O V	$2s^2$–$2s2p$	1u	^1S–$^1P^0$	1·2	0–1	629	1·2	C [22]
	$2s^2$–$2s3p$	2u	^1S–$^1P^0$	0·3	0–1	172	0·3	C
	$2p3s$–$2p3p$	4	$^3P^0$–^3D	3·4	2–3	4123	1·6	C,f
	$2p3p$–$2p3d$	11	^3S–$^3P^0$	1·4	1–2	4158	0·8	C
O VI	$2s$–$2p$	1u	^2S–$^2P^0$	0·41	$\frac{1}{2}$–$1\frac{1}{2}$	1031	0·27	C [1, 22, 30]
	$2s$–$3p$	2u	^2S–$^2P^0$	0·7	$\frac{1}{2}$–$1\frac{1}{2}$	150	0·5	C [1, 15, 30]
	$3s$–$3p$	1	^2S–$^2P^0$	0·67	$\frac{1}{2}$–$1\frac{1}{2}$	3811	0·45	C [1, 15]
Ne IV	$2s^2 2p^3$–$2s2p^4$	1u	$^4S^0$–^4P	1·8	$1\frac{1}{2}$–$2\frac{1}{2}$	543	0·9	C [22]
	$2p^3$–$2p^2 3s$	2u	$^4S^0$–^4P	0·2	$1\frac{1}{2}$–$2\frac{1}{2}$	208	0·1	C
	$2p^3$–$2p^2 3d$	3u	$^4S^0$–^4P	2·1	$1\frac{1}{2}$–$2\frac{1}{2}$	172	1·1	C
Ne V	$2s^2 2p^2$–$2s2p^3$	1u	^3P–$^3D^0$	1·4	2–3	572	0·7	C [22]
	$2p^2$–$2p3s$		^3P–$^3P^0$	0·4	2–2	168	0·2	C
	$2p^2$–$2p3d$		^3P–$^3D^0$	6	2–3	143	3	C
Ne VI	$2s^2 2p$–$2s2p^2$		$^2P^0$–^2D	0·9	$1\frac{1}{2}$–$2\frac{1}{2}$	560	0·5	C [22]
	$2p$–$3d$		$^2P^0$–^2D	3	$1\frac{1}{2}$–$2\frac{1}{2}$	123	2	C
Ne VII	$2s^2$–$2s2p$		^1S–$^1P^0$	0·63	0–1	480	0·63	[22]
Ne VIII	$2s$–$2p$		^2S–$^2P^0$	0·31	$\frac{1}{2}$–$1\frac{1}{2}$	776	0·21	[22, 30]
Na I	$3s$–$3p$	1	^2S–$^2P^0$	1·93	$\frac{1}{2}$–$1\frac{1}{2}$	5889	1·29	[1, 5, 15, 24, 28]
	$3s$–$4p$	2	^2S–$^2P^0$	0·028	$\frac{1}{2}$–$1\frac{1}{2}$	3302	0·019	[1]
	$3p$–$4s$	3	$^2P^0$–^2S	1·02	$1\frac{1}{2}$–$\frac{1}{2}$	11403	0·67	[1, 15]
	$3p$–$5s$	5	$^2P^0$–^2S	0·10	$1\frac{1}{2}$–$\frac{1}{2}$	6160	0·07	[1, 5, 15]
	$3p$–$6s$	8	$^2P^0$–^2S	0·024	$1\frac{1}{2}$–$\frac{1}{2}$	5153	0·016	[5]
	$3p$–$3d$	4	$^2P^0$–^2D	5·4	$1\frac{1}{2}$–$2\frac{1}{2}$	8194	3·2	[1, 15]
	$3p$–$4d$	6	$^2P^0$–^2D	0·55	$1\frac{1}{2}$–$2\frac{1}{2}$	5688	0·33	[1, 5]
	$3p$–$5d$	9	$^2P^0$–^2D	0·16	$1\frac{1}{2}$–$2\frac{1}{2}$	4982	0·10	[1, 5]
Mg I	$3s^2$–$3s3p$	1u	^1S–$^1P^0$	1·6	0–1	2852	1·6	[1, 8, 24, 27, 28]
		1	^1S–$^3P^0$	$0·0^5 2$	0–1	4571	$0·0^5 2$	[1, 8]
	$3s3p$–$3s4s$	2	$^3P^0$–^3S	1·05	2–1	5183	0·58	,,
		6	$^1P^0$–^1S	0·5	1–0	11828	0·5	,,
	$3s3p$–$3s5s$	4	$^3P^0$–^3S	0·15	2–1	3336	0·08	[8]
		8	$^1P^0$–^1S	0·03	1–0	5711	0·03	,,
	$3s3p$–$3s3d$	3	$^3P^0$–^3D	4·9	2–3	3838	2·3	[1, 8]
		7	$^1P^0$–^1D	1·1	1–2	8806	1·1	,,

Atom	Transition	Multiplet			Line			Notes
		No.	Desig.	$g_t f$	J	λ	gf	
						Å		
Mg I	$3s3p-3s4d$	5	$^3P^0-^3D$	1·1	2–3	3096	0·5	[8]
		9	$^1P^0-^1D$	0·18	1–2	5528	0·18	[1, 8]
	$3s3p-3s5d$	11	$^1P^0-^1D$	0·19	1–2	4702	0·19	,,
	$3s3p-3s6d$	14	$^1P^0-^1D$	0·10	1–2	4351	0·10	[8]
	$3s3p-3p^2$	6u	$^3P^0-^3P$	4·5	2–2	2779	1·9	,,
Mg II	$3s-3p$	1u	$^2S-^2P^0$	1·8	$\frac{1}{2}-1\frac{1}{2}$	2795	1·2	[1, 15]
	$3p-4s$	2u	$^2P^0-^2S$	0·74	$1\frac{1}{2}-\frac{1}{2}$	2936	0·5	[1]
	$3p-3d$	3u	$^2P^0-^2D$	4·8	$1\frac{1}{2}-2\frac{1}{2}$	2797	2·7	[1, 15]
	$3d-4f$	4	$^2D-^2F^0$	9·5	$2\frac{1}{2}-3\frac{1}{2}$	4481	5·4	[1]
	$4p-4d$	8	$^2P^0-^2D$	7	$1\frac{1}{2}-2\frac{1}{2}$	7896	4	[15]
Mg IX	$2s^2-2s2p$		$^1S-^1P^0$	0·49	0–1	368	0·49	C [22]
	$2s^2-2s3p$		$^1S-^1P^0$	0·59	0–1	62	0·59	C
Mg X	$2s-2p$		$^2S-^2P^0$	0·25	$\frac{1}{2}-1\frac{1}{2}$	620	0·16	C [22, 30]
	$2s-3p$		$^2S-^2P^0$	0·6	$\frac{1}{2}-1\frac{1}{2}$	58	0·4	C [30]
Al I	$3p-4s$	1	$^2P^0-^2S$	0·7	$1\frac{1}{2}-\frac{1}{2}$	3961	0·5	[8, 28]
	$4s-5p$	5	$^2S-^2P^0$	0·068	$\frac{1}{2}-1\frac{1}{2}$	6695	0·045	[5]
	$4s-6p$	6	$^2S-^2P^0$	0·014	$\frac{1}{2}-1\frac{1}{2}$	5557	0·009	,,
	$3s^23p-3s3p^2$		$^2P^0-^2S$	2·0	$1\frac{1}{2}-\frac{1}{2}$	1936	1·4	[25]
Al II	$3s^2-3s3p$	2u	$^1S-^1P^0$	1·5	0–1	1670	1·5	f [30]
Al III	$3s-3p$	1u	$^2S-^2P^0$	1·9	$\frac{1}{2}-1\frac{1}{2}$	1854	1·3	C [22]
	$3s-4p$	2u	$^2S-^2P^0$	0·03	$\frac{1}{2}-1\frac{1}{2}$	695	0·02	
Si I	$3p^2-3p4s$	1u	$^3P-^3P^0$	0·7	2–2	2516	0·3	[1]
		43u	$^1D-^1P^0$	0·32	2–1	2881	0·32	,,
		3	$^1S-^1P^0$	0·13	0–1	3905	0·13	[8]
	$3p^2-3p3d$	3u	$^3P-^3D^0$	7	2–3	2216	3·5	C
	$3s^23p^2-3s3p^3$	5u	$^3P-^3D^0$	7	2–3	2054	3	[22]
	$3p4s-3p4p$	4	$^3P^0-^3D$	4·9	2–3	12031	2·3	[1, 5]
		5	$^3P^0-^3P$	3·4	2–2	10827	1·4	,,
		6	$^3P^0-^3S$	1·1	2–1	10585	0·6	,,
		13	$^1P^0-^1D$	1·9	1–2	10869	1·9	,,
Si II	$4s-4p$	2	$^2S-^2P^0$	2·6	$\frac{1}{2}-1\frac{1}{2}$	6347	1·7	[1, 15]
	$3d-4f$	3	$^2D-^2F^0$	9	$2\frac{1}{2}-3\frac{1}{2}$	4130	5	,,
	$3s^23p-3s3p^2$	1u	$^2P^0-^2D$	4·0	$1\frac{1}{2}-2\frac{1}{2}$	1816	2·4	C [22]
	$3p-3d$	4u	$^2P^0-^2D$	4	$1\frac{1}{2}-2\frac{1}{2}$	1265	2	C [15]
	$3p-4s$	2u	$^2P^0-^2S$	0·5	$1\frac{1}{2}-\frac{1}{2}$	1533	0·3	,,
	$3p-4d$	6u	$^2P^0-^2D$	0·7	$1\frac{1}{2}-2\frac{1}{2}$	993	0·4	,,
Si III	$3s^2-3s3p$	2u	$^1S-^1P^0$	1·9	0–1	1206	1·9	C, f [22]
	$3s^2-3s4p$	3u	$^1S-^1P^0$	0·04	0–1	566	0·04	C
	$3s4s-3s4p$	2	$^3S-^3P^0$	3·8	1–2	4552	2·1	C [1]
		4	$^1S-^1P^0$	1·1	0–1	5739	1·1	C
Si IV	$3s-3p$	1u	$^2S-^2P^0$	1·6	$\frac{1}{2}-1\frac{1}{2}$	1393	1·1	C [15, 22, 30]
	$3s-4p$	2u	$^2S-^2P^0$	0·06	$\frac{1}{2}-1\frac{1}{2}$	457	0·04	C [31]
	$4s-4p$	1	$^2S-^2P^0$	2·3	$\frac{1}{2}-1\frac{1}{2}$	4088	1·5	[1, 15, 31]
Si XI	$2s^2-2s2p$		$^1S-^1P^0$	0·39	0–1	304	0·39	C [22]
	$2s^2-2s3p$		$^1S-^1P^0$	0·6	0–1	44	0·6	C

Atom		Transition	Multiplet			Line			Notes
			No.	Desig.	$g_t f$	J	λ	gf	
							Å		
P	I	$3p^24s-3p^24p$	1	^{4}P–^{4}D^0	6·0	$2\frac{1}{2}$–$3\frac{1}{2}$	10581	2·4	[5]
S	I	$3p^34s-3p^34p$	1	^{5}S^0–^{5}P	5·2	2–3	9212	2·4	C [5]
			3	^{3}S^0–^{3}P	3·1	1–2	10455	1·7	C
		$3s^23p^4-3s3p^5$	7u	^{3}P–^{3}P^0	8	2–2	1388	3	[22]
S	III	$3s^23p^2-3s3p^3$	1u	^{3}P–^{3}D^0	3	2–3	1200	2	C [22]
		$3p^2-3p4s$	6u	^{3}P–^{3}P^0	0·9	2–2	683	0·4	C
		$3p^2-3p3d$	7u	^{3}P–^{3}D^0	10	2–3	680	5	C
S	IV	$3s^23p-3s3p^2$	1u	^{2}P^0–^{2}D	2·5	$1\frac{1}{2}$–$2\frac{1}{2}$	1072	1·5	C [22]
		$3p-3d$	4u	^{2}P^0–^{2}D	5	$1\frac{1}{2}$–$2\frac{1}{2}$	661	3	
		$3p-4s$	5u	^{2}P^0–^{2}S	0·4	$1\frac{1}{2}$–$\frac{1}{2}$	551	0·3	
S	V	$3s^2-3s3p$	1u	^{1}S–^{1}P^0	1·9	0–1	786	1·9	C [22]
S	VI	$3s-3p$	1u	^{2}S–^{2}P^0	1·5	$\frac{1}{2}$–$1\frac{1}{2}$	933	1·0	C [22, 30]
K	I	$4s-4p$	1	^{2}S–^{2}P^0	1·98	$\frac{1}{2}$–$1\frac{1}{2}$	7664	1·32	[1, 5, 15]
		$4s-5p$	3	^{2}S–^{2}P^0	0·03	$\frac{1}{2}$–$1\frac{1}{2}$	4044	0·02	[1, 5]
		$4p-5s$	5	^{2}P^0–^{2}S	1·1	$1\frac{1}{2}$–$\frac{1}{2}$	12523	0·7	[5]
Ca	I	$4s^2-4s4p$	2	^{1}S–^{1}P^0	1·6	0–1	4226	1·6	[8, 26, 27]
			1	^{1}S–^{3}P^0	0·04^5	0–1	6572	0·04^5	[8]
		$4s4p-4s5s$	3	^{3}P^0–^{3}S	0·80	2–1	6162	0·44	,,
		$4s4p-4s6s$	6	^{3}P^0–^{3}S	0·12	2–1	3973	0·067	,,
		$4s4p-4s7s$	10	^{3}P^0–^{3}S	0·040	2–1	3487	0·022	,,
		$4s4p-4s4d$	4	^{3}P^0–^{3}D	2·8	2–3	4454	1·3	,,
		$4s4p-4s5d$	9	^{3}P^0–^{3}D	0·7	2–3	3644	0·33	,,
			49	^{1}P^0–^{1}D	0·7	1–2	5188	0·7	,,
		$4s4p-4s6d$	11	^{3}P^0–^{3}D	0·38	2–3	3361	0·18	,,
		$4s4p-4p^2$	5	^{3}P^0–^{3}P	3·5	2–2	4302	1·5	,,
			47	^{1}P^0–^{1}D	1·66	1–2	5857	1·66	,,
		$3d4s-3d4p$	18	^{3}D–^{3}F^0	2·5	3–4	6439	1·1	,,
			21	^{3}D–^{3}D^0	4·5	3–3	5588	1·9	,,
			22	^{3}D–^{3}P^0	3·6	3–2	5270	1·7	
Ca	II	$4s-4p$	1	^{2}S–^{2}P^0	2·1	$\frac{1}{2}$–$1\frac{1}{2}$	3933	1·4	[1, 31]
		$3d-4p$	2	^{2}D–^{2}P^0	0·6	$2\frac{1}{2}$–$1\frac{1}{2}$	8542	0·4	,,
		$4p-5s$	3	^{2}P^0–^{2}S	0·8	$1\frac{1}{2}$–$\frac{1}{2}$	3736	0·5	,,
		$4p-4d$	4	^{2}P^0–^{2}D	6	$1\frac{1}{2}$–$2\frac{1}{2}$	3179	3·6	[1, 15]
Sc	I	$3d^24s-3d^24p$	12	^{4}F–^{4}G^0	7·8	$4\frac{1}{2}$–$5\frac{1}{2}$	5671	2·6	[8]
			14	^{4}F–^{4}D^0	5·6	$4\frac{1}{2}$–$3\frac{1}{2}$	4743	1·9	,,
			15	^{2}F–^{2}G^0	3·8	$3\frac{1}{2}$–$4\frac{1}{2}$	5520	2·1	,,
			16	^{2}F–^{2}F^0	3·9	$3\frac{1}{2}$–$3\frac{1}{2}$	5481	2·2	,,
		$3d4s^2-3d4s4p$	5	^{2}D–^{2}F^0	0·03	$2\frac{1}{2}$–$3\frac{1}{2}$	4779	0·02	,,
			6	^{2}D–^{2}P^0	0·31	$2\frac{1}{2}$–$1\frac{1}{2}$	4082	0·19	,,
Ti	I	$3d^34s-3d^34p$	38	^{5}F–^{5}G^0	12·9	5–6	4981	3·8	[13]
			42	^{5}F–^{5}F^0	10·4	5–5	4533	3·0	,,
			104	^{3}F–^{3}G^0	1·4	4–5	6258	0·4	,,
			145	^{5}P–^{5}D^0	5·9	3–4	4617	2·0	,,
		$3d^24s^2-3d^24s4p$	4	^{3}F–^{3}F^0	0·35	4–4	5210	0·14	,,
			6	^{3}F–^{3}G^0	0·18	4–5	4681	0·08	,,
			12	^{3}F–^{3}F^0	2·19	4–4	3998	0·83	,,
			24	^{3}F–^{3}G^0	2·6	4–5	3371	1·2	,,
		$3d^34s-3d^24s4p$	110	^{3}F–^{3}G^0	3·7	4–5	5035	1·5	,,
Ti	II	$3d^24s-3d^24p$	1	^{4}F–^{4}G^0	4·8	$4\frac{1}{2}$–$5\frac{1}{2}$	3349	1·5	[13]
			2	^{4}F–^{4}F^0	4·6	$4\frac{1}{2}$–$4\frac{1}{2}$	3234	1·2	,,

Atom	Transition	Multiplet			Line			Notes
		No.	Desig.	$g_t f$	J	λ	gf	
						Å		
Ti II	$3d^3-3d^24p$	7	$^4F-^4F^o$	1·6	$4\frac12-4\frac12$	3322	0·47	[13]
		34	$^2G-^2G^o$	1·5	$4\frac12-4\frac12$	3900	0·83	,,
		41	$^4P-^4D^o$	0·9	$2\frac12-3\frac12$	4300	0·31	,,
		82	$^2H-^2G^o$	1·3	$5\frac12-4\frac12$	4549	0·72	,,
V I	$3d^44s-3d^44p$	21	$^6D-^6P^o$	1·9	$4\frac12-3\frac12$	4460	0·7	[8]
		22	$^6D-^6F^o$	13	$4\frac12-5\frac12$	4379	4	,,
		27	$^6D\rightarrow^6D^o$	9	$4\frac12-4\frac12$	4111	2·6	,,
		35	$^4D-^4F^o$	3·7	$3\frac12-4\frac12$	5727	1·0	,,
		88	$^4H-^4H^o$	11	$6\frac12-6\frac12$	4268	4	,,
		109	$^4F-^4G^o$	8	$4\frac12-5\frac12$	4545	2·7	,,
	$3d^34s^2-3d^34s4p$	4	$^4F-^4G^o$	0·6	$4\frac12-5\frac12$	4594	0·25	,,
		14	$^4F-^4G^o$	11	$4\frac12-5\frac12$	3185	3·3	,,
	$3d^44s-3d^34s4p$	29	$^6D-^6P^o$	4·4	$4\frac12-3\frac12$	3703	1·5	,,
		41	$^4D-^4F^o$	4·4	$3\frac12-4\frac12$	4090	1·9	,,
	$3d^34s4p-3d^34s5s$	125	$^6F^o-^6F$	4·8	$5\frac12-5\frac12$	5193	1·6	,,
	$3d^34s4p-3d^34s4d$	114	$^6G^o-^6H$	35	$6\frac12-7\frac12$	3695	9	,,
V II	$3d^34s-3d^34p$	1	$^5F-^5G^o$	10·5	5-6	3093	3·0	f
		5	$^3F-^3D^o$	3·5	4-3	3556	1·5	,,
		25	$^5P-^5D^o$	5·8	3-4	4202	2·1	,,
Cr I	$3d^54s-3d^54p$	1	$^7S-^7P^o$	1·4	3-4	4254	0·6	[8]
		7	$^5S-^5P^o$	2·6	2-3	5208	1·2	,,
		38	$^5G-^5H^o$	33	6-7	3963	9	,,
	$3d^44s^2-3d^44s4p$	22	$^5D-^5F^o$	1·3	4-5	4351	0·4	,,
	$3d^54s-3d^44s4p$	4	$^7S-^7P^o$	3·9	3-4	3578	1·7	,,
		43	$^5G-^5G^o$	30	6-6	3743	8	,,
Mn I	$3d^64s-3d^64p$	5	$^6D-^6D^o$	14	$4\frac12-4\frac12$	4041	3·8	[8]
		6	$^6D-^6F^o$	18	$4\frac12-5\frac12$	3806	5·3	,,
	$3d^54s^2-3d^54s4p$	2	$^6S-^6P^o$	0·51	$2\frac12-3\frac12$	4030	0·28	,,
		1u	$^6S-^6P^o$	5·5	$2\frac12-3\frac12$	2794	2·4	
	$3d^54s4p-3d^54s4d$	18	$^8P^o-^8D$	36	$4\frac12-5\frac12$	3569	11	
Fe I	$3d^74s-3d^74p$	20	$^5F-^5D^o$	5·5	5-4	3820	1·8	[8]
		23	$^5F-^5G^o$	10·7	5-6	3581	4·1	,,
		41	$^3F-^5G^o$	5·6	4-5	4383	2·7	,,
		42	$^3F-^3G^o$	6·0	4-5	4271	1·3	,,
		43	$^3F-^3F^o$	8·7	4-4	4045	3·0	,,
		45	$^3F-^3D^o$	5·9	4-3	3815	2·6	,,
	$3d^64s^2-3d^6-4s4p$	4	$^5D-^5D^o$	0·57	4-4	3859	0·19	,,
		5	$^5D-^5F^o$	1·00	4-5	3719	0·32	,,
		2	$^5D-^7F^o$	0·007	4-5	4375	0·002	,,
	$3d^74s-3d^64s4p$	15	$^5F-^5D^o$	0·28	5-4	5269	0·06	,,
		68	$^5P-^5D^o$	2·0	3-4	4528	0·7	,,
	$3d^64s4p-3d^64s5s$	152	$^7D^o-^7D$	11·8	5-5	4260	3·5	,,
Fe II	$3d^64s-3d^64p$	27	$^4P-^4D^o$	4	$2\frac12-3\frac12$	4233	1	?f[1]
		38	$^4F-^4D^o$	5	$4\frac12-3\frac12$	4583	2	,,
		49	$^4G-^4F^o$	6	$5\frac12-4\frac12$	5316	2	,,
Co I	$3d^84s-3d^84p$	22	$^4F-^4G^o$	7·6	$4\frac12-5\frac12$	3453	3·2	[8]
		23	$^4F-^4F^o$	6·5	$4\frac12-4\frac12$	3405	2·2	,,
		35	$^2F-^2F^o$	4·6	$3\frac12-3\frac12$	3569	2·7	,,
	$3d^74s^2-3d^74s4p$	5	$^4F-^4G^o$	0·72	$4\frac12-5\frac12$	3465	0·4	,,
	$3d^84s-3d^74s4p$	28	$^2F-^2G^o$	1·18	$3\frac12-4\frac12$	4121	0·5	,,
		62	$^4P-^4P^o$	1·7	$2\frac12-2\frac12$	3732	0·5	,,
	$3d^74s4p-3d^74s5s$	158	$^6G^o-^6F$	13	$6\frac12-5\frac12$	4867	3	,,

Atom	Transition	Multiplet			Line			Notes
		No.	Desig.	$g_t f$	J	λ (Å)	gf	
Ni I	$3d^9 4s - 3d^9 4p$	19	$^3D-^3F^0$	2·9	3–4	3414	0·8	[8]
		35	$^1D-^1F^0$	1·4	2–3	3619	1·4	,,
	$3d^8 4s^2 - 3d^8 4s 4p$	7	$^3F-^3G^0$	0·35	4–5	3232	0·16	,,
		78	$^3P-^3D^0$	0·5	2–3	3181	0·2	,,
	$3d^9 4s - 3d^8 4s 4p$	25	$^3D-^3F^0$	4	3–4	3050	1·0	,,
	$3d^8 4s 4p - 3d^8 4s 5s$	111	$^5F^0-^5F$	5	5–5	5017	1·8	,,
	$3d^8 4s 4p - 3d^8 4s 4d$	106	$^5G^0-^5H$	28	6–7	3374	8	,,
		123	$^5F^0-^5F$	11·5	5–5	3516	3	,,
	$3d^9 4p - 3d^9 4d$	130	$^3P^0-^3P$	3·6	2–2	4855		,,
		143	$^3F^0-^3G$	13·5	4–5	5080	5·5	,,
		162	$^3D^0-^3F$	5·5	3–4	5084	2·2	,,
		194	$^1F^0-^1G$	5·4	3–4	5081	5·4	,,
Cu I	$4s - 4p$	1	$^2S-^2P^0$	1·2	$\frac{1}{2}-1\frac{1}{2}$	3247	0·8	f, etc.
	$3d^9 4s^2 - 3d^{10} 4p$	2	$^2D-^2P^0$	0·009	$2\frac{1}{2}-1\frac{1}{2}$	5105	0·006	[5]
	$4p - 4d$	7	$^2P^0-^2D$	0·55	$1\frac{1}{2}-2\frac{1}{2}$	5218	0·3	,,
Zn I	$4s4p - 4s5s$	2	$^3P^0-^3S$	1·3	2–1	4810	0·7	,,
	$4s4p - 4s4d$	6	$^1P^0-^1D$	1·1	1–2	6362	1·1	,,
Sr I	$5s^2 - 5s5p$	2	$^1S-^1P^0$	1·7	0–1	4607	1·7	[5, 27]
	$5s5p - 5s6s$	3	$^3P^0-^3S$	1·6	2–1	7070	0·9	[5]
Sr II	$5s - 5p$	1	$^2S-^2P^0$	1·8	$\frac{1}{2}-1\frac{1}{2}$	4077	1·2	[1]
	$4d - 5p$	2	$^2D-^2P^0$	0·76	$2\frac{1}{2}-1\frac{1}{2}$	10327	0·46	,,
	$5p - 6s$	3	$^2P^0-^2S$	1·1	$1\frac{1}{2}-\frac{1}{2}$	4305	0·7	[5]
Ba I	$6s^2 - 6s6p$	2	$^1S-^1P^0$	1·5	0–1	5535	1·5	f [27]
Ba II	$6s - 6p$	1	$^2S-^2P^0$	2·1	$\frac{1}{2}-1\frac{1}{2}$	4554	1·4	C, f [5]
	$5d - 6p$	2	$^2D-^2P^0$	0·88	$2\frac{1}{2}-1\frac{1}{2}$	6141	0·53	[1, 5]
	$6p - 6d$	4	$^2P^0-^2D$	5·8	$1\frac{1}{2}-2\frac{1}{2}$	4130	3·7	,,
Hg I	$6s^2 - 6s6p$		$^1S-^1P^0$	1·3	0–1	1849	1·3	[1]
			$^1S-^3P^0$	0·03	0–1	2536	0·03	,,
	$6s6p - 6s7s$	1	$^3P^0-^3S$	0·7	2–1	5460	0·38	,,
	$6s6p - 6s6d$	4	$^1P^0-^1D$	2·2	1–2	5790	2·2	,,
Pb I	$6p - 7s$	1	$^3P-^3P^0$	8	2–1	4057	1·8	[5, 14]

[1] *A.Q.* **1**, § 29.
[2] C. E. Moore, *Multiplet Table, Revised*, Princeton, 1945.
[3] C. E. Moore, *Ultra-violet Multiplet Table*, N.B.S. Circ. No. 488, 1950, 1952.
[4] D. R. Bates and A. Damgaard, *Phil. Trans.*, A. **242**, 101, 1949.
[5] L. Goldberg, Müller, and Aller, *Ap. J. Supp.*, **5**, 1, 1960.
[6] C. M. Varsavsky, Thesis, Harvard, Nov. 1958.
[7] P. W. Merrill, *Lines of the Chem. Elements in Astron. Spectra*, Carnegie Pub. 610, 1956.
[8] C. W. Allen, *M.N.*, **117**, 622, 1957; **121**, 299, 1960.
[9] H. Maecker, *Z. Phys.*, **135**, 13, 1953; **136**, 119, 1953.
[10] J. Richter, *Z. Phys.*, **151**, 114, 1958.
[11] E. W. Foster, *Proc. Phys. Soc.*, **79**, 94, 1962; *Com. U. Lond. Ob.* No. 48.
[12] R. H. Garstang, *Camb. Phil. Soc.*, **57**, 115, 1961; *Com. U Lond. Ob.*, No. 40.
[13] J. B. Tatum, *Com. U. Lond. Ob.*, No. 41, 1961.
[14] G. D. Bell and R. B. King, *A.J.*, **65**, 483, 1960.
[15] L. Houziaux and M.-P. Sadoine, *Liège Inst. d'Ap.*, No. 423, 1961.
[16] L. C. Green, Rush and Chandler, *Ap. J. Supp.*, **3**, 37, 1957.
[17] E. Trefftz, et al., *Z. Ap.*, **44**, 1, 1957.
[18] A. L. Osherovich and I. G. Savich, *Opt. e. Sp.*, **4**, 715, 1958.

[19] G. Jürgens, Z. Phys., 138, 613, 1954.
[20] P. J. Nawrocki and R. Papa, Atmospheric Processes, Geophys. Corp. of America, 1961.
[21] J. Mastrup and W. Wiese, Z. Ap., 44, 259, 1958.
[22] C. M. Varsavsky, Ap. J. Supp., 6, 75, 1961.
[23] H. Motschmann, Z. Phys., 143, 77, 1955.
[24] V. Weidemann, Z. Ap., 36, 101, 1955.
[25] J. A. Eddy, House, and Zirin, Ap. J., 133, 299, 1961.
[26] K. H. Olsen, Routly, and King, Ap. J., 130, 688, 1959.
[27] N. P. Penkin and L. N. Shabanova, Opt. e. Sp., 12, 3, 1962.
[28] B. Brehm, Demtröder, and Osberghaus, Preprint, Bonn, 1961.
[29] W. L. Wiese and J. B. Shumaker, J.O.S.A., 51, 937, 1961.
[30] G. S. Ivanov-Kholodnyi and G. M. Nukolskii, A. Zh., 38, 828, 1961; 5, 632, 1962.
[31] A. S. Douglas and R. H. Garstang, Proc. Camb. Phil. Soc., 58, 377, 1962.

§ 29. Forbidden Line Transition Probabilities

The unit used for expressing the intensities of forbidden spectrum lines is the transition probability A. From § 25 it can be seen that the line intensity would normally be proportional to $g_2 A_{21}$ where subscript 2 represents the upper level (which appears on the right in the table). Normally $g_2 = 2J_2 + 1$, but for the 21·1 cm line of H$_I$ we have $g_2 = 1\frac{1}{2}$, $g_1 = \frac{1}{2}$ on the weighting system adopted.

The lines tabulated are forbidden in the sense that they disobey the parity rule, hence the transitions involve no change in parity. The list has been prepared by R. H. Garstang in connection with [2] where detailed references are to be found.

Forbidden lines

Atom	Array	Designation lower upper	J lower upper	λ	A
				Å	s^{-1}
H I	$1s$	^2S	$\frac{1}{2}$	21·1 cm	$2\cdot85 \times 10^{-15}$
C I	$2p^2$	$^1D\text{–}^1S$	2–0	8727	0·8
N I	$2p^3$	$^4S^0\text{–}^2D^0$	$1\frac{1}{2}\text{–}1\frac{1}{2}$	5198	$1\cdot6 \times 10^{-5}$
		$^4S^0\text{–}^2D^0$	$1\frac{1}{2}\text{–}2\frac{1}{2}$	5200	$7\cdot0 \times 10^{-6}$
N II	$2p^2$	$^1D\text{–}^1S$	2–0	5754	1·1
		$^3P\text{–}^1D$	1–2	6548	0·001 0
		$^3P\text{–}^1D$	2–2	6583	0·003 0
O I	$2p^4$	$^1D\text{–}^1S$	2–0	5577	1·3
		$^3P\text{–}^1D$	2–2	6300	0·006 9
		$^3P\text{–}^1D$	1–2	6363	0·002 2
		$^3P\text{–}^1S$	1–0	2972	0·078
O II	$2p^3$	$^4S^0\text{–}^2D^0$	$1\frac{1}{2}\text{–}2\frac{1}{2}$	3728	$4\cdot2 \times 10^{-5}$
		$^4S^0\text{–}^2D^0$	$1\frac{1}{2}\text{–}1\frac{1}{2}$	3726	$1\cdot8 \times 10^{-4}$
		$^2D^0\text{–}^2P^0$	$2\frac{1}{2}\text{–}1\frac{1}{2}$	7319	0·12
		$^2D^0\text{–}^2P^0$	$1\frac{1}{2}\text{–}\frac{1}{2}$	7329	0·10
O III	$2p^2$	$^1D\text{–}^1S$	2–0	4363	1·6
		$^3P\text{–}^1D$	1–2	4958	0·007 1
		$^3D\text{–}^1D$	2–2	5006	0·021
F IV	$2p^2$	$^3P\text{–}^1D$	2–2	4059	0·10

Atom	Array	Designation lower upper	J lower upper	λ	A
				Å	s^{-1}
Ne III	$2p^4$	$^3P-^1D$	$2-2$	3868	0·20
		$^3P-^1D$	$1-2$	3967	0·060
		$^1D-^1S$	$2-0$	3342	2·8
Ne IV	$2p^3$	$^2D^0-^2P^0$	$2\frac{1}{2}-1\frac{1}{2}$	4714	0·40
		$^2D^0-^2P^0$	$2\frac{1}{2}-\frac{1}{2}$	4716	0·11
		$^2D^0-^2P^0$	$1\frac{1}{2}-1\frac{1}{2}$	4724	0·44
		$^2D^0-^2P^0$	$1\frac{1}{2}-\frac{1}{2}$	4726	0·39
Ne V	$2p^2$	$^3P-^1D$	$2-2$	3425	0·38
		$^3P-^1D$	$1-2$	3345	0·14
S I	$3p^4$	$^1D-^1S$	$2-0$	7725	4·1
S II	$3p^3$	$^4S^0-^2P^0$	$1\frac{1}{2}-1\frac{1}{2}$	4068	0·27
		$^4S^0-^2P^0$	$1\frac{1}{2}-\frac{1}{2}$	4076	0·066
		$^4S^0-^2D^0$	$1\frac{1}{2}-2\frac{1}{2}$	6716	0·000 63
		$^4S^0-^2D^0$	$1\frac{1}{2}-1\frac{1}{2}$	6730	0·001 7
S III	$3p^2$	$^1D-^1S$	$2-0$	6310	5·6
		$^3P-^1D$	$1-2$	9069	0·025
Cl III	$3p^3$	$^4S^0-^2D^0$	$1\frac{1}{2}-1\frac{1}{2}$	5537	0·007 2
Cl IV	$3p^2$	$^1D-^1S$	$2-0$	5322	6·6
		$^3P-^1D$	$2-2$	8045	0·20
Ar III	$3p^4$	$^1D-^1S$	$2-0$	5191	6·2
		$^3P-^1D$	$2-2$	7135	0·32
Ar IV	$3p^3$	$^2D^0-^2P^0$	$1\frac{1}{2}-1\frac{1}{2}$	7170	1·0
		$^4S^0-^2D^0$	$1\frac{1}{2}-2\frac{1}{2}$	4711	0·002 6
		$^4S^0-^2D^0$	$1\frac{1}{2}-1\frac{1}{2}$	4740	0·027
Ar V	$3p^2$	$^3P-^1D$	$1-2$	6435	0·51
		$^1D-^1S$	$2-0$	4625	7·3
Ar X	$2p^5$	$^2P^0-^2P^0$	$1\frac{1}{2}-\frac{1}{2}$	5534	106
Ar XIV	$2p$	$^2P^0-^2P^0$	$\frac{1}{2}-1\frac{1}{2}$	4359	108
K IV	$3p^4$	$^1D-^1S$	$2-0$	4511	7·0
		$^3P-^1D$	$2-2$	6101	0·84
Ca V	$3p^4$	$^3P-^1D$	$2-2$	5309	2·0
Ca XII	$2p^5$	$^2P^0-^2P^0$	$1\frac{1}{2}-\frac{1}{2}$	3328	484
Ca XIII	$2p^4$	$^3P-^3P$	$2-1$	4086	330
Ca XV	$2p^2$	$^3P-^3P$	$1-2$	5445	77
		$^3P-^3P$	$0-1$	5694	95

Atom	Array	Designation lower	upper	J lower	upper	λ	A
						Å	s^{-1}
Fe II	$3d^6 4s$	^{6}D	^{4}P	$3\frac{1}{2}$	$2\frac{1}{2}$	4889	0·36
		^{6}D	^{4}F	$4\frac{1}{2}$	$4\frac{1}{2}$	4416	0·46
	$3d^6 4s - 3d^5 4s^2$	^{6}D	^{6}S	$4\frac{1}{2}$	$2\frac{1}{2}$	4287	1·1
		^{6}D	^{6}S	$3\frac{1}{2}$	$2\frac{1}{2}$	4359	0·83
	$3d^7$	^{4}F	^{2}D	$3\frac{1}{2}$	$2\frac{1}{2}$	5527	0·27
Fe III	$3d^6$	^{5}D	^{3}F	4	4	4658	0·44
		^{5}D	^{3}P	3	2	5270	0·40
Fe IV	$3d^5$	^{4}G	^{4}F	$5\frac{1}{2}$	$4\frac{1}{2}$	4906	0·32
Fe V	$3d^4$	^{5}D	^{3}F	4	4	3891	0·74
		^{5}D	^{3}P	3	2	3896	0·71
Fe VI	$3d^3$	^{4}F	^{4}P	$4\frac{1}{2}$	$2\frac{1}{2}$	5677	0·20
		^{4}F	^{2}G	$4\frac{1}{2}$	$4\frac{1}{2}$	5176	0·56
Fe VII	$3d^2$	^{3}F	^{3}P	4	2	5276	0·20
		^{3}F	^{1}D	2	2	5721	0·30
Fe X	$3p^5$	^{2}P^0	^{2}P^0	$1\frac{1}{2}$	$\frac{1}{2}$	6374	69
Fe XI	$3p^4$	^{3}P	^{1}D	1	2	3987	9·5
		^{3}P	^{3}P	2	1	7891	43
Fe XIII	$3p^2$	^{3}P	^{3}P	0	1	10747	14
		^{3}P	^{3}P	1	2	10798	9·6
		^{3}P	^{1}D	2	2	3387	91
Fe XIV	$3p$	^{2}P^0	^{2}P^0	$\frac{1}{2}$	$1\frac{1}{2}$	5303	60
Fe XV	$3s3p$	^{3}P^0	^{3}P^0	1	2	7060	38
Ni II	$3d^9 - 2d^8 4s$	^{2}D	^{2}F	$2\frac{1}{2}$	$2\frac{1}{2}$	6667	0·062
		^{2}D	^{2}D	$2\frac{1}{2}$	$2\frac{1}{2}$	4326	1·4
Ni III	$3d^8$	^{3}F	^{3}P	3	1	6402	0·038
Ni XII	$3p^5$	^{2}P^0	^{2}P^0	$1\frac{1}{2}$	$\frac{1}{2}$	4231	237
Ni XIII	$3p^4$	^{3}P	^{1}D	1	2	3643	18
		^{3}P	^{3}P	2	1	5116	156
Ni XV	$3p^2$	^{3}P	^{3}P	0	1	6701	56
		^{3}P	^{3}P	1	2	8024	22
Ni XVI	$3p$	^{2}P^0	^{2}P^0	$\frac{1}{2}$	$1\frac{1}{2}$	3601	191

[1] A.Q. 1, § 29.
[2] R. H. GARSTANG, Atomic and Molecular Processes, ed. Bates, Ch. 1, Academic Press, 1962.

§ 30. Band Oscillator Strengths

In the spectra of diatomic molecules the strengths S_{12} (of § 25) are replaced by electronic, vibrational, and rotational factors. We have for a particular line in a band

$$(2J'+1)f_{em} = (2J''+1)f_{abs} = \frac{8\pi^2 m\nu}{3he^2} \times |R_e|^2 \times |R_{v'v''}|^2 \times \sum_{M'M''} |R_{rot}|^2,$$

and the numerical relations are similar to § 25. Single primes (') denote upper levels, and double primes (") denote lower levels.

Quantum numbers and notation:

S = electron spin, $(2S+1)$ is given as a superscript,

Λ = component of electron orbital angular momentum along axis, symbolized by $\Sigma, \Pi, \Delta, \ldots$

v = vibrational number,

M = magnetic number,

Ω = electronic number = $|\Lambda +$ component of S along axis$|$ for Hund coupling case (a),

K = total angular momentum apart from spin = vector sum of Λ and the rotation N for Hund coupling case (b),

J = total angular momentum
  = vector sum of Ω and N in case (a)
  = vector sum of S and K in case (b).

The rotational factors $|R_{rot}|^2$ are governed by the sum rules

$$\sum_{J'} \sum_{M'M''} |R_{rot}|^2 = 2J''+1; \qquad \sum_{J''} \sum_{M'M''} |R_{rot}|^2 = 2J'+1$$

Here the $\sum_{M'M''}$ sumation is over magnetic states not normally resolved. The sum-rule does not give complete evaluation of $|R_{rot}|^2$, but in simple cases it leads to the approximation for P and R branches

$$\sum_{M'M''} |R_{rot}|^2 \simeq \tfrac{1}{2}(2J''+1).$$

Complete formulae are known in some cases [1] pp. 127, 208, 250, 258, 265, [15, 16, 17]; for intercombination transitions see references in [4]. In the Hund case (b) the number K can play a role similar to J.

The vibrational factors $|R_{v'v''}|^2$ are usually defined by the 'overlap' integrals (Franck-Condon factors).

$$R_{v'v''} = \int \Psi_{v'}^* \Psi_{v''} dr$$

which obey the sum-rule

$$\sum_{v'} |R_{v'v''}|^2 = \sum_{v''} |R_{v'v''}|^2 = 1.$$

Values for C_2, N_2, N_2^+, O_2, O_2^+, CH, CH^+, CO, CO^+, NO, OH, etc. have been tabulated [2, 3].

The absolute oscillator strengths of bands are usually expressed by the f-value for the electronic band; thus

$$f = f_{\text{abs}} = \frac{8\pi^2 m\nu}{3he^2} |R_e|^2.$$

$$f = f_{\text{abs}}$$

Molecule	Band			f	Notes
C_2	$A\ ^3\Pi_g\text{--}X\ ^3\Pi_u$	Swan		0·029	[5, 6, 7, 13]
	$c\ ^1\Pi_g\text{--}b\ ^1\Pi_u$	Deslandres-d'Azambuja		0·06	[5, 6, 13]
N_2	$C\ ^3\Pi_u\text{--}B\ ^3\Pi_g$	2nd positive		0·03	[8]
N_2^+	$B\ ^2\Sigma_u^+\text{--}X\ ^2\Sigma_g^+$	1st negative		0·35	[6, 13]
O_2	$B\ ^3\Sigma_u^-\text{--}X\ ^3\Sigma_g^-$	Schumann-Runge		0·21	[9]
CH	$A\ ^2\Delta\text{--}X\ ^2\Pi$			0·006	[6, 8, 10]
	$C\ ^2\Sigma^+\text{--}X\ ^2\Pi$			0·008	[6, 10]
CN	$B\ ^2\Sigma^+\text{--}X\ ^2\Sigma^+$			0·029	[6, 11]
OH	$A\ ^2\Sigma^+\text{--}X\ ^2\Pi_i$			0·001 2	[12]
CO^+	$A\ ^2\Pi\text{--}X\ ^2\Sigma$	comet-tail		0·003	[6]
H_2	$B\ ^1\Sigma_u^+\text{--}X\ ^1\Sigma_g^+$	Lyman		0·2	[13]
	$C\ ^1\Pi_u\text{--}X\ ^1\Sigma_g^+$	Werner		0·4	[13]
NO	$A\ ^2\Sigma^+\text{--}X\ ^2\Pi$	γ band		0·002	[11, 14]
NH	$A\ ^3\Pi_i\text{--}X\ ^3\Sigma^-$			0·002	[6, 7]

[1] G. HERZBERG, *Spectra of Diatomic Molecules*, 2nd ed., van Nostrand, 1950.
[2] W. R. JARMAIN, FRASER, NICHOLLS, et al., *Ap. J.*, **118**, 228, 1953; **119**, 286, 1954; **122**, 55, 1955; **131**, 399, 1960.
[3] R. W. NICHOLLS, FRASER, and JARMAIN, *Combustion and Flame*, **3**, 13, 1959.
[4] R. H. GARSTANG, *Atomic and Molecular Processes*, ed. Bates, Ch. 1, Academic Press, 1962.
[5] E. CLEMENTI, *Ap. J.*, **132**, 898, 1960.
[6] R. G. BENNETT and F. W. DALBY, *J. Chem. Phys.*, **32**, 1716, 1960; **36**, 399, 1962.
[7] R. H. LYDDANE and F. T. ROGERS, *Phys. Rev.*, **60**, 281, 1941.
[8] G. STEPHENSON, *Proc. Phys. Soc.*, **64A**, 99, 1951.
[9] D. W. O. HEDDLE, *J. Chem. Phys.*, **32**, 1889, 1960.
[10] A. C. HURLEY, *Proc. Roy. Soc.*, A. **249**, 402, 1959.
[11] C. DE JAGER and L. NEVEN, *Molecules in Stars*, Liege Symp., p. 357, 1957.
[12] T. CARRINGTON, *J. Chem. Phys.*, **31**, 1243, 1959.
[13] H. SHULL, *Ap. J.*, **114**, 546, 1951; *J. Chem. Phys.*, **20**, 18, 1952.
[14] S. S. PENNER, *J.O.S.A.*, **50**, 627, 1960.
[15] A. BUDO, *Z. Phys.*, **105**, 73, 1935.
[16] R. S. MULLIKEN, *Rev. Mod. Phys.*, **3**, 89, 1931.
[17] J. G. PHILLIPS, *Ap. J.*, **115**, 183, 1952.

§ 31. Wavelength Standards

Standards of spectral wavelength are expressed in angstroms (Å) or International Angstroms (I.A.) (both $= 10^{-8}$ cm). It is normal to use vacuum wavelengths (λ_{vac}) for

$\lambda < 2000$ Å, and dry air at 15°C, 760 mm-Hg wavelengths (λ_{air}) for $\lambda > 2000$ Å. However vacuum wavelengths are sometimes quoted throughout the spectrum and the primary standard [86]Kr line is expressed in this form.

Wavelength of standard [86]Kr line [2].

$$\lambda_{vac} = 6057 \cdot 80211 \text{ Å} \quad \text{The primary standard}$$
$$\lambda_{air} = 6056 \cdot 12525 \text{ Å}$$
$$1 \text{ m} = 1\ 650\ 763 \cdot 73\ \lambda_{vac}$$

Other [86]Kr lines [2]	4377·3502	5651·1288
λ_{vac} in Å	4455·1666	6013·8196
	4464·9416	6458·0721
	4503·6159	
Lines of [198]Hg [2]	4047·7144	5771·1985
λ_{vac} in Å	4359·5622	5792·2684
	5462·2706	
λ_{air} (green line) [1]	5460·7532	
Lines of Cd	4799·9139	
λ_{air} in Å [1]	5085·8230	
	6438·4696	

Conversion from air to vacuum

$$\lambda_{vac} = n\lambda_{air}$$

where n is refractive index of dry air at 15°C and 760 mm-Hg.

Wavelength conversion $= \lambda_{vac} - \lambda_{air} = (n-1)\lambda_{air}$ [1, 3]

λ_{air}	000	100	200	300	400	500	600	700	800	900
Å	Å	Å	Å	Å	Å	Å	Å	Å	Å	Å
2000	0·648	0·667	0·687	0·708	0·731	0·754	0·777	0·801	0·825	0·850
3000	0·875	0·900	0·925	0·950	0·976	1·001	1·027	1·053	1·079	1·105
4000	1·131	1·157	1·183	1·210	1·236	1·262	1·289	1·315	1·342	1·368
5000	1·395	1·421	1·448	1·475	1·501	1·528	1·555	1·581	1·608	1·635
6000	1·662	1·689	1·715	1·742	1·769	1·796	1·823	1·850	1·877	1·904
7000	1·931	1·957	1·984	2·011	2·038	2·065	2·092	2·119	2·146	2·173
8000	2·200	2·227	2·254	2·281	2·308	2·335	2·362	2·389	2·417	2·444
9000	2·471	2·498	2·525	2·552	2·579	2·606	2·633	2·660	2·687	2·714
10000	2·741	2·769	2·796	2·823	2·850	2·877	2·904	2·931	2·958	2·985

λ	0000	1000	2000	3000	4000	5000	6000	7000	8000	9000
Å	Å	Å	Å	Å	Å	Å	Å	Å	Å	Å
10000	2·741	3·012	3·284	3·556	3·827	4·099	4·371	4·643	4·915	5·188
20000	5·460	5·732	6·004	6·276	6·549	6·821	7·094	7·366	7·638	7·911
30000	8·183	8·455	8·728	9·000	9·273	9·545	9·818	10·090	10·363	10·635
40000	10·908	11·180	11·453	11·725	11·998	12·270	12·543	12·815	13·088	13·360
50000	13·633	13·906	14·178	14·451	14·723	14·996	15·268	15·540	15·813	16·086

Tables are available [3, 4] for direct conversion of λ_{air} (in I.A.) to wave-number ($= 1/\lambda_{vac}$). The wave-number unit is the kayser (K) ($= \text{cm}^{-1}$).

[1] *A.Q.* **1**, § 30.
[2] *Trans. I.A.U.*, **11**, 97, 1961.
[3] *Table of Wavenumbers*, N.B.S. Monograph 3, 1960.
[4] H. KAYSER, *Tabelle der Schwingungszahlen*, Leipzig, 1925.

§ 32. Stark Effect

The Stark effect displacement is quoted in wave-number units for an electric field of 100 kV/cm. Only the stronger Stark components are quoted. The lines are selected on astrophysical interest, and in the case of Fe the seven lines quoted are those with the largest known Stark displacements. $+ \equiv$ displaced towards violet.

When the displacement is proportional to the electric field (near 100 kV/cm) the line is type 1 (linear), and when proportional to the square of the field it is q (quadratic). For the π polarization the electric vector of the radiation is parallel to the electric field, and for σ it is normal to the field. When the polarizations are not separated or unknown the values are placed in the centre of the column.

Average microscopic electric field $F_0 = 46 \cdot 8 (P_1/T)^{2/3}$ E.S.U.

where the electron and ion pressures are both P_1, and T = temperature.

$$F_0 = 2 \cdot 61 e N^{2/3}$$

where N is the ion density in cm^{-3}.

Stark Effect

Atom	λ	Designation	Type	Displacement for 100 kV/cm	
				π	σ
	Å			cm^{-1}	cm^{-1}
H	1216	Lα	1	$\pm 12 \cdot 8$	0
	1026	Lβ	1	$\pm 38 \cdot 5$	$\pm 19 \cdot 3$
	973	Lγ	1	± 77	$\pm 51 \cdot 4$
	6563	Hα	1	$\pm 25 \cdot 7, 19 \cdot 2$	$\pm 6 \cdot 4, 0$
	4861	Hβ	1	$\pm 64, 51 \cdot 4$	$\pm 38 \cdot 5, 25 \cdot 7$
	4340	Hγ	1	$\pm 116, 96$	$\pm 83, 64, 0$
	4102	Hδ	1	$\pm 181, 154$	$\pm 141, 116, 64, 39$
He	3889	2 ^{3}S–3 ^{3}P^0	q?	$-0 \cdot 8$	$-0 \cdot 8$
	5016	2 ^{1}S–3 ^{1}P^0	q	$+5$	$+3$
	3188	2 ^{3}S–4 ^{3}P^0	q	$-6 \cdot 0$	
	3965	2 ^{1}S–4 ^{1}P^0	q?	$+38$	$+30$
	7065	2 ^{3}P^0–3 ^{3}S	q?	$-0 \cdot 3$	$-0 \cdot 3$
	4713	2 ^{3}P^0–4 ^{3}S	q	$-2 \cdot 8$	$-2 \cdot 8$
	5048	2 ^{1}P^0–4 ^{1}S	q	$-5 \cdot 2$	$-5 \cdot 2$
	5876	2 ^{3}P^0–3 ^{3}D	q?	$+0 \cdot 8$	$+0 \cdot 7$
	6678	2 ^{1}P^0–3 ^{1}D	q	$-3 \cdot 4, -2 \cdot 9$	$-3 \cdot 4, -2 \cdot 9$
	4471	2 ^{3}P^0–4 ^{3}D	1	-23	-23
	4922	2 ^{1}P^0–4 ^{1}D	1	-41	$-41, -23$
Li	4603	2 ^{2}S–2 ^{2}P^0	q	-24	-23
Na	5896	3 ^{2}S–3 ^{2}P$^0_{\frac{1}{2}}$	q	$-0 \cdot 008$	$-0 \cdot 008$
	5890	3 ^{2}S–3 ^{2}P$^0_{1\frac{1}{2}}$	q	$-0 \cdot 011$	$-0 \cdot 011, -0 \cdot 004$
Mg	5184	3 ^{3}P$_2$–4 ^{3}S	q?	$-0 \cdot 05$	$-0 \cdot 05$
	5173	3 ^{3}P$_1$–4 ^{3}S	q?	$-0 \cdot 05$	$-0 \cdot 05$
	3838	3 ^{3}P$_2$–3 ^{3}D	q	$+1 \cdot 8$	$+2 \cdot 5$
	5528	3 ^{1}P–4 ^{1}D	q	$-1 \cdot 3$	—
	4703	3 ^{1}P–5 ^{1}D	q	$-4 \cdot 3$	—
	4352	3 ^{1}P–6 ^{1}D	q	$-11 \cdot 3$	—

Atom	λ	Designation	Type	Displacement for 100 kV/cm	
				π	σ
K	Å			cm^{-1}	cm^{-1}
	4047	4 ^{2}S–5 ^{2}P$_{\frac{1}{2}}$	q	$-0{\cdot}37$	
	4044	4 ^{2}S–5 ^{2}P$_{1\frac{1}{2}}$	q	$-0{\cdot}41, -0{\cdot}21$	
Ca	4227	4 ^{1}S–4 ^{1}P	q	$-0{\cdot}002$	
Fe	5065	y ^{5}F$_3^0$–e ^{3}G$_4$	q	$+2{\cdot}14$	$+1{\cdot}77$
	5079	a ^{5}P$_2$–y ^{5}P$_1^0$	q	$+1{\cdot}67$	$+2{\cdot}18$
	5134	y ^{5}F$_5^0$–f ^{5}G$_6$	q	$+3{\cdot}14$	$+2{\cdot}90$
	5162	y ^{5}F$_5^0$–g ^{5}F$_5$	q	$-8{\cdot}8$	$-6{\cdot}15$
	5367	z ^{5}G$_3^0$–e ^{5}H$_4$	q	$+1{\cdot}91$	$+1{\cdot}17$
	5424	z ^{5}G$_6^0$–e ^{5}H$_7$	q	$+1{\cdot}70$	$+1{\cdot}27$
	5455	z ^{5}G$_6^0$–f ^{5}G$_6$	q	$+3{\cdot}00$	$+2{\cdot}86$
Sr	4607	5 ^{1}S–5 ^{1}P^0	q	$-0{\cdot}008$	$+0{\cdot}002\,5$

[1] *A.Q.* **1**, § 31.

§ 33. Line Broadening

The total width B of a spectrum line at half its maximum intensity (the whole $-\frac{1}{2}-$ width) may be obtained by combining the contributing factors, doppler, collision, instrumental, etc. For this purpose it is convenient to resolve each factor into, (i) a Gaussian term with half $-(1/e)-$ width g in the intensity expression $\exp(-x^2/g^2)$, and (ii) a damping term with half $-\frac{1}{2}-$ width d in the expression $1/(1+x^2/d^2)$. The resolution can be made by selecting the values of d/b, d/g, etc. to fit the tabulated Voigt profiles [1, 2]. b is the whole $-\frac{1}{2}-$ width of the broadening factor.

Voigt profiles [1, 2]

Parameters				
$\dfrac{d}{b}$	$\dfrac{d}{g}$	$\dfrac{g}{b}$	$\dfrac{g^2}{b^2}$	p
0·00	0·000	0·601	0·361	1·064
0·05	0·088	0·568	0·322	1·108
0·10	0·188	0·533	0·284	1·154
0·15	0·302	0·497	0·247	1·201
0·20	0·436	0·459	0·210	1·251
0·25	0·599	0·417	0·174	1·302
0·30	0·807	0·372	0·138	1·354
0·35	1·091	0·321	0·103	1·408
0·40	1·533	0·261	0·068	1·462
0·45	2·451	0·184	0·034	1·517
0·50	∞	0·000	0·000	1·571

$\dfrac{d}{b}$	Ordinates in terms of central ordinate											
	0·9	0·8	0·7	0·6	0·5	0·4	0·3	0·2	0·1	0·05	0·02	0·01
	Width in terms of whole-$\frac{1}{2}$-width											
0·00	0·39	0·57	0·72	0·86	1·00	1·15	1·32	1·52	1·82	2·08	2·38	2·58
0·05	0·39	0·56	0·71	0·86	1·00	1·15	1·33	1·54	1·87	2·19	2·64	3·11
0·10	0·38	0·56	0·71	0·85	1·00	1·16	1·34	1·57	1·94	2·33	3·08	4·04
0·15	0·38	0·56	0·71	0·85	1·00	1·16	1·35	1·59	2·01	2·52	3·64	4·91
0·20	0·38	0·55	0·70	0·85	1·00	1·16	1·36	1·63	2·12	2·76	4·16	5·71
0·25	0·37	0·55	0·70	0·85	1·00	1·17	1·38	1·67	2·24	3·02	4·67	6·48
0·30	0·37	0·54	0·69	0·84	1·00	1·18	1·40	1·72	2·37	3·29	5·14	7·22
0·35	0·36	0·54	0·69	0·84	1·00	1·19	1·43	1·78	2·52	3·56	5·69	7·94
0·40	0·36	0·53	0·68	0·83	1·00	1·20	1·45	1·85	2·68	3·83	6·09	8·63
0·45	0·35	0·52	0·67	0·83	1·00	1·21	1·49	1·92	2·84	4·09	6·61	9·30
0·50	0·33	0·50	0·65	0·82	1·00	1·22	1·53	2·00	3·00	4·36	7·00	9·95

The method of combining becomes

$$b \simeq (d^2 + 2{\cdot}80g^2)^{1/2} + d \quad (\pm 0{\cdot}8\%) \qquad B \simeq (D^2 + 2{\cdot}80G^2)^{1/2} + D$$
$$G = (g_1^2 + g_2^+ + \cdots)^{1/2} \qquad\qquad D = d_1 + d_2 + \cdots$$

Area under intensity curve of unit central intensity $= pB$ (or pb for components)

Resolving pattern of a perfect spectrograph (narrow slit)

$$d = 0{\cdot}14l \qquad\qquad g = 0{\cdot}43l$$

where l is resolving distance (maximum to first minimum).

Effect of slit width s $\qquad\qquad d = 0 \qquad\qquad g \simeq 0{\cdot}41s$

Thermal doppler broadening $\qquad d = 0 \qquad\qquad g = \dfrac{\lambda}{c}\left(\dfrac{2kT}{m_a}\right)^{1/2}$

where g is in wavelength units, and $m_a =$ atomic mass.

Collision damping $\qquad\qquad d = 1/2\pi\tau \qquad\qquad g = 0$

where d is in frequency units and $\tau =$ mean free time between collisions.

Radiation damping $\qquad\qquad d = \gamma/4\pi \qquad\qquad g = 0$

where d is in frequency units and $\gamma =$ damping constant (§ 25).

Classical radiation damping $\qquad d = 5{\cdot}901 \times 10^{-5}$ Å $\quad g = 0$

where d becomes constant when expressed in angstroms.

Holtzmark distribution function $W(\beta)$ [4]

$$d \simeq 0{\cdot}61 \qquad\qquad g \simeq 3{\cdot}0$$

in the units of β. β is the linear Stark effect displacement of a spectrum line caused by ionic fields in terms of the displacement due to an ion at mean distance $r_0 = (3/4\pi N_1)^{1/3}$ where N_1 is the ion density.

When (d/g) is small, as is normally the case for stellar spectra, the Voigt profiles are more suitably expressed [3] in terms of $a = (d/g)$ in the form

$$I_x/I_0 = H_0(u) + aH_1(u) + a^2 H_2(u) + a^3 H_3(u) + \cdots$$

where x is spectral shift from the line centre in the same units as g, d etc., $u = x/g$, I_x and I_0 are line intensities at the point x and a fictitous value in the centre.

The H functions for Voigt profiles

u	$H_0(u)$	$H_1(u)$	$H_2(u)$	$H_3(u)$
0·0	+1·000	−1·128	+1·000	−0·752
0·2	+0·961	−1·040	+0·884	−0·637
0·4	+0·852	−0·803	+0·580	−0·342
0·6	+0·698	−0·486	+0·195	+0·007
0·8	+0·527	−0·168	−0·148	+0·280
1·0	+0·368	+0·086	−0·368	+0·405
1·2	+0·237	+0·245	−0·445	+0·386
1·4	+0·141	+0·314	−0·411	+0·280
1·6	+0·077	+0·316	−0·318	+0·153
1·8	+0·039 2	+0·280	−0·215	+0·051
2·0	+0·018 3	+0·232	−0·128	−0·010
2·5	+0·001 9	+0·130	−0·022	−0·036
3·0	+0·000 1	+0·079	−0·002	−0·017
3·5	+0·000 0	+0·053 4	−0·000 1	−0·006 8
4·0	0·000 0	+0·039 2	0·000 0	−0·003 3
5·0	0·000 0	+0·024 1	0·000 0	−0·001 1
6·0	0·000 0	+0·016 5	0·000 0	−0·000 5
7·0	0·000 0	+0·011 9	0·000 0	−0·000 2
8·0	0·000 0	+0·009 0	0·000 0	−0·000 2
10·0	0·000 0	+0·005 7	0·000 0	−0·000 1
12·0	0·000 0	+0·004 0	0·000 0	−0·000 0

Collision broadening.

The frequency change associated with a collision takes the form

$$\Delta\nu = C_n/r^n$$

where C_n is a constant and r^n the distance from the disturbing particle.

γ_{col} = collision damping constant = $2/\tau$

τ = mean time between collisions

v = mean relative speed of disturbing particle

= $\{(8kT/\pi)(1/m_a + 1/m_b)\}^{1/2}$

$n = 4$: The quadratic Stark effect.

$$\gamma_{col} = 2/\tau = 39\,C_4^{2/3}\,v^{1/3}\,N_e$$

where N_e = electron (or ion) density.

$C_4 = 6·15 \times 10^{-15} \times$ displacement in cm^{-1} for 100 kV/cm field.

$n = 6$: The van der Waals forces

$$\gamma_{col} = 2/\tau = 17\,C_6^{2/5}\,v^{3/5}\,N_H$$

where N_H = neutral H atom density.

$$C_6 \simeq 1·61 \times 10^{-33}\left(\frac{13·6}{\chi - W}\right)^2 \qquad [4]$$

where $\chi - W$ is energy in volts required to ionize the excited level.

Merging of Balmer lines due to line broadening (Inglis and Teller formula, with constant from [5]).

$$\log N_e = 23{\cdot}46 - 7{\cdot}5 \log n_m$$

where N_e is electron density, and n_m is the principal quantum number of the last resolved line.

[1] *A.Q.* **1**, § 32.
[2] G. ELSTE, *Z. Ap.*, **33**, 39, 1953.
[3] D. L. HARRIS, *Ap. J.*, **108**, 112, 1948.
[4] K.-H. BÖHM, *Stellar Atmospheres*, ed. Greenstein, p. 88, Chicago, 1961.
[5] L. H. ALLER, *Gaseous Nebulae*, p. 216, Chapman and Hall, 1956.

CHAPTER 5

RADIATION

§ 34. Radiation Quantities and Inter-relations

THE quantitative concepts of radiation are defined in terms of I, the flux of radiation at a given point in a given direction across unit surface normal to that direction per unit time and per unit solid angle. This is called *specific intensity*, or simply *intensity*.

Flux of radiation through a unit surface = *surface flux*, or *flux density*

$$\mathscr{F} = \int_{4\pi} I \cos \theta \, d\omega$$

where θ is the angle between the ray and the outward normal and $\int_{4\pi} \ldots d\omega$ represents integration in all directions.

Emittance = flux of radiation emitted from a unit surface

$$\mathscr{F} = \int_{2\pi} I \cos \theta \, d\omega$$

$$= \text{for isotropic radiation } \pi I$$

where in this case the integration $\int_{2\pi} \ldots d\omega$ is over the outward hemisphere.

Radiation density
$$u = \frac{1}{c} \int_{4\pi} I \, d\omega = \frac{4\pi}{c} \bar{I}.$$

Radiation quantities per unit frequency and wavelength ranges are written I_ν, I_λ, $\mathscr{F}_\nu$, etc.

$$I = \int I_\nu \, d\nu = \int I_\lambda \, d\lambda$$

$$I_\lambda = \frac{c}{\lambda^2} I_\nu = \frac{\nu^2}{c} I_\nu \qquad \lambda I_\lambda = \nu I_\nu$$

$$d\lambda = -\frac{\lambda^2}{c} \, d\nu = -\frac{c}{\nu^2} \, d\nu \qquad c = \lambda \nu$$

Linear absorption coefficient = κ_s

$$dI/ds = -\kappa_s I$$

Scattering coefficient σ_s, as for absorption coefficient but radiation scattered. It is used in the sense that $\kappa_s - \sigma_s$ represents absorption and transference into heat.

Mass absorption coefficient κ_m (subscript is usually omitted)

$$dI/ds = -\rho \kappa_m I \quad [\rho = \text{density}]$$

Atomic or particle absorption coefficient a

$$dI/ds = -NaI$$

where there are N atoms or particles per unit volume. a has the dimensions of area and represents the effective area over which incident radiation is fully absorbed.

7—A.Q.

Emission coefficient j = radiant flux emitted per unit volume and unit solid angle.

Uniform scattering

$$j = \sigma/4\pi \quad \times \quad \int_{4\pi} I \, d\omega$$

$\underbrace{\quad}$ scattering $\quad$ $\underbrace{\qquad}$ incident radiation

Scattering by electrons, atoms, and molecules

$$j = \frac{\sigma}{4\pi} \int_{4\pi} \tfrac{3}{4} (1 + \cos^2 \theta) \, I \, d\omega$$

θ = angle between incident and scattered light.

Optical thickness or depth $\qquad \tau = \int \kappa_s \, ds$

Source function or ergiebigkeit $\qquad S = j/\kappa_s$

Intensity emitted from an absorbing medium

$$I = \int_0^\infty j \exp(-\tau) \, ds = \int_0^\infty S \exp(-\tau) \, d\tau$$

Kirchhoff law (a) in a volume element

$$j_\nu = \kappa_{s,\nu} \, B_\nu(T)$$

where $B_\nu(T)$ is black body intensity at temperature T.

Kirchhoff law (b) at a surface element

$$I_\nu = A_\nu B_\nu(T)$$

where A_ν is fraction of incident radiation absorbed, i.e. $(1 - A_\nu)$ = reflection coefficient.

Atomic polarizability α = induced dipole moment per unit electric field ($\bar{\alpha}$ for steady or low frequency field)

$$\bar{\alpha} = 4a_0^3 \sum_n \frac{f_n}{(\nu_n/cR_\infty)^2}$$

$$= 5 \cdot 926 \times 10^{-25} \sum_n \frac{f_n}{(\nu_n/cR_\infty)^2} \text{ cm}^3$$

$$= 7 \cdot 128 \times 10^{-23} \sum_n f_n \lambda_n^2 \text{ cm}^3 \quad [\lambda \text{ in } \mu]$$

where ν_n/cR_∞ = frequency in Rydbergs of lines connecting the ground level, f_n = corresponding oscillator strength.

Scattering $\qquad \sigma_s = \dfrac{128\pi^5}{3} N \left(\dfrac{\nu}{c}\right)^4 \alpha^2 = \dfrac{128\pi^5}{3\lambda^4} N\alpha^2$

$$= 1 \cdot 305 \; 7 \times 10^{20} N\alpha^2/\lambda^4 \quad [\lambda \text{ in } \mu]$$

Index of refraction n $\qquad n - 1 = 2\pi N\alpha$

$$= \text{(for s.t.p.) } 1 \cdot 689 \times 10^{20}\alpha$$

Molecular refraction $\qquad R = \dfrac{n^2 - 1}{n^2 + 2} \dfrac{M}{\rho} = \dfrac{4\pi}{3} N_0 \alpha$

where M = molecular weight, ρ = density, N_0 = Avogadro number.

[1] A.Q. 1, § 33.

§ 35. Refractive Index and Polarizability

Refractive index and polarizability of atomic and molecular gases

n = refractive index at S.T.P.

$$n - 1 = A(1 + B/\lambda^2) \quad [\lambda \text{ in } \mu]$$

$\bar{\alpha}$ = polarizability at low frequency

Atom	$\bar{\alpha}$	n (D lines)	A	B
	10^{-25} cm^3		10^{-5}	10^{-3}
H	6·70			
He	2·07	1·000 035 0	3·48	2·3
Li	200			
Be	93			
O	1·5			
Ne	3·96	1·000 067 1	6·66	2·4
Na	270			
Ar	16·54	1·000 283 7	27·92	5·6
K	380			
Kr	24·8	1·000 427 3	41·89	6·97
Rb	500			
X	40·4	1·000 702	68·23	10·14
Cs	500			
Hg	52	1·000 935	87·8	22·65

Molecule	n (D lines)	A	B
		10^{-5}	10^{-3}
Air	1·000 291 8	28·71	5·67
H_2	1·000 138 4	13·58	7·52
O_2	1·000 272	26·63	5·07
N_2	1·000 297	29·06	7·7
H_2O	1·000 254	516 (radio freq.)	
CO_2	1·000 449 8	43·9	6·4
CO	1·000 334	32·7	8·1
NH_3	1·000 375	37·0	12·0
NO	1·000 297	28·9	7·4
CH_4	1·000 441		

Refractive indices of optical media

λ	Calcspar		Glass		Fluorite	Quartz		Fused silica	Rock salt	Sylvine KCl	Water
	ord. ray	extr. ray	BSC crown	DF flint	CaF$_2$	ord. ray	extr. ray				
μ											
0·2	1·91	1·58			1·495	1·651	1·663	1·550	1·792	1·724	1·423
0·3	1·722	1·515	1·557		1·455	1·579	1·589	1·489	1·602	1·547	1·358
0·4	1·683	1·499	1·531	1·650	1·442	1·558	1·567	1·471	1·568	1·510	1·343
0·5	1·666	1·491	1·522	1·627	1·437	1·549	1·558	1·463	1·552	1·497	1·336
0·6	1·657	1·486	1·517	1·616	1·434	1·544	1·553	1·458	1·543	1·490	1·332
0·7	1·652	1·483	1·513	1·610	1·432	1·541	1·550	1·455	1·538	1·486	1·330
0·8	1·648	1·481	1·511	1·605	1·430	1·539	1·548		1·535	1·483	1·328
1·0	1·643	1·479	1·507	1·600	1·429	1·536	1·544		1·532	1·480	1·325
2	1·626	1·476	1·496		1·424	1·520	1·528		1·526	1·476	1·315
5					1·398	1·42			1·519	1·471	
10					1·303				1·494	1·457	
20									1·384	1·395	
Temp. coeff.	$+0.0^5\,5$	$+0.0^4\,14$	$-0.0^5\,1$	$+0.0^5\,3$	$-0.0^4\,1$	$-0.0^5\,5$	$-0.0^5\,6$	$-0.0^5\,3$	$-0.0^4\,4$	$-0.0^4\,4$	$-0.0^4\,8$
Spectral limits low λ high λ	0·23 2·2	4	0·32 2·2	0·37 2·8	0·14 9·0	0·18 3·6		0·17 21	0·20 17	0·38 22	<0·2 1·14

Atmospheric refraction see § 54.

Refractive indices of optical media. The values quoted are relative to air at 15 °C. The temperatures of the media are about 18 °C and the temperature coefficients quoted are the change in D line refractive index for 1 °C temperature rise. Manufacturers' reports must be consulted for indices that are accurate enough for optical computing. The table gives also the spectral limits (λ in μ) within which the absorption is less than 1 exp cm^{-1} (i.e. 1 cm transmission $> 37\%$).

$$[1] \ A.Q. \ 1, \ \S \ 34.$$

§ 36. Absorption and Scattering by Particles

Scattering of free electrons σ_e

$$\sigma_e = \frac{8\pi}{3} \left(\frac{e^2}{mc^2} \right)^2 \left(1 - 2\frac{h\nu}{mc^2} \right) = 0 \cdot 665 \ 20 \times 10^{-24} \left(1 - 2\frac{h\nu}{mc^2} \right) \quad \text{cm}^2$$

where σ_e is the (exponential) scattering coefficient per electron (§ 34) and the relativity term $2h\nu/mc^2$ is usually negligible.

Rayleigh scattering of atoms or molecules

$$\sigma_s = \frac{32\pi^3}{3N} \frac{(n-1)^2}{\lambda^4}$$

$$= 3 \cdot 307 \times 10^{18}(n-1)^2/\lambda^4 N \quad \text{cm}^{-1} \quad [\lambda \text{ in } \mu]$$

where N = atoms or molecules per unit volume, n = refractive index of medium, and σ_s represents a linear scattering coefficient.

Rayleigh scattering per atom or molecule

$$\sigma_a = \frac{32\pi^3}{3\lambda^4} \left(\frac{n-1}{N} \right)^2 = \frac{128\pi^5}{3\lambda^4} \alpha^2$$

$$= 1 \cdot 306 \times 10^{20}\alpha^2/\lambda^4 \quad \text{cm}^2 \quad [\lambda \text{ in } \mu]$$

where α = polarizability.

Rayleigh linear scattering for small particles

$$\sigma_s = \frac{24\pi^3 N_p V^2 (n^2 - 1)^2}{\lambda^4 (n_p^2 + 2)^2}$$

where N_p = particles per unit volume, V = volume of particles, and n_p their refractive index.

Atomic scattering at some distance from any absorption line

$$\sigma_a = \frac{8\pi}{3} \left(\frac{e^2}{mc^2} \right)^2 \left(\sum_2 \frac{f_{12}\nu^2}{\nu_{12}^2 - \nu^2} \right)^2$$

where f_{12} is the oscillator strength (1 is the ground level when excitation is low).

Absorption of small spherical particles a_p expressed in terms of the area πr^2 [2]. r = radius of particle, $x = 2\pi r/\lambda$, and n = refractive index.

a_p

x	Water drops $n = 4/3$	Totally reflecting spheres $n = \infty$	Iron spheres at 4000 Å
	πr^2	πr^2	πr^2
small	$0 \cdot 11 x^4$	$2 \cdot 7 x^4$	$2 \cdot 9 x$
0·1	0·000 01	0·000 3	0·3
0·2	0·000 2	0·005	0·6
0·5	0·007	0·22	1·7
1·0	0·07	2·0	3·0
2·0	0·5	2·2	3·0
5·0	3·6	2·1	2·6
∞	2·0	2·0	2·0

Absorption and scattering for $x > 10$

		Diffraction		Reflection and scattering
Absorption $a_\text{p}/\pi r^2 =$		1·0	+	1·0
Scattering $\sigma_\text{p}/\pi r^2 =$		1·0	+	albedo

Note, however, that for very large x the diffraction angle is so small that the diffracted light is effectively added to the original beam, giving $a_\text{p}/\pi r^2 = 1$ and $\sigma_\text{p}/\pi r^2 = $ albedo.

The determination of the precise value of a_p for particular dimensions of particles and wavelengths is complicated [2].

[1] *A.Q.* **1**, § 35.
[2] H. C. van de Hulst, *Res. Astr. Ob. Utrecht*, **9**, 1 and 2, 1946–9.

§ 37. Continuous Atomic Absorption and Recombination

Quantities

ϵ = energy of free electron. Unit = Rydberg energy = $hcR = 2 \cdot 18 \times 10^{-11}$ erg
   $= 13 \cdot 60$ ev

χ = ionization energy in same units; $\nu_0 = cR\chi$

ν = frequency $= cR(\chi + \epsilon)$; $d\nu = cR d\epsilon$

a_ν = atomic absorption coefficient at frequency ν; i.e. a_ν = cross-section of atom for ionization by a photon

$\dfrac{df}{d\nu}$ and $\dfrac{df}{d\epsilon}$ = differentials of continuum oscillator strength with frequency and with free electron energy

f_c = integrated oscillator strength of continuum $= \displaystyle\int_{\nu_0}^{\infty} \dfrac{df}{d\nu} d\nu$

α = recombination coefficient such that $\alpha N_e N_1$ gives the total number of recombinations per sec per cm^3 (N_e electrons cm^{-3}, N_1 ions cm^{-3})

α_t = corresponding recombination coefficient to a particular level, term, configuration, etc., labelled t.

Q_t = recombination cross-section of ion for capture on a particular level, term, etc.

$\tilde{\omega}_1, \tilde{\omega}_t$ = statistical weights of ion and atom at particular level, term, or configuration (the symbol g is used in other sections)

v = mean electron velocity (in cm/s)

T = temperature (in °K)

Z = stage of ionization ($=1$ for neutral atom, 2 for first ion, etc.)

= charge on upper ion

Inter-relations

$$\alpha_t = vQ_t$$

$$a_v = \frac{\pi e^2}{mRc^2}\frac{df}{d\epsilon} = 8\cdot067 \times 10^{-18}\frac{df}{d\epsilon}$$

$$a_v = \frac{mc}{2\pi e^2 R}\frac{2\tilde{\omega}_1}{\tilde{\omega}_t}\frac{\epsilon^{1/2}\alpha_t}{(\chi_t+\epsilon)^2} = 1\cdot713 \times 10^{-4}\frac{2\tilde{\omega}_1}{\tilde{\omega}_t}\frac{\epsilon^{1/2}\alpha_t}{(\chi_t+\epsilon)^2} \quad [1] \text{ (the Milne relation)}$$

$$v = \frac{2\pi e^2}{h}\epsilon^{1/2} = \left(\frac{\pi kT}{2m}\right)^{1/2} = 2\cdot188 \times 10^8 \epsilon^{1/2} = 4\cdot880 \times 10^5 T^{1/2}$$

using reciprocal mean v in this case [1]

$$\epsilon = \frac{h^2 k}{8\pi e^4 m}T = 4\cdot975 \times 10^{-6}T$$

$$\alpha_t T^{1/2} = \frac{4\pi e^2}{m}\left(\frac{hR^3}{\pi ck}\right)^{1/2}(\chi_t+\epsilon)^2\frac{\tilde{\omega}_t}{2\tilde{\omega}_1}a_v = 2\cdot612 \times 10^6(\chi_t+\epsilon)^2\frac{\tilde{\omega}_t}{2\tilde{\omega}_1}a_v$$

General approximations

A general procedure for calculating a_v is available [2].

Generalized value of recombination coefficient [1]

α (to ground state) $\simeq 1 \times 10^{-11}Z^2 T^{-1/2}$

α (to all states) $\quad \simeq 3 \times 10^{-10}Z^2 T^{-3/4}$

Generalized recombination cross-section [1]

Q (to ground state) $\simeq 2 \times 10^{-17}Z^2 T^{-1}$

Q (to all states) $\quad \simeq 6 \times 10^{-16}Z^2 T^{-5/4}$

where Z is charge on upper ion.

Absorption and recombination for hydrogen-like atoms

$$a_v = \frac{64\pi^4}{3\sqrt{3}}\frac{Z^4 me^{10}}{ch^6 n^5}\frac{1}{v^3}g$$

$$= 2\cdot815 \times 10^{29}\frac{Z^4}{n^5}\frac{1}{v^3}g$$

$$= 1\cdot045 \times 10^{-14}\frac{Z^4\lambda^3}{n^5}g \quad [\lambda \text{ in } \mu]$$

where $Z = 1$ for hydrogen, n is total quantum number, and g the Gaunt factor [3] of order unity.

At the absorption edge, frequency v_0

$$a_{v_0} = \frac{8}{3\sqrt{(3)}\pi^2}\frac{h^3 g}{m^2 ce^2 Z^2}n = 7\cdot906 \times 10^{-18}\frac{ng}{Z^2} \quad \text{cm}^2$$

$$\left(\frac{df}{d\epsilon}\right)_{v_0} = \frac{16}{3\sqrt{(3)}\pi}\frac{ng}{Z^2} = 0\cdot98014\frac{ng}{Z^2}$$

Continuum oscillator strength f_c

$$f_c = \frac{8\bar{g}}{3\sqrt{(3)}\pi n} = 0 \cdot 4901 \frac{\bar{g}}{n}$$

where $\bar{g}$ is a mean value of the Gaunt factor [3].

Extensive tabulations of Gaunt factors are available [4]. Approximations are given below.

The Gaunt factor for various configurations of the hydrogen atom

Configuration	g at absorption edge		$\bar{g}$ for whole continuum	
1s		0·80		0·89
2s	0·95 ⎫		1·47 ⎫	
2p	0·89 ⎬ 0·89		0·80 ⎬ 1·00	
3s	1·08 ⎧		1·79 ⎧	
3p	1·10 ⎬ 0·91		1·32 ⎬ 1·04	
3d	0·76 ⎭		0·61 ⎭	
4s	1·19 ⎧		2·02 ⎧	
4p	1·25 ⎨ 0·92		1·75 ⎨ 1·06	
4d	⎬		1·22 ⎬	
4f	⎭		0·47 ⎭	
5		0·93		1·07
6		0·94		
7		0·95		

Recombination cross-section on to the nth hydrogen level [12]

$$Q_n = \frac{2^4 h e^2}{3\sqrt{(3)}m^2 c^3} \frac{(hcR)^2}{h\nu\frac{1}{2}mv^2} \frac{g}{n^3} = 2 \cdot 11 \times 10^{-22} \frac{g}{n\epsilon(1+n^2\epsilon)}$$

Recombination coefficient on to the nth hydrogen level [12]

$$\alpha_n = vQ_n = 2 \cdot 07 \times 10^{-11} \frac{g}{nT^{1/2}(1+n^2\epsilon)}$$

$$= \frac{2^9 \pi^5}{(6\pi)^{3/2}} \frac{e^{10}}{m^2 c^3 h^3} \left(\frac{m}{kT}\right)^{3/2} \frac{1}{n^3} \exp\left(\chi_n/kT\right) \mathrm{Ei}\left(\chi_n/kT\right) = 3 \cdot 262 \times 10^{-6} M(n, T)$$

where $M(n, T) = n^{-3} T^{-3/2} \exp\left(\chi_n/kT\right) \mathrm{Ei}\left(\chi_n/kT\right)$ has been tabulated [5] and is of the order 10^{-8} for 10^4 °K. For factors of the type (χ_n/kT), χ_n is in ergs, but the factor may be written $(157\,900\chi_n/T)$ with χ_n in Rydbergs (i.e. with $\chi_n = 1/n^2$) The function $\mathrm{Ei}(x)$ has been tabulated [6]. Note that $\exp(x)\,\mathrm{Ei}(x) \simeq 1/x$ for $x > 5$.

Recombination coefficient onto all levels of hydrogen [8]

$$\alpha_H = 2 \cdot 07 \times 10^{-11} T^{-1/2} \phi \quad \mathrm{cm^3\ s^{-1}}$$

where ϕ changes slowly with T as follows:

$\log T$	2	3	4	5
ϕ	4·6	3·4	2·3	1·2

[1] *A.Q.* **1**, § 36.
[2] A. BURGESS and M. J. SEATON, *M.N.*, **120**, 121, 1960.
[3] J. A. GAUNT, *Phil. Trans.*, **229**, 163, 1930.
[4] W. J. KARZAS and R. LATTER, *Ap. J. Supp.*, **6**, 167, 1961.
[5] G. CILLIÉ, *M.N.*, **92**, 820, 1932.
[6] E. JAHNKE and F. EMDE, *Tables of Functions*, Dover, 1945.
[7] L. SPITZER, *Ap. J.*, **107**, 6, 1948.
[8] H. ZANSTRA, *Obs.*, **74**, 66, 1954.

§ 38. Table of Atomic Absorption and Recombination Coefficients

The notation is from § 37. The columns give the atom, the term designation, the ionization potential, the atomic absorption coefficient at the absorption edge, the corresponding $df/d\epsilon$ at the absorption edge and at $\epsilon = 0.05$, remarks on the variation of the absorption coefficient with frequency, the integrated oscillator strength f_c, the recombination coefficient and cross-section for a temperature of 10 000 °K, and references. The temperature 10 000 °K was selected for recombination factors because that is the order of the temperature usually met in this connection in astrophysics. For other temperatures one may use the approximations

$$\alpha \propto T^{-0.5} \text{ (ground states)} \qquad \propto T^{-0.8} \text{ (total recombination)}$$
$$Q \propto T^{-1.0} \text{ (ground states)} \qquad \propto T^{-1.3} \text{ (total recombination)}$$

The recombination factors have usually been determined from the relation for $\alpha_t T^{1/2}$ (§ 37), which for 10 000 °K becomes

$$\alpha(10\ 000\ °K) = 10.54 \times 10^{-14} (\tilde{\omega}_t/\tilde{\omega}_1)(\chi + 0.05)^2 \, (df/d\epsilon)_{0.05}.$$

Atom	Term	χ	a_{v_0}	$df/d\epsilon$		Variation with ϵ	f_c	α_t	Q_t	Ref.
				$\epsilon = 0$	$\epsilon = 0.05$			10 000 °K		
		Rydberg	10^{-18} cm^2	Rydberg^{-1}				10^{-14} cm^3 s^{-1}	10^{-22} cm^2	
H I	$1s$	1.000	6.3	0.78	0.69	$(\chi+\epsilon)^{-3}$	0.436	15.8	32	[1, 6]
	$2s$	0.250	15	1.86	1.1	$(\chi+\epsilon)^{-2.5}$	0.362	2.3	4.7	,,
	$2p$	0.250	14	1.74	1.1	$(\chi+\epsilon)^{-3}$	0.196	5.3	11	,,
	$3s$	0.111	26	3.1	1.0	$(\chi+\epsilon)^{-2}$	0.293	0.8	1.6	,,
	$3p$	0.111	26	3.2	1.0	$(\chi+\epsilon)^{-3}$	0.217	2.0	4.1	,,
	$3d$	0.111	18	2.2	0.7	$(\chi+\epsilon)^{-3}$	0.100	2.0	4.1	,,
	$4s$	0.062	38	4.65	1.3	$(\chi+\epsilon)^{-2}$	0.248	0.4	0.7	,,
	$4p$	0.062	40	4.9	1.1	$(\chi+\epsilon)^{-2}$	0.214	1.0	2.0	,,
	$4d$	0.062	39	4.8	0.8		0.149	1.0	2.0	,,
	$4f$	0.062	15	1.8	0.3		0.057	0.6	1.2	,,
	Total							43	88	,,
He I	$1s^2\ ^1S$	1.807	7.6	0.95	0.91	$(\chi+\epsilon)^{-2}$	1.50	15.9	33	[1, 6]
	$1s2s\ ^3S$	0.351	2.80	0.35	0.33	$(\chi+\epsilon)^{-1}$	0.25	1.4	2.9	,,
	$1s2s\ ^1S$	0.292	10.5	1.30	1.0	$(\chi+\epsilon)^{-2}$	0.40	0.55	1.1	,,
	Total							43	88	,,
He II	$1s$	4.000	1.8	0.22	0.21	$(\chi+\epsilon)^{-3}$	0.44	73	150	
Li I	$2s\ ^2S$	0.397	3.0	0.37	0.31	$(\chi+\epsilon)^{-2}$	0.2	1.3	2.7	[4]
Li II	$1s^2\ ^1S$	0.557	2	0.25	0.2		1.0	0.4	0.8	[2]
Be I	$2s^2\ ^1S$	0.685	8.2	1.02	0.72	$e^{-\epsilon/0.15}$	0.15	2.0	4.1	[2]
B I	$2p\ ^2P^0$	0.610	12	1.5	1.3	$(\chi+\epsilon)^{-2}$	0.9	35	70	[2]
C I	$2p^2\ ^3P$	0.828	11	1.4	1.4	$(\chi+\epsilon)^{-1}$	2	17	35	[2]
C II	$2p\ ^2P^0$	1.790	3.7	0.46	0.45	$(\chi+\epsilon)^{-1}$	1.1	96	200	[2]
N I	$2p^3\ ^4S^0$	1.069	9	1.1	1.2	max at 0.4	3	7	14	[2]
N II	$2p^2\ ^3P$	2.177	6.4	0.79	0.77	$(\chi+\epsilon)^{-1}$	3	60	120	[2]

Atom	Term	χ	a_{v_0}	$df/d\epsilon$ $\epsilon = 0$	$\epsilon = 0.05$	Variation with ϵ	f_c	α_t	Q_t	Ref.
								10 000 °K		
		Rydberg	10^{-18} cm^2	Rydberg^{-1}				10^{-14} cm^3 s^{-1}	10^{-22} cm^2	
O I	$2p^4\,^3$P Total	1·001	2·6	0·32	0·36	max at 0·3	0·9	8	16	[2]
								22	45	[1]
O II	$2p^3\,^4$S	2·584	8·1	1·00	1·0	$(\chi+\epsilon)^{-1}$	4	32	65	[2]
F I	$2p^5\,^2$P^0	1·282	4·5	0·56	0·56	constant	2	7	13	[2]
F II	$2p^4\,^3$P	2·67	2·5	0·31	0·31	constant	1·6	54	110	[2]
Ne I	$2p^6\,^1$S	1·586	5·5	0·63	0·65	max at 0·6	2·0	3·0	6	[4]
Ne II	$2p^5\,^2$P^0	3·02	4·5	0·56	0·56	constant	3·4	37	76	[2]
Na I	$3s\,^2$S	0·378	0·116	0·014	0·005	min at 0·07	0·001	0·02	0·05	[1]
	$3p\,^2$P^0	0·223	7·7	0·95	0·39	$(\chi+\epsilon)^{-4}$	0·07	2·5	5·1	,,
	$4s\,^2$S	0·143	0·16	0·020	<0·001	min at 0·05	0·002	0·01	0·02	,,
	$4p\,^2$P^0	0·102	16	2·0	0·58	$(\chi+\epsilon)^{-3}$	0·10	0·85	1·7	,,
Na II	$2p^6\,^1$S	3·48	7·1	0·88	0·88	constant	6	19	39	[2]
Mg I	$3s^2\,^1$S	0·563	1·2	0·15	0·04		0·006			[5]
Mg II	$3s\,^2$S	1·105	0·24	0·030	0·034	max at 0·2	0·12	1·0	2·0	[3]
	$3p\,^2$P^0	0·780	0·6	0·08	0·06	min at 1	0·10	2·6	5	,,
	$3d\,^2$D	0·454	5·7	0·70	0·49	$(\chi+\epsilon)^{-3}$	0·15	13	27	,,
Si II	$3p\,^2$P^0	1·200	4·8	0·59	0·52	$(\chi+\epsilon)^{-3}$	0·28	51	104	[3]
	$4s\,^2$S	0·604	0·06	0·007	0·010	max at 0·2	0·05	0·1	0·2	,,
	$3d\,^2$D	0·478	4·8	0·59	0·42	$(\chi+\epsilon)^{-3}$	0·11	12	25	,,
	$4p\,^2$P^0	0·461	7·2	0·89	0·70	$(\chi+\epsilon)^{-3}$	0·25	11	22	,,
Ar I	$3p^6\,^1$S	1·18	35	4·3			4			[4]
K I	$4s\,^2$S	0·319	0·012	0·001 5	0·002 4	min at 0·02		0·05	0·1	[1]
K II	$3p^6\,^1$S	2·339	32	4·0	3·9	$(\chi+\epsilon)^{-1}$	7	37	75	[1]
Ca I	$4s^2\,^1$S	0·449	0·47	0·058	0·021	min at 0·02	0·12	0·08	0·16	[4]
	,,	0·574	0·88	0·11	0·07	min at 0·13	0·003			
Ca II	$4s\,^2$S	0·873	0·11	0·014	0·016	max at 0·3	0·026	0·3	0·6	[1]
	$3d\,^2$D	0·750	17	2·0	1·6	$(\chi+\epsilon)^{-3}$	0·8	110	250	,,
	$4p\,^2$P^0	0·643	5·5	0·68	0·59	$(\chi+\epsilon)^{-2.5}$	0·23	18	37	,,
Rb I	$5s\,^2$S	0·307	0·11	0·014	0·001					[1]
Cs I	$6s\,^2$S	0·286	0·23	0·03	0·005	min at 0·5		0·03	0·06	[1]
	$6p\,^2$P^0	0·182	36	4·5						
	$5d\,^2$D	0·154	30	3·7						

[1] *A.Q.* **1**, § 37.
[2] D. R. Bates (and M. J. Seaton), *M.N.*, **106**, 423, 432, 1946; **109**, 698, 1949.
[3] L. Biermann, *Ver. U.-S. Gottingen*, No. 87, 1946.
[4] R. W. Ditchburn (and R. D. Hudson), *Proc. Roy. Soc.*, A **236**, 216, 1956; A **256**, 53, 1960.
[5] R. W. Ditchburn and G. V. Marr, *Proc. Phys. Soc.*, A **66**, 655, 1953.
[6] A. Burgess and M. J. Seaton, *M.N.*, **121**, 471, 1960.

§ 39. Absorption of Material of Stellar Interiors

Mass absorption coefficient

Photoelectric (Rosseland mean) [1, 2]

$$\bar{\kappa} = 3 \cdot 9 \times 10^{25} \rho (1+X)(1-X-Y) T^{-3 \cdot 5} t^{-1} + 4 \cdot 1 \times 10^{22} (1+X)(X+Y)$$

Electron scattering [1]

$$\bar{\kappa}_e = 0 \cdot 19 (1+X)$$

where ρ = density in g cm^{-3}, T = temperature, t = guillotine factor, X, Y = fraction by mass of H, He ($X \simeq 0 \cdot 63$, $Y \simeq 0 \cdot 36$, $1-X-Y \simeq 0 \cdot 014$ for population I stars).

The guillotine factor t is tabulated with the arguments T and $\ln\{G(T)/N_e\}$ where $G(T) = 2(2\pi m k T)^{3/2}/h^3 = 4 \cdot 830 \times 10^{15} T^{3/2}$, and the heavy element mixture used is 60% O and 40% Russell mixture.

log t

T	ln $\{G(T)/N_e\}$					
	2	3	4	5	6	∞
1×10^6 °K			0·40	0·34	0·30	0·22
2×10^6 °K			0·38	0·32	0·28	0·24
4×10^6 °K	0·80	0·54	0·34	0·20	0·11	0·03
6×10^6 °K	0·97	0·73	0·53	0·39	0·31	0·24
8×10^6 °K	1·11	0·88	0·71	0·59	0·51	0·45
10×10^6 °K	1·18	0·97	0·80	0·67	0·59	0·54
15×10^6 °K	1·23	1·01	0·83	0·72	0·66	0·61
20×10^6 °K	1·27	1·02	0·84	0·72	0·67	0·63
25×10^6 °K	1·33	1·09	0·91	0·81	0·76	0·72
30×10^6 °K	1·42	1·20	1·06	0·98	0·94	0·92

The guillotine factor and density ρ [1]

log ρ (ρ in g cm^{-3}) log t	-3 0·28	-2 0·27	-1 0·27	0 0·28	1 0·78	2 1·2

Tabulations of the absorption coefficient as a function of temperature, density and composition are available [3, 4].

X-ray atomic absorption coefficient for shells K($n = 1$), L($n = 2$), M($n = 3$), etc. [1]

$$= 0 \cdot 021 z^4 \lambda^3 n^{-3} \quad [\lambda \text{ in cm}]$$

z = atomic number. The probable error is about 10% near the absorption edge at λ_E, but for $\lambda < 0 \cdot 1 \lambda_E$ the absorption is greater than the formula.

[1] *A.Q.* 1, § 38.
[2] A. G. MASEVICH and T. G. VOLKONSKAYA, *A. Zh.*, **37**, 42, 1960; *Sov. A.*, **4**, 40.
[3] G. KELLER and R. E. MEYEROTT, *Ap. J.*, **122**, 32, 1955.
[4] H. ZIRIN, *Ap. J.*, **128**, 342, 1958.

§ 40. Absorption of Material of Stellar Atmospheres

The value tabulated is log κ_m, where κ_m is the exponential mass absorption coefficient in $g^{-1} cm^2$ [2].

The low temperature limit of the table, $T = 3\,840\ °K$ or $\Theta = 5\,040°/T = 1·3$ is set by the appearance of considerable molecular band absorption. The main sources of true absorption above this temperature are H, H$^-$, He, He$^+$, C, and metals. The absorption coefficients are multipled by $(1 - e^{-h\nu/kT})$ to cater for stimulated emissions. No such factor is applied to electron and Rayleigh scattering which, however, are included in the total absorption κ_m.

The main table gives log κ_m at wavelengths chosen to illustrate various features as follows :

λ	Feature	λ	Feature
900	includes Lyman continuum	3500	includes Balmer continuum
1000	includes C continuum	4000	excludes Balmer continuum
1100	excludes C continuum	8000	includes Paschen continuum, max. H$^-$
1500	peak metal absorption	10000	excludes Paschen continuum
2500	includes Mg continuum	17000	excludes Brackett continuum, min. H$^-$

The arguments are $\Theta = 5\,040°/T$, and the electron pressure P_e in dyn cm^{-2}. The Rosseland mean is given in the last column of this table [2].

In the table giving log $\bar{\kappa}_m$ as a function of Θ, log P_e and log P, where P is the total pressure, information from various sources has been used [2, 3, 4] and the values are not necessarily the Rosseland mean. A tabulation for the absorption coefficient at $\lambda 4235$ Å is available [5].

[1] A.Q. 1, § 39.
[2] E. VITENSE, Z. Ap., 28, 81, 1951.
[3] B. STRÖMGREN, Pub. Kobenhavn Ob., No. 138, 1944.
[4] S. CHANDRASEKHAR and G. MÜNCH, Ap. J., 104, 446, 1946.
[5] L. H. ALLER, Stellar Atmospheres, ed. Greenstein, p. 239, Chicago, 1961.

$\log \kappa_m$ [2]

log P_e	Θ	200	900	1000	1100	1500	2000	2500	3000	3500	4000	5000	6000	8000	10000	17000	30000	50000	Rosseland mean
1	= 1·3		+6·45	+3·11	+2·13	+2·65	+0·52	+0·13	−0·30	−0·21	−0·77	−0·04	+0·03	+0·07	+0·04	−0·77	−0·32	+0·05	−0·18
0			+6·45	+3·08	+2·10	+2·54	+0·58	+0·05	−1·24	−1·20	−1·17	−0·97	−0·97	−0·93	−0·96	−1·77	−1·32	−0·95	−1·18
−1			+6·45		+1·97	+2·6	+0·47	−0·26	−1·90	−2·07	−2·09	−1·97	−1·97	−1·93	−1·96	−2·77	−2·32	−1·95	−2·18
1	= 1·2		+6·45	+3·08	+2·12	+2·53	+1·05	+·016	−0·44	−0·39	−0·31	−0·21	−0·13	−0·09	−0·13	−0·83	−0·39	+0·19	−0·29
0			+6·45	+3·11	+2·01	+2·46	+0·68	+0·07	−1·22	−1·32	−1·30	−1·21	−1·13	−1·09	−1·13	−1·83	−1·39	−0·81	−1·28
−1			+6·45		+1·61	+2·02	+0·29	−0·64	−1·88	−2·11	−2·18	−2·18	−2·13	−2·09	−2·13	−2·83	−2·39	−1·81	−2·26
2	= 1·1			+3·09	+2·14	+2·58	+1·15	+0·63	+0·38	+0·43	+0·51	+0·63	+0·70	+0·74	+0·73	+0·10	+0·58	+1·03	+0·55
1				+3·09	+2·07	+2·50	+0·90	+0·19	−0·54	−0·55	−0·48	−0·37	−0·29	−0·26	−0·27	−0·90	−0·42	+0·03	−0·43
0				+3·09	+1·71	+2·13	+0·47	−0·37	−1·33	−1·44	−1·43	−1·36	−1·28	−1·25	−1·26	−1·89	−1·42	−0·97	−1·39
−1					+0·98	+1·37	−0·24	−1·13	−2·05	−2·23	−2·32	−2·33	−2·26	−2·23	−2·25	−2·88	−2·41	−1·97	−2·35
3	= 1·0			+3·02	+3·18	+2·80	+1·70	+1·23	+1·20	+1·27	+1·33	+1·43	+1·52	+1·57	+1·54	+1·02	+1·51	+1·87	+1·40
2				+3·09	+2·12	+2·54	+1·23	+0·65	+0·27	+0·30	+0·34	+0·43	+0·52	+0·57	+0·54	+0·02	+0·51	+0·87	+0·42
1				+3·09	+2·05	+2·22	+0·83	+0·13	−0·50	−0·60	−0·60	−0·55	−0·47	−0·43	−0·46	−0·97	−0·49	−0·13	−0·55
0				+3·09	+1·82	+1·52	+0·10	−0·70	−1·36	−1·48	−1·55	−1·53	−1·46	−1·42	−1·45	−1·96	−1·48	−1·13	−1·52
−1					+1·90	+0·60	−0·75	−1·52	−2·10	−2·23	−2·44	−2·48	−2·44	−2·41	−2·44	−2·94	−2·47	−2·13	−2·42
3	= 0·9			+3·11	+2·17	+2·61	+1·48	+1·16	+1·02	+1·09	+1·15	+1·23	+1·32	+1·37	+1·33	+0·93	+1·43	+1·82	+1·23
2				+3·11	+1·93	+2·32	+1·07	+0·56	+0·17	+0·15	+0·17	+0·25	+0·33	+0·38	+0·33	−0·06	+0·44	+0·82	+0·27
1				+3·09	+1·62	+1·63	+0·37	−0·21	−0·71	−0·76	−0·78	−0·74	−0·67	−0·62	−0·66	−1·05	−0·56	−0·18	−0·70
0					+1·42	+0·75	−0·51	−1·10	−1·50	−1·50	−1·74	−1·73	−1·66	−1·57	−1·65	−2·04	−1·55	−1·17	−1·60
−1					+1·65	−0·14	−1·28	−1·72	−1·75	−1·67	−2·40	−2·45	−2·39	−2·33	−2·43	−2·57	−2·26	−1·84	−2·35
3	= 0·8			+3·13	+2·16	+2·41	+1·50	+1·05	+0·78	+0·91	+0·93	+1·05	+1·13	+1·18	+1·18	+0·86	+1·36	+1·76	+1·05
2				+3·10	+2·00	+1·77	+0·79	+0·25	+0·00	+0·03	−0·01	+0·06	+0·14	+0·19	+0·19	−0·11	+0·38	+0·77	+0·08
1				+3·06	+2·20	+0·86	−0·11	−0·60	−0·72	−0·62	−1·00	−0·93	−0·84	−0·68	−0·79	−1·06	−0·56	−0·15	−0·84
4	= 0·7		+6·4	+3·18	+2·37	+2·50	+1·18	+1·66	+1·66	+1·71	+1·75	+1·85	+1·93	+1·97	+1·96	+1·78	+2·30		+1·78
3			+6·4	+3·11	+1·99	+1·89	+1·06	+0·82	+0·76	+0·82	+0·76	+0·86	+0·95	+1·00	+0·97	+0·79	+1·30		+0·84
2			+6·4	+3·02	+1·73	+0·98	+0·24	+0·06	+0·13	+0·27	+0·19	+0·09	+0·01	+0·08	+0·02	−0·10	+0·43		−0·02
1			+6·4	+2·54	+1·79	+0·08	−0·35	−0·24	−0·05	+0·12	−0·98	−0·82	−0·65	−0·43	−0·67	−0·58	−0·03		−0·66

$\log \kappa_m$ [2]

log P_e	100	200	900	1000	1100	1500	2000	2500	3000	3500	4000	5000	6000	8000	10000	17000	30000	Rosse-land mean
										λ in A								
Θ = 0·6																		
4			+6·30	+3·06	+2·01	+2·01	+1·54	+1·47	+1·53	+1·64	+1·52	+1·65	+1·72	+1·79	+1·76	+1·71	+2·22	+1·60
3			+6·30	+2·93	+1·77	+1·15	+0·79	+0·87	+1·05	+1·23	+0·59	+0·72	+0·84	+0·99	+0·88	+0·94	+1·55	+0·85
2			+6·23	+2·39	+1·50	+0·41	+0·42	+0·69	+0·89	+1·06	−0·06	+0·16	+0·37	+0·67	+0·42	+0·62	+1·24	+0·36
1			+5·87	+1·73	+1·20	−0·10	+0·08	+0·33	+0·59	+0·72	−0·40	−0·14	−0·01	+0·26	+0·02	+0·23	+0·80	+0·00
Θ = 0·5																		
4		+4·99	+6·28	+3·10	+1·9	+1·49	+1·60	+1·80	+2·03	+2·17	+1·45	+1·62	+1·79	+2·01	+1·89	+2·15	+2·60	+1·69
3		+4·93	+6·15	+2·55	+1·9	+1·01	+1·28	+1·53	+1·78	+1·94	+0·92	+1·17	+1·42	+1·69	+1·52	+1·86	+2·38	+1·29
2		+4·86		+1·90	+1·1	+0·35	+0·67	+0·90	+1·16	+1·33	+0·29	+0·53	+0·77	+1·06	+0·87	+1·22	+1·7	+0·65
1				+1·00	+0·2	−0·34	−0·15	+0·06	+0·26	+0·42	−0·39	−0·25	−0·08	+0·15	+0·00	+0·33	+0·8	−0·12
Θ = 0·4																		
5		+4·95	+6·24	+2·58	+1·77	+2·15	+2·47	+2·73	+2·97	+3·10	+2·38	+2·64	+2·79	+3·07	+2·99	+3·28	+3·9	+2·47
4		+4·83	+5·82	+1·78	+1·27	+1·65	+1·97	+2·27	+2·50	+2·65	+1·79	+2·07	+2·29	+2·60	+2·50	+2·79	+3·2	+1·94
3		+4·73	+4·94	+0·85	+0·43	+0·79	+1·13	+1·42	+1·66	+1·81	+0·92	+1·21	+1·43	+1·74	+1·64	+1·91	+2·3	+1·09
2			+3·95	−0·05	−0·32	−0·08	+0·20	+0·48	+0·70	+0·81	+0·05	+0·27	+0·49	+0·77	+0·68	+0·95	+1·4	+0·22
1			+2·95	−0·51	−0·57	−0·51	−0·40	−0·27	−0·15	−0·06	−0·48	−0·39	−0·28	−0·10	−0·15	+0·23	+0·4	−0·36
Θ = 0·3																		
5		+4·82	+5·24	+1·79	+1·74	+2·16	+2·49	+2·78	+2·99	+3·14	+2·48	+2·76	+3·00	+3·25	+3·26	+3·60	+4·1	+2·27
4		+4·85	+4·26	+0·84	+0·83	+1·22	+1·55	+1·82	+2·03	+2·16	+1·54	+1·80	+2·03	+2·29	+2·31	+2·65	+3·1	+1·33
3		+4·85	+3·27	+0·00	+0·02	+0·35	+0·64	+0·89	+1·10	+1·19	+0·63	+0·86	+1·09	+1·34	+1·34	+1·68	+2·2	+0·47
2			+2·28	−0·58	−0·46	−0·32	−0·17	+0·02	+0·18	+0·15	−0·18	−0·01	+0·17	+0·40	+0·41	+0·72	+1·2	−0·18
1			+1·28	−0·58	−0·57	−0·55	−0·52	−0·47	−0·40	−0·38	−0·52	−0·47	−0·40	−0·31	−0·30	−0·13	+0·3	−0·50
Θ = 0·2																		
6		+4·76	+4·50	+2·00	+2·14	+2·34	+2·84	+3·12	+3·32	+3·46	+3·09	+3·34	+3·57	+3·83	+3·89	+4·24	+4·8	+2·49
5		+4·76	+3·50	+1·05	+1·16	+1·36	+1·87	+2·14	+2·36	+2·46	+2·12	+2·36	+2·58	+2·84	+2·90	+3·25	+3·8	+1·54
4		+4·79	+2·50	+0·14	+0·24	+0·40	+0·90	+1·16	+1·36	+1·46	+1·13	+1·38	+1·60	+1·85	+1·91	+2·25	+2·8	+0·61
3			+1·50	−0·42	−0·39	−0·40	+0·00	+0·21	+0·44	+0·48	+0·18	+0·41	+0·62	+0·86	+0·92	+1·26	+1·8	−0·10
2			+0·53	−0·56	−0·55	−0·53	−0·47	−0·39	−0·31	−0·26	−0·40	−0·31	−0·18	−0·02	+0·03	+0·33	+0·8	−0·39
1			−0·21	−0·58	−0·58	−0·58	−0·57	−0·56	−0·55	−0·54	−0·56	−0·55	−0·52	−0·48	−0·47	−0·34	−0·1	−0·53
Θ = 0·1																		
6	+3·74	+4·68		+1·19	+1·31	+1·69	+1·98	+2·10	+2·17	+2·42	+2·32	+2·55	+2·72	+2·97	+3·10			+1·76
5	+3·18	+4·00		+0·36	+0·47	+0·82	+1·10	+1·17	+1·24	+1·50	+1·40	+1·65	+1·80	+2·04	+2·16			+0·76
4	+2·79	+3·02		−0·29	−0·24	−0·03	+0·19	+0·26	+0·30	+0·56	+0·46	+0·69	+0·82	+1·05	+1·20			−0·06
3	+2·66	+2·03		−0·50	−0·49	−0·44	−0·36	−0·34	−0·40	−0·21	−0·26	−0·13	−0·04	+0·15	+0·27			−0·40
2	+2·66	+1·05		−0·53	−0·53	−0·52	−0·51	−0·51	−0·51	−0·49	−0·50	−0·46	−0·44	−0·39	−0·34			−0·50
1		+0·14		−0·54	−0·54	−0·54	−0·53	−0·53	−0·53	−0·53	−0·53	−0·53	−0·53	−0·52	−0·51			−0·52

log κ_m [2]

log P_e									λ in A									Rosseland mean
	100	200	900	1000	1100	1500	2000	2500	3000	3500	4000	5000	6000	8000	10000	17000	30000	
Θ = 0·07																		
7	+3·19	+3·99	+2·72	+1·86	+1·95	+2·33	+2·63	+2·73	+2·93	+3·04	+3·00	+3·23	+3·40	+3·64	+3·80			+1·79
6	+2·77	+2·99	+1·74	+0·89	+1·00	+1·36	+1·65	+1·74	+1·94	+2·04	+2·02	+2·25	+2·41	+2·65	+2·80			+0·79
5	+2·76	+1·99	+0·76	+0·02	+0·11	+0·40	+0·67	+0·77	+0·97	+1·06	+1·04	+1·27	+1·43	+1·66	+1·81			+0·04
4	+2·68	+1·00	−0·08	−0·41	−0·38	−0·28	−0·14	−0·08	+0·07	+0·15	+0·19	+0·32	+0·47	+0·69	+0·83			−0·36
3	0·00	+0·14	−0·45	−0·52	−0·52	−0·50	−0·46	−0·46	−0·41	−0·39	−0·39	−0·32	−0·24	−0·12	−0·03			−0·50
2	−0·50	−0·39	−0·52	−0·52	−0·52	−0·52	−0·52	−0·52	−0·51	−0·51	−0·50	−0·50	−0·49	−0·45	−0·44			−0·52
1	−0·52	−0·51	−0·53	−0·53	−0·52	−0·52	−0·52	−0·52	−0·52	−0·52	−0·52	−0·52	−0·52	−0·52	−0·52			−0·52
Θ = 0·05																		
7	+2·53	+2·60	+2·08	+1·38	+1·45	+1·90	+2·15	+2·33	+2·51	+2·64	+2·64	+2·85	+3·01	+3·27	+3·43			+1·05
6	+1·98	+1·60	+1·09	+0·42	+0·49	+0·91	+1·15	+1·33	+1·51	+1·64	+1·64	+1·85	+2·01	+2·27	+2·43			+0·26
5	−0·10	+0·64	+0·16	−0·31	−0·20	+0·04	+0·24	+0·40	+0·57	+0·68	+0·67	+0·85	+1·01	+1·27	+1·43			−0·26
4	−0·46	−0·16	−0·36	−0·48	−0·47	−0·42	−0·35	−0·27	−0·20	−0·14	−0·14	0·00	+0·13	+0·33	+0·48			−0·46
3	−0·52	−0·45	−0·51	−0·52	−0·52	−0·52	−0·51	−0·50	−0·48	−0·47	−0·46	−0·43	−0·40	−0·30	−0·24			−0·52
2	−0·52	−0·52	−0·53	−0·52	−0·52	−0·52	−0·52	−0·52	−0·52	−0·52	−0·52	−0·52	−0·52	−0·51	−0·50			−0·52
1	−0·52	−0·52	−0·52	−0·52	−0·52	−0·52	−0·52	−0·52	−0·52	−0·52	−0·52	−0·52	−0·52	−0·52	−0·52			−0·52

log κ_m

log P_e

Θ	−1	0	1	2	3	4	5	6	7
0·05			1̄·48	1̄·48	1̄·48	1̄·54	1̄·74	0·26	1·05
0·07			1̄·48	1̄·48	1̄·50	1̄·64	0·04	0·80	1·80
0·1			1̄·48	1̄·50	1̄·60	1̄·94	0·82	1·82	
0·2		1̄·48	1̄·48	1̄·61	1̄·90	0·70	1·66	2·51	
0·3		1̄·48	1̄·50	1̄·76	0·58	1·46	2·42		
0·4		1̄·50	1̄·64	0·37	1·25	2·10	2·62		
0·5		1̄·50	1̄·95	0·83	1·45	1·83			
0·6		1̄·51	1̄·15	0·52	0·95	1·70			
0·7		1̄·50	1̄·50	0·10	0·94	1·92			
0·8		1̄·50	1̄·26	0·18	1·15	2·15			
0·9	5̄·70	2̄·60	1̄·39	0·38	1·35	2·35			
1·0	5̄·62	2̄·46	1̄·60	0·53	1·54	2·54			
1·2	5̄·80	2̄·57	1̄·85	0·85	1·88	2·88			
1·4		2·85	1̄·18	1·18	2·22	3·22			
1·6		1̄·18	1̄·50	1·50	2·55	3·55			
1·8		1̄·50	1̄·80	1·80	2·85	3·85			
				2·08	3·13	4·18			

log P

Θ	1	2	3	4	5	6	7	8
0·05	1̄·48	1̄·48	1̄·49	1̄·53	1̄·64	0·06	0·80	1·82
0·07	1̄·48	1̄·48	1̄·50	1̄·59	1̄·88	0·59	1·48	2·6
0·1	1̄·48	1̄·50	1̄·55	1̄·82	0·50	1·46	2·46	
0·2	1̄·48	1̄·56	1̄·78	0·36	1·27	2·21	3·2	
0·3	1̄·50	1̄·69	0·23	1·06	1·92	2·9	3·3	
0·4	1̄·53	1̄·99	0·79	1·63	2·22	2·50	2·8	
0·5	1̄·72	0·39	1·03	1·40	1·63	1·86	2·27	2·15
0·6	1̄·84	0·18	0·37	0·58	0·88	1·23	1·66	1·90
0·7	1̄·24	0·28	1̄·48	1̄·83	0·26	0·73	1·27	1·80
0·8	3·64	5̄·74	2̄·76	1̄·23	1·79	0·40	1·10	1·80
0·9			5̄·17	2·83	1·59	0·33	0·95	1·62
1·0			3·90	2·72	1·53	0·22	0·83	1·39
1·2			3·80	2·58	1·19	1̄·81	0·42	1·05

§ 41. Absorption of Negative Hydrogen Ion

The table gives $\log a(\mathrm{H}^-)$, where $a(\mathrm{H}^-)$ is the continuous absorption coefficient of negative hydrogen ions due to free-free and bound-free transitions and after allowing for the stimulated emission factor $(1 - e^{-h\nu/kT})$. The coefficients are per neutral hydrogen atom and per unit electron pressure. $\Theta = 5\,040\ ^{\circ}\mathrm{K}/T$, $T = $ temperature, and $\lambda = $ wavelength.

* For long wavelengths add $+\log \lambda^2$ [λ in μ] to the first line,

** For short wavelengths add $-0\cdot21/\lambda$ [λ in μ] to the last line.

The mean is a straight average weighted in accordance with the monochromatic fluxes in a stellar atmosphere [1].

$$\log a(\mathrm{H}^-)\ [1,\ 5]$$

λ	Θ										
	0·5	0·6	0·7	0·8	0·9	1·0	1·2	1·4	1·6	1·8	2·0
μ	in 10^{-30} cm^4 dyn^{-1}										
*	3·30	3·50	3·58	3·64	3·71	3·74	3·85	3·93	3·98	4·04	4·10
5	4·84	4·93	5·00	5·05	5·10	5·15	5·22	5·28	5·33	5·38	5·42
3	4·40	4·48	4·55	4·60	4·65	4·70	4·77	4·83	4·88	4·93	4·97
2	4·05	4·13	4·20	4·25	4·30	4·34	4·42	4·48	4·53	4·57	4·61
1·8	3·95	4·04	4·10	4·16	4·21	4·25	4·32	4·38	4·43	4·48	4·52
1·6	3·87	3·97	4·05	4·14	4·22	4·31	4·49	4·70	4·93	5·17	5·41
1·4	3·85	4·00	4·15	4·30	4·46	4·61	4·92	5·21	5·50	5·78	6·04
1·2	3·89	4·10	4·30	4·49	4·68	4·87	5·20	5·52	5·81	6·09	6·36
1·0	3·92	4·16	4·39	4·60	4·80	4·99	5·34	5·65	5·95	6·23	6·49
0·8	3·92	4·18	4·42	4·64	4·84	5·03	5·37	5·69	5·98	6·26	6·52
0·6	3·86	4·12	4·36	4·58	4·78	4·97	5·31	5·63	5·92	6·20	6·46
0·5	3·80	4·06	4·29	4·51	4·71	4·90	5·25	5·56	5·85	6·13	6·40
0·4	3·70	3·96	4·19	4·41	4·60	4·80	5·15	5·46	5·75	6·03	6·30
0·3	3·53	3·79	4·03	4·24	4·45	4·63	4·98	5·29	5·58	5·86	6·13
**	4·24	4·50	4·73	4·95	5·15	5·34	5·67	5·99	6·28	6·55	6·82
Mean	3·74	4·04	4·33	4·57	4·76	4·94	5·26	5·55	5·82	6·08	6·32

[1] *A.Q.* **1**, § 40.
[2] S. CHANDRASEKHAR, *Ap. J.*, **128**, 114, 1958.
[3] W. E. MITCHELL, *Ap. J.*, **130**, 872, 1959.
[4] T. OHMURA and H. OHMURA, *Ap. J.*, **131**, 8, 1960.
[5] O. GINGERICH, *Apl. J.*, **134**, 653, 1961.

§ 42. Free-free Absorption and Emission

Free-free linear absorption coefficient [1]

$$\kappa_s = \frac{4\pi}{3\sqrt{3}}\frac{Z^2 e^6}{hcm^2 v}\frac{g}{\nu^3}N_e N_1 \quad [\kappa \text{ in exp cm}^{-1}]$$

$$= 1\cdot801 \times 10^{14}\frac{Z^2 g}{\nu^3 v}N_e N_1 \quad [v \text{ in cm/s}]$$

$$= 6\cdot685 \times 10^{-18}Z^2 g\lambda^3 N_e N_1/v \quad [\lambda \text{ in cm}]$$

where v = electron velocity, g = Gaunt factor representing departure from Kramers' theory, Z = ionic charge, N_e and N_i electronic and ionic concentrations in cm^{-3}. Mean $1/v = (2m/\pi kT)^{1\,2}$ whence

$$\kappa_s = 3 \cdot 692 \times 10^8 Z^2 g T^{-1/2} v^{-3} N_e N_i$$
$$= 1 \cdot 370 \times 10^{-23} Z^2 \lambda^3 g N_e N_i / T^{1/2} \quad [\lambda \text{ in cm}].$$

Effective linear absorption coefficient κ' after allowance for stimulated emissions

$$\kappa_s' = 3 \cdot 692 \times 10^8 \{1 - \exp(-h\nu/kT)\} Z^2 g T^{-1/2} v^{-3} N_e N_i$$

For small $h\nu/kT$ $(= 1 \cdot 438/\lambda T)$, e.g. for radio waves

$$\kappa_s' = \frac{8}{3} \left(\frac{\pi}{6}\right)^{1/2} \frac{e^6}{c(mkT)^{3/2}} \frac{Z^2 g}{\nu^2} N_e N_i \quad [\kappa_s' \text{ in exp cm}^{-1}]$$
$$= 0 \cdot 0178 Z^2 g \nu^{-2} T^{-3/2} N_e N_i$$
$$= 1 \cdot 98 \times 10^{-23} Z^2 g \lambda^2 N_e N_i T^{-3/2} \quad [\lambda \text{ in cm}]$$

Gaunt factor in visible and near ultra violet spectrum

$$g \simeq 1 \cdot 0$$

For variations in extreme cases see [7].

Gaunt factor for radio waves

$$g = \frac{\sqrt{3}}{\pi} \ln (b_2/b_1) \simeq \frac{\sqrt{3}}{\pi} \ln (kT/e^2 N_e^{1/3})$$
$$= 1 \cdot 269 \ 5 \ (2 \cdot 78 + \log T - \tfrac{1}{3} \log N_e)$$

where b_2 and b_1 are the outer and inner limits of the collision parameters. The expression given does not suit all circumstances and more comprehensive formulations are available [2, 3, 4].

For a fully ionized plasma (with 12% He by number) the radio absorption becomes

$$\kappa_s' = \frac{\zeta N_e^2}{\nu^2 T^{3/2}}$$

with $\zeta = 0 \cdot 0132 \ln (600 T N_e^{-1/3})$ in suitable cases. Approximate values of ζ [1, 6]

Solar corona $\zeta \simeq 0 \cdot 19$
Solar chromosphere $\zeta \simeq 0 \cdot 11$
Galactic clouds $\zeta \simeq 0 \cdot 16$

Free-free emission (Bremsstrahlung) per unit solid angle per unit volume and per unit frequency range

$$j_\nu = \kappa_\nu' B_\nu \quad \text{(black body)}$$
$$= \frac{16}{3} \left(\frac{\pi}{6}\right)^{1/2} \frac{e^6 Z^2}{c^3 m^2} \left(\frac{m}{kT}\right)^{1/2} g \exp\left(-\frac{h\nu}{kT}\right) N_e N_i$$
$$= 5 \cdot 443 \times 10^{-39} Z^2 g \exp(-c_2/\lambda T) T^{-1/2} N_e N_i$$
$$\text{erg cm}^{-3} \text{ s}^{-1} \text{ sterad}^{-1} \quad [T \text{ in } °\text{K}, N \text{ in cm}^{-3}]$$

Total free-free emission [1]

$$4\pi \int_0^\infty j_\nu \, d\nu = \frac{64\pi}{3} \left(\frac{\pi}{6}\right)^{1/2} \frac{e^6 Z^2}{hc^3 m} \left(\frac{kT}{m}\right)^{1/2} g N_e N_i$$
$$= 1 \cdot 435 \times 10^{-27} Z^2 T^{1/2} g N_e N_i \quad \text{erg cm}^{-3} \text{ s}^{-1}.$$

[1] A.Q. 1, § 41.
[2] L. OSTER, Z. Ap., 47, 169, 1959.
[3] P. A. G. SCHEUER, M.N., 120, 231, 1960.
[4] M. RUDKJÖBING, Ann. d'Ap., 22, 111, 1959.
[5] C. DE JAGER, Handb. der Phys., 52, p. 284, 1959.
[6] F. MORIYAMA, Ann. Tokyo Ob., 7, 127, 1961.
[7] W. J. KARZAS and R. LATTER, Ap. J. Supp., 6, 167, 1961.

§ 43. Black Body Radiation

Stefan-Boltzmann constant $= \dfrac{2\pi^5 k^4}{15 c^2 h^3} = \dfrac{\pi^4 c_1}{14 c_2^4}$

$$\sigma = (5\cdot669\,2 \pm 0\cdot000\,7) \times 10^{-5} \quad \text{erg cm}^{-2}\,\text{s}^{-1}\,\text{deg}^{-4}$$

Black-body emittance $\mathscr{F} =$ total flow of radiation outward from unit black-body surface at absolute temperature T

$$\mathscr{F} = \sigma T^4$$

Black-body intensity

$$B = (\sigma/\pi)T^4 = 1\cdot804\,6 \times 10^{-5}T^4 \quad \text{erg cm}^{-2}\,\text{s}^{-1}\,\text{sterad}^{-1}\,\text{deg}^{-4}$$

Radiation density u in a cavity at temperature T

$$u = aT^4 = (4\sigma/c)T^4 = 7\cdot564\,1 \times 10^{-15}T^4 \quad \text{erg cm}^{-3}\,\text{deg}^{-4}$$

In a medium of refractive index n

$$B = n^2(\sigma/\pi)T^4$$

$$u = n^3(4\sigma/c)T^4.$$

A similar factor applies for the Planck law with n_ν and n_λ.

Photon emission constant $= 15\cdot106\,11 \, c/c_2^3$

$$p = 1\cdot520\,5 \times 10^{11} \text{ photons cm}^{-2}\,\text{s}^{-1}\,\text{deg}^{-3}$$

Photon flux from unit black-body surface

$$N = pT^3$$

Polarization. Black-body radiation is unpolarized, hence the intensity of radiation linearly polarized in a specified direction will be half the value quoted in the formulae.

Planck function (wavelength units)

$$(c/4)u_\lambda = \pi B_\lambda = \mathscr{F}_\lambda = 2\pi hc^2\lambda^{-5}/(e^{hc/k\lambda T} - 1)$$

$$= c_1\lambda^{-5}/(e^{c_2/\lambda T} - 1)$$

$$c_1 = 2\pi hc^2 = 3\cdot741\,2 \times 10^{-5} \text{ erg cm}^2\,\text{s}^{-1} \quad [\lambda \text{ in cm}]$$

$$a_1 = 4c_1/c = 4\cdot991\,8 \times 10^{-15} \text{ erg cm}$$

$$c_2 = hc/k = 1\cdot438\,79 \pm 0\cdot000\,05 \quad \text{cm deg}$$

$$c_2' = c_2 \log e = 0\cdot624\,86 \text{ cm deg (use with common logs).}$$

u_λ, B_λ, and $\mathscr{F}_\lambda$ are the radiation density, intensity, and emittance for unit wavelength range.

Planck function (frequency units)

$$(c/4)u_\nu = \pi B_\nu = \mathscr{F}_\nu = 2\pi h\nu^3 c^{-2}/(e^{h\nu/kT} - 1)$$

Photon distribution law $N_\lambda = 2\pi c\lambda^{-4}/(e^{c_2/\lambda T} - 1)$

$$N_\nu = 2\pi c^{-2}\nu^2/(e^{h\nu/kT} - 1) \; \equiv \; \mathscr{F}_\nu/h\nu$$

N_λ and N_ν, are the emittance of photons per cm^2 per sec and per unit wavelength and frequency range.

Rayleigh-Jeans distribution (for red end of spectrum)

$$\mathscr{F}_\lambda = 2\pi ckT\lambda^{-4} = (c_1/c_2)T\lambda^{-4}$$

$$\mathscr{F}_\nu = 2\pi c^{-2}kT\nu^2 = 2\pi kT\lambda^{-2}$$

8—A.Q.

Wien distribution (for violet end of spectrum)

$$\mathscr{F}_\lambda = 2\pi hc^2\lambda^{-5}e^{-c_2/\lambda T} = c_1\lambda^{-5}e^{-c_2/\lambda T}$$

$$\mathscr{F}_\nu = 2\pi hc^{-2}\nu^3 e^{-h\nu/kT}$$

Wien law. Wavelength of maximum $\mathscr{F}_\lambda$ or B_λ, λ_{max}

$$T\lambda_{max} = 0{\cdot}201\ 405\ 2\ c_2 = 0{\cdot}289\ 78\ \text{cm deg}$$

Wavelength of maximum photon emission, λ_m

$$T\lambda_m = 0{\cdot}255\ 057\ 1\ c_2 = 0{\cdot}366\ 97\ \text{cm deg}$$

Frequency of maximum $\mathscr{F}_\nu$ or B_ν, ν_m

$$Tc/\nu_m = 0{\cdot}354\ 429\ 0\ c_2 = 0{\cdot}509\ 95\ \text{cm deg}$$

The three numerical constants above are $1/y$ in $y = 5(1-e^{-y})$, $y = 4(1-e^{-y})$, and $y = 3(1-e^{-y})$ respectively.

The tables of the Planck function give:

$$\mathscr{F}_{0-\lambda} = \int_0^\lambda \mathscr{F}_\lambda\,d\lambda \quad \text{in terms of } \mathscr{F}_{0-\infty} \quad (= \mathscr{F})$$

$$\mathscr{F}_\lambda \qquad\qquad\quad \text{,, \quad ,, \quad ,, } \mathscr{F}_{\lambda max}$$

$$N_{0-\lambda} = \int_0^\lambda N_\lambda\,d\lambda \quad \text{,, \quad ,, \quad ,, } N_{0-\infty} \quad (= N)$$

$$N_\lambda \qquad\qquad\quad \text{,, \quad ,, \quad ,, } N_{\lambda m}$$

$$\mathscr{F}_\nu \qquad\qquad\quad \text{,, \quad ,, \quad ,, } \mathscr{F}_{\nu m}$$

Asymptotic expressions for long and short wavelengths are given as functions of $x = c_2/\lambda T = h\nu/kT$.

Absolute values may be obtained by using the following data:

$$\mathscr{F}_{0-\infty} = 6{\cdot}493\ 939\ c_1(T/c_2)^4 = 5{\cdot}669\ 3\times 10^{-5}T^4 \quad \text{erg cm}^{-2}\,\text{s}^{-1}\,\text{deg}^{-4}$$

$$\mathscr{F}_{\lambda max} = 21{\cdot}201\ 44\ c_1(T/c_2)^5 = 1{\cdot}286\ 4\times 10^{-4}T^5 \quad \text{erg cm}^{-3}\,\text{s}^{-1}\,\text{deg}^{-5}$$

For λ in microns and $T = 10\ 000\ °\text{K}$ $\quad \mathscr{F}_{\lambda max} = 1{\cdot}286\times 10^{12}\quad \text{erg }\mu^{-1}\,\text{cm}^{-2}\,\text{s}^{-1}$

$$N_{0-\infty} = 15{\cdot}106\ 11\ c(T/c_2)^3 = 1{\cdot}520\ 5\times 10^{11}T^3 \quad \text{photons cm}^{-2}\,\text{s}^{-1}\,\text{deg}^{-3}$$

$$N_{\lambda m} = 30{\cdot}032\ 63\ c(T/c_2)^4 = 2{\cdot}100\ 9\times 10^{11}T^4 \quad \text{photons cm}^{-3}\,\text{s}^{-1}\,\text{deg}^{-4}$$

$$\mathscr{F}_{\nu m} = 1{\cdot}421\ 436\ (c_1/c)(T/c_2)^3 = 5{\cdot}955\ 4\times 10^{-16}T^3 \quad \text{erg cm}^{-2}\,\text{deg}^{-3}$$

For wave-number units and $T = 10\ 000\ °\text{K}$ $\quad \mathscr{F}_{\nu m} = 1{\cdot}785\ 4\times 10^7\ \text{erg cm}^{-1}\,\text{s}^{-1}$.

[1] *A.Q.* **1**, § 42.
[2] K.-H. Böhm and B. Schlender, *Z. Ap.*, **43**, 95, 1957.
[3] J. K. McDonald, *Pub. D. A. O. Victoria*, **10**, 127, 1955.

Tables of the Planck function

λT	$x = c_2/\lambda T$	$\dfrac{\mathscr{F}_{0-\lambda}}{\mathscr{F}_{0-\infty}}$	$\dfrac{\mathscr{F}_{\lambda}}{\mathscr{F}_{\lambda\max}}$	$\dfrac{N_{0-\lambda}}{N_{0-\infty}}$	$\dfrac{N_{\lambda}}{N_{\lambda m}}$	$\dfrac{\mathscr{F}_{\nu}}{\mathscr{F}_{\nu m}}$
cm deg	large x	$\dfrac{x^3 e^{-x}}{6\cdot 493\,9}$	$\dfrac{x^5 e^{-x}}{21\cdot 201}$	$\dfrac{x^2 e^{-x}}{2\cdot 404}$	$\dfrac{x^4 e^{-x}}{4\cdot 780}$	$\dfrac{x^3 e^{-x}}{1\cdot 421\,4}$
0·00	↑	↑	↑	↑	↑	↑
0·01	143·85	$0\cdot 0^{56}\,16$	$0\cdot 0^{53}\,98$	$0\cdot 0^{58}\,29$	$0\cdot 0^{54}\,30$	$0\cdot 0^{56}\,70$
0·02	71·925	$0\cdot 0^{26}\,35$	$0\cdot 0^{23}\,52$	$0\cdot 0^{27}\,12$	$0\cdot 0^{24}\,33$	$0\cdot 0^{25}\,15$
0·03	47·950	$0\cdot 0^{16}\,27$	$0\cdot 0^{13}\,18$	$0\cdot 0^{17}\,14$	$0\cdot 0^{14}\,17$	$0\cdot 0^{15}\,12$
0·04	35·962	$0\cdot 0^{11}\,19$	$0\cdot 0^{9}\,683$	$0\cdot 0^{12}\,13$	$0\cdot 0^{10}\,84$	$0\cdot 0^{11}\,79$
0·05	28·770	$0\cdot 0^{8}\,130$	$0\cdot 0^{6}\,297$	$0\cdot 0^{9}\,118$	$0\cdot 0^{7}\,458$	$0\cdot 0^{8}\,536$
0·06	23·975	$0\cdot 0^{7}\,932$	$0\cdot 0^{4}\,145$	$0\cdot 0^{7}\,100$	$0\cdot 0^{5}\,267$	$0\cdot 0^{6}\,375$
0·07	20·550	$0\cdot 0^{5}\,186$	$0\cdot 0^{3}\,206$	$0\cdot 0^{6}\,230$	$0\cdot 0^{4}\,444$	$0\cdot 0^{5}\,726$
0·08	17·981	$0\cdot 0^{4}\,165$	0·001 38	$0\cdot 0^{5}\,223$	$0\cdot 0^{3}\,339$	$0\cdot 0^{4}\,635$
0·09	15·983	$0\cdot 0^{4}\,872$	0·005 63	$0\cdot 0^{4}\,138$	0·001 56	$0\cdot 0^{3}\,329$
0·10	14·385	$0\cdot 0^{3}\,321$	0·016 44	$0\cdot 0^{4}\,559$	0·005 07	0·001 18
0·12	11·988	0·002 14	0·072 64	$0\cdot 0^{3}\,439$	0·026 87	0·007 54
0·14	10·275	0·007 80	0·186 27	0·001 84	0·080 41	0·026 31
0·16	8·9906	0·019 74	0·345 18	0·005 22	0·170 31	0·063 69
0·18	7·9917	0·039 38	0·520 26	0·011 51	0·288 77	0·121 58
0·20	7·1925	0·066 79	0·683 44	0·021 32	0·421 44	0·196 59
0·25	5·7540	0·161 45	0·946 12	0·061 55	0·729 36	0·426 22
0·30	4·7950	0·273 36	0·997 12	0·119 37	0·922 41	0·646 87
0·35	4·1100	0·383 06	0·922 71	0·186 24	0·995 74	0·814 74
0·40	3·5962	0·481 02	0·800 10	0·255 11	0·986 74	0·922 72
0·45	3·1967	0·564 44	0·671 36	0·321 58	0·931 61	0·979 96
0·50	2·8770	0·633 86	0·554 67	0·383 37	0·855 19	0·999 52
0·60	2·3975	0·737 89	0·373 78	0·490 20	0·691 55	0·969 93
0·70	2·0550	0·808 12	0·253 94	0·575 52	0·548 15	0·896 89
0·80	1·7981	0·856 31	0·175 98	0·643 06	0·434 08	0·811 77
0·90	1·5983	0·890 04	0·124 71	0·696 69	0·346 13	0·728 20
1·00	1·4385	0·914 18	0·090 37	0·739 68	0·278 70	0·651 50
1·20	1·1988	0·945 06	0·050 40	0·802 85	0·186 52	0·523 30
1·40	1·0275	0·962 86	0·030 10	0·846 05	0·129 97	0·425 36
1·60	0·8991	0·973 77	0·019 02	0·876 56	0·093 79	0·350 87
1·80	0·7992	0·980 81	0·012 57	0·898 95	0·069 74	0·293 53
2·0	0·7192	0·985 56	0·008 62	0·915 85	0·053 18	0·248 59
3·0	0·4795	0·995 24	0·001 94	0·959 45	0·017 98	0·126 06
4·0	0·3596	0·997 90	$0\cdot 0^{3}\,655$	0·976 25	0·008 08	0·075 60
5·0	0·2877	0·998 90	$0\cdot 0^{3}\,279$	0·984 52	0·004 30	0·050 25
10	0·1438	$0\cdot 9^{3}\,848$	$0\cdot 0^{4}\,188$	0·995 92	$0\cdot 0^{3}\,579$	0·013 54
20	0·0719	$0\cdot 9^{4}\,801$	$0\cdot 0^{5}\,122$	0·998 93	$0\cdot 0^{4}\,751$	0·003 51
50	0·0288	$0\cdot 9^{5}\,878$	$0\cdot 0^{7}\,318$	$0\cdot 9^{3}\,828$	$0\cdot 0^{5}\,491$	$0\cdot 0^{3}\,574$
100	0·0144	$0\cdot 9^{6}\,848$	$0\cdot 0^{8}\,200$	$0\cdot 9^{4}\,570$	$0\cdot 0^{6}\,618$	$0\cdot 0^{3}\,145$
	↓	↓	↓	↓	↓	↓
	small x	$1 - 0\cdot 051\,34\,x^3$	$0\cdot 047\,17\,x^4$	$1 - 0\cdot 208\,0\,x^2$	$0\cdot 209\,2\,x^3$	$0\cdot 703\,5\,x^2$

§ 44. Reflection from Metallic Mirrors

No attempt has been made to differentiate between different methods of deposition.

λ	Silver	Aluminium	Speculum	Mercury	Nickel	Copper	Gold	Silicon	Platinum	Steel	Tungsten
μ	%	%	%	%	%	%	%	%	%	%	%
0·20	20	72			35	34	18	68	20	24	15
0·22	25	78			40	34	27	68	29	27	16
0·24	27	81	26		42	31	32	68	35	30	18
0·26	27	82	33	58	40	29	34	68	37	33	20
0·28	23	82	38	61	39	28	34	67	38	36	21
0·30	12	82	44	64	39	29	35	65	39	39	23
0·32	7	82	48	67	41	30	33	61	40	41	25
0·34	63	83	51	69	43	32	33	56	42	44	27
0·36	77	83	54	71	45	34	33	50	43	46	30
0·38	82	84	56	73	47	36	34	41	45	49	34
0·40	85	85	58	74	50	38	34	35	48	51	38
0·45	90	86	61	74	57	42	37	30	56	55	45
0·50	91	87	63	73	61	47	51	30	59	57	49
0·55	92	88	65	73	63	60	77	30	60	57	52
0·60	93	89	66	74	65	74	84	30	61	56	51
0·65	94	88	67	74	67	82	89	30	63	55	52
0·70	95	87	68	75	69	85	93	30	66	56	53
0·80	97	85	70	70	70	89	95	29	70	59	56
0·90	98	88	71	72	72	90	96	29	72	61	58
1·00	98	93	72	73	73	92	97	28	74	63	60
1·5	98	97	79	78	81	94	98	28	79	71	75
2·0	98	96	82	82	84	96	98	28	81	77	87
5·0	99	97	89	89	92	98	99	28	91	90	95
10·0	99	98	92	92	96	99	99	28	95	93	98

Measurements have been made of the extreme ultra-violet reflections from various optical surfaces [2]. However the results are dependent on the age of the surface and details of deposition, and no suitable summary can be made.

[1] A.Q. 1, § 43.
[2] G. HASS and R. TOUSEY, J.O.S.A., 49, 593, 1959.
[3] W. C. WALKER, RUSTGI, and WEISSLER, J.O.S.A., 49, 471, 1959.

§ 45. Visual Photometry

Units of visual photometry are given in § 12.

Relative visibility factor K_λ for normal brightness (about 5×10^{-4} stilb or greater), the photoptic curve (International) (cone vision at fovea):

$$K_\lambda$$

λ Å	0	100	200	300	400	500	600	700	800	900
3000Å									$0 \cdot 0^{4}4$	$0 \cdot 0^{3}12$
4000	0·0004	0·0012	0·0040	0·0116	0·023	0·038	0·060	0·091	0·139	0·208
5000	0·323	0·503	0·710	0·862	0·954	0·995	0·995	0·952	0·870	0·757
6000	0·631	0·503	0·381	0·265	0·175	0·107	0·061	0·032	0·017	0·0082
7000	0·0041	0·0021	0·00105	$0 \cdot 0^{3}52$	$0 \cdot 0^{3}25$	$0 \cdot 0^{3}12$	$0 \cdot 0^{4}6$	$0 \cdot 0^{4}3$		

$$\text{Equivalent width of } K_\lambda \text{ curve} = \int K_\lambda \, d\lambda$$
$$= 1068 \text{ Å}$$

Mechanical equivalent of light [1]

$$K_\lambda \text{ lumens} \equiv 0 \cdot 001 \ 47 \text{ watts}$$

Luminous energy (in lumergs)
$$= 680 \int K_\lambda e_\lambda \, d\lambda$$

where $e_\lambda \, d\lambda$ is element of energy in joules.

1 lumen (5550 Å radiation) $= 4 \cdot 11 \times 10^{15}$ photons

Relative visibility for dark-adapted eye (about 10^{-7} stilb or less), the scotoptic curve [1] (rod vision):

λ Å	0	100	200	300	400	500	600	700	800	900
4000Å	0·0185	0·040	0·076	0·132	0·213	0·302	0·406	0·520	0·650	0·770
5000	0·900	0·985	0·960	0·840	0·680	0·500	0·350	0·228	0·140	0·083
6000	0·0490	0·0300	0·0175	0·0100	0·0058	0·0032	0·0017	$0 \cdot 0^{3}87$	$0 \cdot 0^{3}44$	$0 \cdot 0^{3}21$
7000	$0 \cdot 0^{3}10$									

Dark-adapted eye, 1 lumen at 5100 Å (scotoptic)
$$\equiv 0 \cdot 000 \ 58 \text{ watts}$$

Quantum threshold for a single scintillation with most favourable conditions for human eye $= 4$ quanta in $0 \cdot 15$ sec (absorbed)
$$\equiv 60 \text{ quanta in } 0 \cdot 15 \text{ sec (incident)}$$

Threshold intensity for large steady source [2]
$$= 1 \cdot 4 \times 10^{-10} \text{ stilb}$$

Size of retinal image for 1′ arc $= 4 \cdot 9 \ \mu$

Eye resolving power $\simeq 1' \simeq 5 \ \mu$ at fovea

Density of rods and cones in the retina [2]

Rods: 30×10^{6} rods/sterad $= 2 \cdot 7$ rods/$(')^{2}$

Cones: $1 \cdot 2 \times 10^{6}$ cones/sterad $= 0 \cdot 1$ cones/$(')^{2}$

Density of cones in the fovea　　　　　　$\simeq 50 \times 10^6$ cones/sterad

Equivalent diameter of fovea region containing no rods [3]
$$= 1° \, 40'.$$

The rod/cone ratio increases with distance from fovea.

Diameters of individual cones　　　　　$= 2\mu \equiv 25''$ (variable)

　　　,,　　　　,,　　　,,　　rods　　　$= 1\mu \equiv 12''$.

Approximate brightness of common objects [4]

Candle	0·6 stilb
Acetylene (Kodak burner)	10·8 ,,
Welsbach (high pressure) mantle	25 ,,
Tungsten lamp filament	800 ,,
Sodium vapour lamp	70 ,,
Mercury vapour lamp (high pressure)	150 ,,
Arc crater (plain carbon)	16 000 ,,
Clear blue sky	0·2 to 0·6 ,,
Overcast sky	0·3 to 0·7 ,,
Zenith sun (from sea level)	165 000 ,,

Approximate albedos [5]

White cartridge paper	0·80
Black cloth	0·012
Black velvet	0·004

[1] *A.Q.* **1**, § 44.
[2] M. H. Pirenne, *Endeavour*, **20**, 197, 1961.
[3] L. C. Martin, *Technical Optics*, **1**, 144, 1948.
[4] J. W. T. Walsh, *Photometry*, p. 529, 2nd ed., 1953.
[5] R. A. Houstoun, *Treatise on Light*, 1924.

§ 46. Photography

Photographic density $D = \log(I_0/I)$ where I is the intensity of light transmitted by the plate and I_0 the intensity transmitted in an unexposed part of the plate.

Photographic sensitivity S may be expressed by the ratio D/F, where F is the flux of radiation on the plate (in erg cm^{-2}).

Sensitivity of rather fast blue plates to 4300 Å radiation, about 1 sec exposure and low densities [1]
$$S = 5 \text{ cm}^2 \text{ erg}^{-1}$$

Change of sensitivity S with wavelength (in cm^2 erg^{-1})

λ in Å	3000	3500	4000	4500	5000	5500	6000	6500	7000
Blue-sensitive plates	3	4	4	5	3	0			
Panchromatic plates	3	4	5	3·5	2·0	3·5	3·5	0·3	0·01

Density per unit photon flux—blue sensitive plates, low densities, and 4300 Å radiation
$$= 2 \cdot 5 \times 10^{-11} \ cm^2 \ photon^{-1}$$

Mass of silver deposited for unit photographic density
$$= 1 \cdot 1 \times 10^{-4} \ g \ cm^{-2}$$

Photographic grain diameters $\simeq 0 \cdot 7 \, \mu$

Number of grains for unit photographic density
$$\simeq 2 \times 10^8 \ grains \ cm^{-2}$$

Typical thickness of photographic emulsion
$$\simeq 0 \cdot 003 \ cm$$

Photographic resolution—resolvable lines per mm

Fast emulsions	65
Medium speed emulsions	100
Special maximum resolution emulsions	1 000

Density of star images, 1 h exposure time on fast blue plates
$$\log D = 2 \log d - 2 \log w - 0 \cdot 4 \, m_{pg} - 0 \cdot 7$$

where d = telescope O.G. diameter in inches, w = diameter of image on plate in cm, and m_{pg} = photographic magnitude. The photographic density D is assumed < 1.

Number of lumens L entering a telescope of diameter D in inches for star m_v near zenith (clear conditions)
$$\log L = 2 \log D - 0 \cdot 4 \, m_v - 9 \cdot 05$$

[1] *A.Q.* **1**, § 45.

CHAPTER 6

EARTH

§ 47. Earth Dimensions

SPHEROID [1, 2, 3, 4, 7]

Equatorial radius	a	$= 6\ 378 \cdot 17 \pm 0 \cdot 04$ km
Polar radius	c	$= 6\ 356 \cdot 79$ km
Mean radius	$\mathscr{R}_{\oplus} = (a^2 c)^{1/3}$	$= 6\ 371 \cdot 03$ km
Length of equatorial quadrant		$= 10\ 018 \cdot 81$ km
Length of meridional quadrant		$= 10\ 002 \cdot 02$ km
Ellipticity	$(a-c)/a$	$= 1/298 \cdot 26$
Eccentricity	$(a^2-c^2)^{1/2}/a$	$= 0 \cdot 081\ 82$
Surface area		$= 5 \cdot 100\ 70 \times 10^{18}$ cm^2
Volume		$= 1 \cdot 083\ 22 \times 10^{27}$ cm^3

Depression from spheroid at lat. 45° ($\kappa = 6 \times 10^{-7}$) 1, 10
$$= 4 \text{ metres}$$

Ellipticity of the equator [5, 11]
$$(a_{\max} - a_{\min})/a_{\text{mean}} = 2 \cdot 6 \times 10^{-5} \quad (\equiv 166 \text{ m})$$
Longitude of maximum $= 22°$ W.

Earth mass [1] $\qquad\qquad \mathscr{M}_{\oplus} = (5 \cdot 977 \pm 0 \cdot 004) \times 10^{27}$ g

Earth mass × gravitational constant [1, 2, 6]
$$k_e^2 = 3 \cdot 986\ 16 \times 10^{20} \text{ cm}^3 \text{ s}^{-2}$$
$$k_e = 1 \cdot 996\ 536 \times 10^{10} \text{ cm}^{3/2} \text{ s}^{-1}$$
$$= 0 \cdot 001\ 239\ 46\ a^{3/2} \text{ s}^{-1}$$
$$= 0 \cdot 074\ 367\ 8\ a^{3/2} \text{ min}^{-1}$$

Earth mean density [1] $\qquad \bar{\rho}_{\oplus} = 5 \cdot 517 \pm 0 \cdot 004$ g cm^{-3}

Moment of inertia [4, 5]

about rotation axis
$$C = 0 \cdot 330\ 6\ \mathscr{M}_{\oplus} a^2$$
$$= 8 \cdot 04 \times 10^{44} \text{ g cm}^2$$

about equatorial axis
$$A = 0 \cdot 329\ 5\ \mathscr{M}_{\oplus} a^2$$
$$(C-A)/C = 0 \cdot 003\ 275\ 6 = 1/305 \cdot 29$$
$$\tfrac{2}{3}J = J_2 = (C-A)/(\mathscr{M}_{\oplus} a^2) = 0 \cdot 001\ 082\ 7$$
$$\mathscr{M}_{\oplus} a^2 = 2 \cdot 432 \times 10^{45} \text{ g cm}^2$$

Constants of the earth's gravitational potential [5]
$$U = \frac{G \mathscr{M}_{\oplus}}{a} \frac{a}{r} \left\{ 1 - \sum_{n=2}^{\infty} J_n \left(\frac{a}{r} \right)^n P_n(\sin \phi) \right\}$$

where
$$r = \text{radial distance from earth centre}$$
$$P_n = \text{Legendre polynomial of degree } n$$
$$\phi = \text{latitude}$$
$$\tfrac{2}{3}J = J_2 = 1\ 082 \cdot 7 \times 10^{-6}$$
$$-\tfrac{2}{5}H = J_3 = \quad -2 \cdot 4 \times 10^{-6}$$

$$-\tfrac{8}{35}D = -\tfrac{8}{30}K = J_4 = \quad -1\cdot7 \times 10^{-6}$$
$$J_5 = \quad -0\cdot1 \times 10^{-6}$$
$$J_6 = \quad +0\cdot8 \times 10^{-6}$$
$$J_7 = \quad -0\cdot4 \times 10^{-6}$$
$$J_8 = \quad +0\cdot1 \times 10^{-6}$$

Angular velocity of earth rotation (1900) [1]
$$= 7\cdot292\ 115\ 15 \times 10^{-5}\ \text{radian s}^{-1}$$
For seasonal change, see § 11.

Angular momentum $= 5\cdot86 \times 10^{40}\ \text{cm}^2\ \text{g s}^{-1}$

Rotational energy $= 2\cdot138 \times 10^{36}\ \text{erg}$

Work required to dissipate earth material to infinity against earth gravitation [1]
$$= 2\cdot46 \times 10^{39}\ \text{erg}$$

Lengthening of day [1] $= 0\cdot001\ 6\ \text{s century}^{-1}$

Increase of sidereal day as a result of tidal action [1]
$$= 0\cdot000\ 72\ \text{s century}^{-1}$$

Energy lost by tidal friction [1]
    spring tide $= 2\cdot2 \times 10^{19}\ \text{erg s}^{-1}$
    mean tide $= 1\cdot1 \times 10^{19}\ \text{erg s}^{-1}$

Earth equatorial rotational velocity $= 0\cdot465\ 10\ \text{km/s}$

Earth escape velocity $= 11\cdot19\ \text{km/s}$

Period of an earth satellite in relation to semi-major axis a_1 of orbit
$$a_1 = 331\cdot3\ P^{2/3} \quad [a_1\ \text{in km},\ P\ \text{in min}]$$

Mean velocity of earth in its orbit $= 29\cdot78\ \text{km/s}$

Earth age [8] $= (4\cdot5 \pm 0\cdot3) \times 10^9\ \text{y}$

Variation of latitude [1, 9]. The movement of the axis of rotation is compounded of two motions,
    (a) free period of 436 d and semi-amplitude $0''\cdot18$;
    (b) annual period of 365 d and semi-amplitude $0''\cdot09$.

Earth surface

Land Area [1] $= 1\cdot48 \times 10^{18}\ \text{cm}^2$

Ocean area $= 3\cdot63 \times 10^{18}\ \text{cm}^2$

Mean land elevation $= 825\ \text{m}$

Mean ocean depth $= 3\ 770\ \text{m}$

Ocean mass $= 1\cdot42 \times 10^{24}\ \text{g}$

Surface gravity g
    (standard) $g_0 = 980\cdot665\ \text{cm s}^{-2}$
    (lat. 45°) $= 980\cdot618\ \text{cm s}^{-2}$

$$g = 980\cdot618 - 2\cdot586\ 5\cos 2\phi + 0\cdot005\ 8\cos^2 2\phi - 0\cdot000\ 308\ h\ \text{cm s}^{-2}$$
$$= 978\cdot037\ 3(1 + 0\cdot005\ 289\sin^2\phi - 0\cdot0^559\sin^2 2\phi - 0\cdot0^6315\ h)\ \text{cm s}^{-2}$$

where ϕ = astronomical or geographical latitude
          h = altitude in metres.

Centrifugal acceleration at equator $= 3\cdot391\ 5\ \text{cm s}^{-2}$

At equator, $g/$(centrifugal acceleration)

$$= 288 \cdot 38 = 1/0 \cdot 003\ 468$$

Difference between astronomical or geographical latitudes ϕ and geocentric latitude ϕ'

$$\phi - \phi' = 695'' \cdot 65 \sin 2\phi - 1'' \cdot 17 \sin 4\phi$$

$$1° \text{ of latitude} \quad = 111 \cdot 133 - 0 \cdot 562 \cos 2\phi + 0 \cdot 001 \cos 4\phi \quad \text{km}$$

$$1° \text{ of longitude} = 111 \cdot 414 \cos \phi - 0 \cdot 094 \cos 3\phi + 0 \cdot 000\ 2 \cos 5\phi \quad \text{km}$$

Distance from sea level to earth centre

$$\rho = a(0 \cdot 998\ 320 + 0 \cdot 001\ 684 \cos 2\phi - 0 \cdot 000\ 004 \cos 4\phi)$$

Geocentric coordinates [12]

$$\rho \sin \phi' = (S + 0 \cdot 1568\ h \times 10^{-6}) \sin \phi$$

$$\rho \cos \phi' = (C + 0 \cdot 1568\ h \times 10^{-6}) \cos \phi$$

$$\tan \phi' = (0 \cdot 993\ 277 + 0 \cdot 0011\ h \times 10^{-6}) \tan \phi$$

ϕ	S	C	ϕ	S	C
0°	0·993 28	1·000 00	50°	0·995 24	1·001 98
10°	0·993 38	1·000 10	60°	0·995 79	1·002 53
20°	0·993 67	1·000 39	70°	0·996 24	1·002 98
30°	0·994 11	1·000 84	80°	0·996 53	1·003 28
40°	0·994 66	1·001 39	90°	0·996 63	1·003 38

[1] *A.Q.* **1**, § 46.
[2] S. HERRICK BAKER, and HILTON, *U.C.L.A. Astron. Papers*, No. 24, 1958.
[3] R. M. L. BAKER and M. W. MAKEMSON, *Astrodynamics*, p. 83, Academic Press, 1960.
[4] A. H. COOK, *Geoph. J.*, **2**, 222, 1959.
[5] D. G. KING-HELE, *Geoph. J.*, **4**, 3, 1961; **6**, 270, 1962.
[6] J. A. O'KEEFE, ECKELS, and SQUIRES, *A.J.*, **64**, 245, 1959.
[7] W. M. KAULA, *J. Geoph. Res.*, **66**, 1799, 1961.
[8] P. COUDERC, *l'Astron.*, **74**, 11, 1960.
[9] A. M. WALKER and A. YOUNG, *M.N.*, **115**, 443, 1955; **117**, 119, 1957.
[10] D. BROUWER and G. M. CLEMENCE, *Planets and Satellites*, ed. Kuiper and Middlehurst
     p. 31, Chicago, 1961.
[11] W. A. HEISKANEN, *J. Geophys. Res.*, **67**, 321, 1962.
[12] *The Astronomical Ephemeris*.

§ 48. Geological Time Scale

Age of earth [2] $\qquad\qquad\qquad = (4 \cdot 5 \pm 0 \cdot 3) \times 10^9 \text{ y}$

End of recent glaciation [1]

$$= 11\ 000 \text{ y ago}$$

Duration of each glaciation about 50 000 y

Period of glaciation and inter-glaciation

$$= 250\ 000 \text{ y but irregular}$$

Period of geological ice-ages [3] $\qquad = 250 \times 10^6 \text{ y}$

Duration of each ice-age is a few million years.

Greatest age yet found geologically [4]

$$= 3 \cdot 3 \times 10^9 \text{ y.}$$

Geological ages

Eras	Periods, Epochs	Age [1, 3, 5, 6]	Life
Kainozoic		10^6 years ago	
	Quaternary, Recent Pleistocene	0 to 1	Man
	Tertiary, Pliocene	1 to 12	Higher mammals
	Tertiary, Miocene	12 to 27	
	Tertiary, Oligocene	27 to 42	
	Tertiary, Eocene	42 to 60	
	Tertiary, Paleocene	60 to 70	
Mesozoic	Cretaceous	70 to 134	Modern vegetation
	Jurassic	134 to 175	Giant reptiles
	Triassic	175 to 220	Mammals
Palaeozoic	Permian	220 to 260	
	Carboniferous	260 to 330	Reptiles
	Devonian	330 to 380	Land animals
	Silurian	380 to 430	Land plants
	Ordovician	430 to 500	Marine vertebrates
	Cambrian	500 to 600	Marine invertebrates
Pre-Cambrian	Late Pre-Cambrian	600 to 700	Algae
	Upper Pre-Cambrian	700 to 900	
	Middle Pre-Cambrian	900 to 1200	
	Lower Pre-Cambrian	1200 to 2000	
	Archaean	2000 +	

[1] *A.Q.* **1**, § 47.
[2] P. COUDERC, *l'Astron.*, **74**, 11, 1960.
[3] E. J. ÖPIK, *Irish A.J.*, **5**, 97, 1958.
[4] I.U.G.G., *Geoph. J.*, **3**, 472, 1960.
[5] A. HOLMES, *Trans. Edinburgh Geol. Soc.*, **17**, 183, 1960.
[6] C. F. DAVIDSON, *Nature*, **184**, 1310, 1473, 1959.

§ 49. Earth Crust

The earth crust may be considered to extend from the surface to the Mohorovičić discontinuity at a depth below land of about 35 km. Since the discontinuity is higher and the solid surface lower under the oceans the crustal thickness is very small, perhaps 5 km, in some ocean areas. The typical crust is made of

(i) Surface sediments   2 km   both continents and oceans
(ii) Granite   25 km   continents only
(iii) Basalt   10 km   both continents and oceans.

Earth surface density [1] $= 2 \cdot 64 \pm 0 \cdot 05 \text{ g cm}^{-3}$

Specific heat: Granite $0 \cdot 20 \text{ cal g}^{-1} \, {}^{\circ}\text{C}^{-1}$
              Basalt $0 \cdot 22 \text{ cal g}^{-1} \, {}^{\circ}\text{C}^{-1}$

Surface heat conductivity [4] $= 5 \times 10^{-3} \text{ cal deg}^{-1} \text{ cm}^{-1} \text{ s}^{-1}$

Surface temperature gradient [4] $= 2 \cdot 0 \times 10^{-4} \, {}^{\circ}\text{C cm}^{-1}$

Outflow of heat [2, 4] $= 1\cdot 2 \times 10^{-6}$ cal cm^{-2} s^{-1}
    Range from $0\cdot 8$ to $2\cdot 4 \times 10^{-6}$

Radioactive heat generation of rocks [1, 2]

Rock	U	Th	K	Total
	10^{-6} cal g^{-1} year^{-1}			
Granite	2·8	2·2	0·9	5·9
Basalt	0·6	0·9	0·2	1·7
Dunite	0·010	0·011	0·000	0·021
(Chrondrites)	0·008	0·009	0·021	0·038

Heat production of radioactive elements [1, 2]
    Uranium series   0·73   cal (g of U)$^{-1}$ year^{-1}
    Thorium series   0·20   cal (g of Th)$^{-1}$ year^{-1}
    Potassium 26×10^{-6} cal (g of K)$^{-1}$ year^{-1}

Velocities of seismic waves [1, 5]
        $P = 8\cdot 11$ km/s $P_g = 5\cdot 598$ km/s
        $S = 4\cdot 34$ km/s $S_g = 3\cdot 402$ km/s

    where P = longitudinal, S = transverse, and subscript $_g$ = direct surface wave.

Release of earthquake energy [1]
    Mean annual $= 10^{26}$ erg
    Great earthquake (about 1 in ten years) $= 3 \times 10^{26}$ erg

Electrical factors for surface materials (very variable) [1, 3]

	Dielectric constant	Resistivity
	× free space	Ω cm
Sea water	81	22
Fresh water	80	10 000
Rich loams, clays	20	1 000
Industrial areas	5	30 000
Sand, coarse gravel	10	300 000

[1] *A.Q.* **1**, § 48.
[2] G. J. F. MacDonald, *J. Geoph. Res.*, **64**, 1967, 1959.
[3] F. E. Terman, *Electronic and Radio Engineering*, ed. 4, p. 808, McGraw-Hill, 1955.
[4] E. C. Bullard and D. T. Griggs, *Geoph. J.*, **6**, 118, 1961.
[5] R. Stoneley, *R.A.S. Geoph. Supp.*, **7**, 71, 279, 1954–7.

§ 50. Earth Interior

Main layers of the earth interior

	Depth range	σ
Crust	0 to 33 (variable) km	0·25
Mantle	33 to 2 900 km	0·28
Core	2 900 to 5 000 km	0·5
Inner core	5 000 to 6 371 km	

Earth interior physical data

r = distance from earth centre, $\mathscr{R}_\oplus$ = earth radius, T = temperature, ρ = density, g = gravity, P = pressure, $\mathscr{M}_r$ = mass within radius r and $\mathscr{M}_\oplus$ = earth mass, k = bulk modulus, μ = shear modulus, and σ = Poisson's ratio, and $\lambda = k - \frac{2}{3}\mu$. * in the first column of the table represents a *discontinuity*.

Depth	$r/\mathscr{R}_\oplus$	T [1, 4, 5] (?)	ρ [1, 2, 3, 6]	g [1, 2, 3]	P [1, 2]	$\mathscr{M}_r/\mathscr{M}_\oplus$ [1, 2, 3]	Velocity of seismic waves long (P) [1, 2, 3]	trans (S)	Elastic constants μ [1, 2, 3]	λ
km		°K	g cm^{-3}	cm s^{-2}	10^{12} dyn cm^{-2}		km/s		10^{12} c.g.s.	
0	1·000	287	2·60	981	0·000	1·000	5·6	3·4	0·26	0·27
10	0·998	460	2·7	982	0·003	0·998	6·0	3·6	0·3	0·31
			3·0				6·6	3·8	0·4	0·41
33*	0·995	700		983	0·009	0·992				
			3·4				7·9	4·4	0·63	0·75
100	0·984	1 200	3·5	986	0·031	0·972	8·0	4·5	0·67	0·81
200	0·969	1 700	3·6	989	0·068	0·944	8·2	4·55	0·76	0·95
300	0·953	2 000	3·7	992	0·104	0·915	8·55	4·70	0·83	1·07
400	0·937	2 200	3·8	994	0·142	0·886	9·00	4·95	0·92	1·23
600	0·906	2 500	4·1	995	0·218	0·827	10·20	5·65	1·32	1·70
800	0·874	2 800	4·3	994	0·303	0·767	10·95	6·10	1·67	1·98
1 000	0·843	3 000	4·5	990	0·395	0·705	11·43	6·35	1·87	2·28
1 500	0·765	3 500	4·9	985	0·63	0·584	12·17	6·67	2·17	2·86
2 000	0·686	3 800	5·1	986	0·87	0·474	12·80	6·92	2·48	3·48
2 500	0·608	4 100	5·3	1 005	1·12	0·380	13·35	7·16	2·78	4·07
			5·5				13·62	7·31	3·00	4·50
2 900*	0·545	4 300		1 040	1·36	0·315				
			9·5				8·1			6·3
3 000	0·529	4 500	9·7	1 020	1·45	0·296	8·2			6·6
3 500	0·451	5 000	10·3	915	1·93	0·193	8·9			8·2
4 000	0·372	5 500	10·9	802	2·38	0·115	9·5			9·8
4 500	0·294	5 800	11·2	690	2·83	0·060	10·0			11·2
			11·7				10·4			12·7
5 000*	0·215	6 000		600	3·20	0·030				
			16·0							
5 500	0·137	6 200	16·5	410	3·5	0·009	11·2			
6 000	0·058	6 300	17·0	170	3·7	0·001	11·3			
6 371	0·000	6 400	17·3	0	3·8	0·000	11·3			

[1] *A.Q.* **1**, § 49.
[2] K. E. Bullen, *Intro. to Theory of Seismology*, Cambridge, 1947; *R.A.S. Geoph. Supp.*, **6**, 50, 383, 1952.
[3] Z. Alterman, Jarosch and Pekeris, *Geoph. J.*, **4**, 219, 1961.
[4] J. J. Gilvarry, *J.A.T.P.*, **10**, 84, 1957.
[5] G. J. F. MacDonald, *J. Geoph. Res.*, **66**, 2489, 1961.
[6] F. Birch, *Geoph. J.*, **4**, 295, 1961.

§ 51. Atmosphere

Dry air at standard temperature and pressure (S.T.P.) [1]

Standard temperature	$T_0 = 0\ {}^\circ\text{C} = 273.16\ {}^\circ\text{K} = 32\ {}^\circ\text{F}$
Standard pressure	$P_0 = 760\ \text{mm-Hg} = 29.921\ \text{inch-Hg}$
	$= 1\ 013.250\ \text{millibar} = 1\ 033.23\ \text{g-wt cm}^{-2}$
Standard gravity	$g_0 = 980.665\ \text{cm s}^{-2} = 32.174\ \text{ft s}^{-2}$
Air density	$\rho = 0.001\ 292\ 8\ \text{g cm}^{-3}$
Molecular weight	$M_0 = 28.970$
Mean molecular mass	$= 4.810 \times 10^{-23}\ \text{g}$

Molecular root-mean-square velocity

$$(3RT_0/M_0)^{1/2} = 4.85 \times 10^4\ \text{cm s}^{-1}$$

Speed of sound	$= (\gamma P_0/\rho_0)^{1/2} = (\gamma RT_0/M_0)^{1/2}$
	$= 3.31 \times 10^4\ \text{cm s}^{-1}$
Specific heats	$c_\text{p} = 0.2403\ \text{cal g}^{-1}\,{}^\circ\text{C}^{-1}$
	$c_\text{v} = 0.1715\ \text{cal g}^{-1}\,{}^\circ\text{C}^{-1}$
Ratio	$c_\text{p}/c_\text{v} = \gamma = 1.401$
Molecules per cm^3	$N = 2.688 \times 10^{19}$
Molecular diameter	$\sigma = 3.46 \times 10^{-8}\ \text{cm}$
Mean free path $= [\sqrt{(2)}\pi N\sigma^2]^{-1}$	$= 6.98 \times 10^{-6}\ \text{cm}$
Coefficient of viscosity	$= 1.72 \times 10^{-4}\ \text{poise}$
Thermal conductivity	$= 5.6 \times 10^{-5}\ \text{cal cm}^{-1}\,\text{s}^{-1}\,{}^\circ\text{K}^{-1}$
Refractive index	$n = 1 + 2.876 \times 10^{-4} + 1.629 \times 10^{-6}\lambda^{-2}$
	$\qquad\qquad + 1.36 \times 10^{-8}\lambda^{-4} \qquad [\lambda\ \text{in}\ \mu]$

Rayleigh scattering

$$\sigma_\text{s} = 1.043\frac{32\pi^3(n-1)^2}{3N\lambda^4}$$

$$= 344.9\frac{(n-1)^2}{N\lambda^4}\ \text{exp/cm} \quad [\lambda\ \text{in cm}]$$

$$\simeq 1.07 \times 10^{-8}\lambda^{-4.05}\ \text{exp/cm} \quad [\lambda\ \text{in}\ \mu]$$

Water-vapour

Water-vapour pressure e in saturated air

Temperature in °C	-30	-20	-10	0	$+10$	$+20$	$+30$	$+40$
e in mm-Hg	0.29	0.78	1.96	4.58	9.21	17.55	31.86	55.40
e in millibar	0.38	1.04	2.60	6.10	12.28	23.37	42.48	73.8

Water-vapour density	$= 2.886 \times 10^{-4}\ e/T\ \text{g cm}^{-3}$

where T = temperature in °K, and e is in mm-Hg.

1 cm precipitable water	$= 1\ 245\ \text{atmo-cm (i.e. cm S.T.P.) water-vapour}$
Density of moist air	$= 4.645 \times 10^4(B - 0.378\ e)/T\ \text{g cm}^{-3}$

where B = total pressure and B and e are in mm-Hg.

Mean change of water-vapour pressure with height h

$$\log(e_h/e_0) = -h/6 \quad [h\ \text{in km}]$$

Total water-vapour above height h

$$= 0.21\, e_h 10^{-h/22} \text{ cm precipitable water}$$

$$\simeq 0.21\, e_h \text{ cm precipitable water per unit air mass}$$

$$\simeq 260\, e_h \text{ atmo-cm water-vapour per unit air mass}$$

where h is in km, e_h = water-vapour in mm-Hg at height h (using 2·1 instead of 2·3 in Hann's equation).

Composition of atmosphere [1, 2]

1 atmo-cm = thickness of layer in cm when reduced to S.T.P.

$$= 2.687 \times 10^{19} \text{ molecules cm}^{-2}$$

Gas	Molecular weight	Fraction of dry air		Amount	Notes
		by volume	by weight		
		$\times 10^{-6}$	$\times 10^{-6}$	atmo-cm	
N_2	28·02	780 840	755 230	624 000	
O_2	32·00	209 460	231 410	167 400	
H_2O	18·02	1 000 to 28 000	600 to 17 000	800 to 22 000	b d
Ar	39·94	9 340	12 900	7 450	
CO_2	44·01	330	500	260	a
Ne	20·18	18·2	12·7	14·6	
He	4·00	5·24	0·72	4·2	
CH_4	16·05	1·5	0·8	1·2	
Kr	83·7	1·14	3·3	0·91	
CO	28·01	0·06 to 1	0·06 to 1	0·05 to 0·8	a
SO_2	64·06	1	2	1	a
H_2	2·02	0·5	0·04	0·4	
N_2O	44·02	0·5	0·8	0·4	
O_3	48·0	0·01 to 0·1	0·02 to 0·2	0·25	b c
Xe	131·3	0·087	0·39	0·07	
NO_2	46·01	0·000 5 to 0·02	0·000 8 to 0·03	0·000 4 to 0·02	a
Rn	222	$0.0^{13}6$	$0.0^{12}5$	5×10^{-14}	
NO	30·01	trace	trace	trace	a

a = greater in industrial areas
b = meteorological or geographical variations
c = increases in ozone layer, § 59.
d = decreases with height.

Some additional atoms and molecules may be detected spectroscopically in the night sky or aurora, § 62.

Homogeneous atmosphere, scale heights, and gradients [1]

Scale height of atmosphere (height for pressure change of one exponential ratio)

$$= RT/M_0 g = 2.93 \times 10^3 T \quad \text{cm} \quad [T \text{ in } °\text{K}]$$

Height of homogeneous atmosphere H [1]

Ground temperature in °C	-30	-15	0	15	30
H in km	7·113	7·552	7·991	8·430	8·869

Mass of atmosphere per cm^2 $= 1\,035$ g

Total mass of earth atmosphere $= 5{\cdot}30 \times 10^{21}$ g

Adiabatic temperature gradient $= g/Jc_{\mathrm{p}}$

$\qquad\qquad\qquad\qquad\qquad\quad = 9{\cdot}76$ °C per km

Mean temperature gradient in troposphere

$\qquad\qquad\qquad\qquad\qquad\quad = 6{\cdot}5$ °C per km

Mass per unit area of 1 atmo-cm of gas of molecular weight M

$\qquad\qquad\qquad\qquad\qquad\quad = 4{\cdot}461 \times 10^{-5}\,M \quad$ g cm^{-2}

[1] *A.Q.* **1**, § 50.
[2] J. W. TOWNSEND, *I.G.Y. Rocket Rep.*, No. 6, 61, 1960.

§ 52. Variation of Meteorological Quantities with Latitude

The table averages the Northern and Southern hemispheres which differ in detail as a result of the different land distributions.

Latitude	Mean air temperature (sea-level)	Seasonal temperature range (on land)	Ocean temperature	Total pressure (sea-level)	Water-vapour pressure (sea-level)	Tropopause temperature	height	pressure
	°C	°C	°C	mm-Hg	mm-Hg	°C	km	mm-Hg
0°	27	1	27	758	21	−87	17·8	60
10°	26	3	26	759	20	−80	16·5	74
20°	24	6	24	761	18	−73	14·8	97
30°	20	9	20	763	14	−66	12·9	127
40°	13	13	14	761	9	−62	11·2	160
50°	6	17	7	756	5	−58	9·7	198
60°	−2	21	2	751	2	−55	8·5	233
70°	−10	26	0		1	−54	7·6	258
80°	−18	29	−2			−53	7·0	285
90°	−25							

[1] *A.Q.* **1**, § 51.

§ 53. Distribution of Earth Atmospheres with Height

Atmospheric layers and transition levels [2, 3]

	Altitude h km	Characteristics and notes
Troposphere	0 to 12	Weather variations
Tropopause	12	See § 52
Stratosphere	12 to 50	Inversion. T increase with h
Stratopause	50	
Mesosphere	50 to 80	T decrease with h
Mesopause	85	Noctilucent clouds
Thermosphere	> 85 km	Continuous T increase with h
Ozonosphere	12 to 50	Ozone layer, see § 59
Ionosphere	> 70	Ionized layers, see § 61
Exosphere	> 600	Region of no collisions
Homosphere	< 100	Complete mixing of major constituents
Heterosphere	> 100	Diffusion governs molecular composition

Layer in which atoms are more than half ionized [2]
> 1 000 km

Layer in which H dominates number composition [3]
> 1 200 km

Layer in which O^+ dominates density composition [3]
1 200 to 1 800 km

h = height above sea level P = pressure
T = temperature ρ = density
N = number density of molecules + atoms + ions (not electrons)
$\simeq N_e$ (electron density) above 1 000 km
H = scale height of pressure μ = molecular weight
l = mean free path of molecules
ν_e, ν_μ = electronic and molecular collision frequency

ϕ = geopotential altitude $= \displaystyle\int_0^h (g/g_s)\, dh$

where g = gravity, g_s = a standard gravity. In the case g_s = gravity at sea level, we have $\phi = h\mathscr{R}_\oplus/(h + \mathscr{R}_\oplus)$.

Mean physical conditions and altitude [1, 4, 5, 6, 7]

h	$\log P$	T	$\log \rho$	$\log N$	H	$\log l$
km	in dyn cm^{-2}	°K	in g cm^{-3}	in cm^{-3}	km	in cm
0	6·006	288	− 2·912	19·41	8·4	− 5·17
1	5·953	282	− 2·955	19·36	8·3	− 5·13
2	5·900	275	− 3·000	19·31	8·2	− 5·09
3	5·846	269	− 3·042	19·28	8·0	− 5·05
4	5·790	262	− 3·087	19·23	7·8	− 5·00
5	5·732	256	− 3·132	19·19	7·5	− 4·96
6	5·674	249	− 3·177	19·14	7·2	− 4·90
8	5·552	236	− 3·276	19·04	6·8	− 4·82
10	5·423	223	− 3·382	18·94	6·6	− 4·72
15	5·083	217	− 3·706	18·61	6·3	− 4·39
20	4·744	217	− 4·051	18·27	6·4	− 4·05
30	4·075	230	− 4·745	17·58	6·8	− 3·36
40	3·47	257	− 5·396	16·92	7·5	− 2·69
50	2·93	276	− 5·975	16·34	8·2	− 2·13
60	2·38	255	− 6·48	15·83	7·6	− 1·66
70	1·76	215	− 7·03	15·29	6·4	− 1·09
80	1·02	178	− 7·69	14·62	5·2	− 0·43
90	0·15	177	− 8·51	13·79	5·2	+ 0·34
100	− 0·57	207	− 9·35	12·95	6·2	+ 1·18
110	− 1·17	270	− 10·05	12·23	8·4	+ 2·00
120	− 1·60	420	− 10·68	11·63	12·5	+ 2·60
150	− 2·24	1 020	− 11·68	10·56	32	+ 3·60
200	− 2·80	1 250	− 12·35	9·91	43	+ 4·36
250	− 3·31	1 350	− 12·95	9·46	48	+ 4·73
300	− 3·72	1 400	− 13·42	9·02	55	+ 5·15
400	− 4·36	1 500	− 14·17	8·28	70	+ 5·83
500	− 4·9	1 550	− 14·72	7·7	83	+ 6·40
700	− 5·9	1 600	− 15·7	6·8	110	+ 7·36
1 000	− 7·0	1 600	− 16·8	5·7	150	
3 000	[10, 11, 12, 13]	1 700		3·9		
10 000	,,			3·0		
20 000	,, [16]	2×10^5		2·3		
30 000	,,			1·5		

Day and night variations from mean values

upper sign → day value

lower sign → night value

h	P, ρ, N	T	H
km	dex	°K	km
200	± 0·03	± 130	± 5
300	± 0·10	± 280	± 9
400	± 0·23	± 300	± 12
500	± 0·30	± 300	± 16
700	± 0·50	± 300	± 20

Dissociation, composition, molecular weight, and collision frequencies

h	Composition by number [1, 2, 6, 15]			μ [2, 4, 5, 9]	ν_e [1, 14]	ν_μ [8]
	O_2	O	N_2			
km	%	%	%		s^{-1}	s^{-1}
100	21	1	78	28·9	120 000	29 000
150	18	8	74	28·2	600	18
200	11	18	71	26·3	50	5
250	8	27	65	24·0		1·8
300	6	36	56	22·2		0·7
400	3	60	35	19·3		0·14
500	2	80	15	17·1		0·036
700				14·8		0·004

[1] *A.Q.* **1**, § 52.
[2] J. W. TOWNSEND, *I.G.Y. Rocket Rep.*, No. 6, 61, 1960.
[3] C. O. HINES, *J. Geoph. Res.*, **65**, 2563, 1960.
[4] R. A. MINZER, CHAMPION and POND, *The ARDC model atmosphere*, 1959; AFCRC-TR-59-267.
[5] COSPAR *International Reference Atmosphere*, 1961.
[6] H. K. KALLMANN, *J. Geoph. Res.*, **64**, 615, 1959; **66**, 787, 1961.
[7] D. G. KING-HELE and D. M. C. WALKER, *COSPAR Symp.*, Florence, 1961; *Ann. Geophys.*, **17**, 162, 1961.
[8] M. NICOLET, *J. Geoph. Res.*, **64**, 2092, 1959.
[9] M. RÖMER, *Mitt. U.-S. Bonn*, No. 37, 1961.
[10] F. S. JOHNSON, *J. Geoph. Res.*, **65**, 2571, 1960.
[11] J. H. POPE, *J. Geoph. Res.*, **66**, 67, 1961.
[12] G. McK. ALLCOCK, *J.A.T.P.*, **14**, 185, 1959.
[13] R. L. SMITH and R. S. HELLIWELL, *J. Geoph. Res.*, **65**, 2583, 1960.
[14] J. S. KANE, *J. Geoph. Res.*, **64**, 133, 1959.
[15] K. WATANABE and H. F. HINTEREGGER, *J. Geoph. Res.*, **67**, 999, 1962.
[16] H. B. LIEMOHN and F. L. SCARF, *J. Geoph. Res.*, **67**, 1785, 1962.

§ 54. Atmospheric Refraction and Air Path

Refractive index of air n, at pressure $p = 760$ mm-Hg, temperature $t = 15$ °C, and zero water vapour pressure [2]

$$(n-1) \times 10^{-6} = 64\cdot328 + 29\,498\cdot1 \left(146 - \frac{1}{\lambda_0^2}\right)^{-1} + 255\cdot4 \left(41 - \frac{1}{\lambda_0^2}\right)^{-1}$$

where λ_0 is the vacuum wavelength in microns.

Refractive index for other temperatures and pressures [1]

$$(n_{t,p} - 1) = (n_{15,760} - 1) \frac{p[1 + (1\cdot049 - 0\cdot0157\,t) \times 10^{-6}p]}{720\cdot883(1 + 0\cdot003\,661\,t)}$$

where t is in °C and p in mm-Hg.

For water-vapour pressure f (in mm-Hg) the refraction factor $(n-1) \times 10^6$ is *reduced* [1] by

$$\frac{0\cdot0624 - 0\cdot000\,680/\lambda^2}{1 + 0\cdot003\,661\,t} f$$

Refractive index of air for radio waves [1, 6]

$$(n_{t,p,f} - 1) \times 10^6 = 287 \cdot 8 \, \frac{p}{760} \cdot \frac{1}{1 + 0 \cdot 003\,66\,t} + \frac{0 \cdot 33\,f}{1 + 0 \cdot 003\,66\,t} + \frac{6 \cdot 70\,f}{(1 + 0 \cdot 003\,66\,t)^2}$$

independent of λ in the radio band.

Refractive index n and constant of refraction $R_0 = (n^2 - 1)/2n^2$ for air, $t = 0$ °C, $p = 760$ mm-Hg, and $f = 4$ mm-Hg. For other temperatures and pressures multiply by $p/(760 + 2 \cdot 9t)$ where the factor $2 \cdot 9t$ makes an approximate allowance for the change of water-vapour content with temperature [1].

λ	$n-1$	R_0	λ	$n-1$	R_0	λ	$n-1$	R_0
μ	$\times 10^{-6}$	$''$	μ	$\times 10^{-6}$	$''$	μ	$\times 10^{-6}$	$''$
0·20	341·7	70·44	0·40	298·1	61·46	1·2	288·5	59·48
0·22	329·2	67·87	0·45	295·5	60·92	1·4	288·2	59·42
0·24	321·0	66·18	0·50	294·1	60·63	1·6	288·0	59·37
0·26	315·2	64·98	0·55	292·8	60·36	1·8	287·9	59·35
0·28	310·8	64·07	0·60	291·9	60·18	2·0	287·8	59·32
			0·65	291·3	60·05	3·0	287·6	59·30
0·30	307·4	63·37				4·0	287·5	59·27
0·32	304·8	62·84	0·70	290·6	59·91	∞ optical	287·4	59·25
0·34	302·6	62·38	0·80	289·9	59·77			
0·36	300·8	62·01	0·90	289·3	59·64	Radio waves with $f = 10$ mm-Hg		
0·38	299·4	61·72	1·00	289·0	59·58		355	73·2

Refraction and air mass. The refraction is tabulated for $p = 760$ mm-Hg and $t = 10$ °C; for other values of p and t multiply the refraction $R = \zeta - z$ by $p/\{760 \times (0 \cdot 962 + 0 \cdot 0038\,t)\}$. The mass of air in the path varies with p and t in the same way as for refraction. It will be seen that R is given by the residual in the ζ column, and that air mass = $\sec z$ for small z.

Apparent altitude $h = 90° - z$	True zenith distance ζ [1, 3, 4]	$\sec z$	Air mass [1, 5]	Apparent altitude $h = 90° - z$	True zenith distance ζ [1, 3, 4]	$\sec z$	Air mass [1, 5]
0°	90° 35′ 22″	∞	38	10°	80° 5′ 19″	5·759	5·600
1°	89° 24′ 44″	57·30	26·96	15°	75° 3′ 35″	3·864	3·816
2°	88° 18′ 27″	28·65	19·79	20°	70° 2′ 39″	2·924	2·904
3°	87° 14′ 27″	19·11	15·36	25°	65° 2′ 5″	2·366	2·357
4°	86° 11′ 47″	14·34	12·44	30°	60° 1′ 41″	2·000	1·995
5°	85° 9′ 53″	11·47	10·40	40°	50° 1′ 10″	1·556	1·553
6°	84° 8′ 29″	9·567	8·900	50°	40° 0′ 49″	1·305	1·304
7°	83° 7′ 24″	8·206	7·768	60°	30° 0′ 34″	1·155	1·154
8°	82° 6′ 34″	7·185	6·884	70°	20° 0′ 21″	1·064	1·064
9°	81° 5′ 53″	6·392	6·177	80°	10° 0′ 10″	1·015	1·015
10°	80° 5′ 19″	5·759	5·600	90°	0° 0′ 0″	1·000	1·000

[1] *A.Q.* **1**, § 53.
[2] B. EDLÉN, *Vacuum Corrections*, Lund, 1951.
[3] *Inman's Nautical Tables*, 1940.
[4] B. GARFINKEL, *A.J.*, **50**, 169, 1944.
[5] V. G. FESSENKOV, *A. Zh.*, **32**, 265, 1955.
[6] B. R. BEAN, *Proc. I.R.E.*, **50**, 260, 1962.

§ 55. Continuous Absorption of Atmosphere

The table quotes exponential absorption coefficient for a stated quantity of absorbing matter which is approximately the amount in a normal atmosphere. For molecular scattering (Rayleigh scattering) 4·3% has been added to the Rayleigh formula to allow for the non-isotropic factor [2], giving

$$\text{Scattering per atmosphere} = 1\!\cdot\!025 \times 10^5 (n-1)^2/\lambda^4 \quad [\lambda \text{ in } \mu]$$

where n is the refractive index.

For continuous water-vapour absorption, Fowle's values [3] have been divided by 10 leaving this factor almost negligible. For ozone the decadic absorption coefficients quoted [4] are multiplied by 0·691 to give exponential absorption for 0·3 atmo-cm. In the interesting region 2800–3200 Å the empirical formula for the ozone decadic absorption per atmo-cm α is

$$\log \alpha = 17\!\cdot\!58 - 56\!\cdot\!4\lambda \quad [\lambda \text{ in } \mu].$$

The dust absorption represents normally clear conditions for a large object (such as the sun) when the small angle scatter radiation will still reach the wide angle receptor. For pin-hole reception, normally used for stars, this column would represent exceedingly good conditions.

Continuous atmospheric absorption

λ	Molecular scattering [1, 2]	Water vapour [1, 3]	Ozone [1, 4]	Dust, clear conditions [1]	Total	Trans-mission
μ	per atmosphere	per cm precipitable water	per 3 mm at S.T.P.	per atmosphere		
0·20	7·26		2·4	0·24	20 ?	0·00
0·22	4·68		17	0·21	27	0·00
0·24	3·16		65	0·19	68	0·00
0·26	2·21		88	0·17	89	0·00
0·28	1·606		34	0·157	36	0·00
0·30	1·194		3·2	0·143	4·5	0·011
0·32	0·908		0·24	0·132	1·29	0·275
0·34	0·702	0·010	0·02	0·122	0·84	0·43
0·36	0·552	0·006	0·00	0·113	0·67	0·51
0·38	0·441	0·004	0·000	0·106	0·55	0·58
0·40	0·356	0·004	0·00	0·099	0·46	0·63
0·45	0·219	0·003	0·001	0·084	0·31	0·73
0·50	0·142	0·003	0·012	0·074	0·23	0·793
0·55	0·096	0·002	0·031	0·065	0·19	0·827
0·60	0·067 5	0·002	0·044	0·058	0·17	0·844
0·65	0·048 8	0·002	0·023	0·053	0·127	0·881
0·70	0·036 1	0·001	0·008	0·048	0·093	0·911
0·80	0·021 1	0·001	0·001	0·040	0·063	0·939
0·90	0·013 1	0·001	0·00	0·035	0·049	0·952
1·0	0·008 6	0·001		0·030	0·040	0·961
1·2	0·004 1			0·024	0·029	0·971
1·4	0·002 2			0·019	0·022	0·978
1·6	0·001 3			0·016	0·018	0·982
1·8	0·000 8			0·014	0·015	0·985
2·0	0·000 5			0·012	0·013	0·987
3·0	0·000 1			0·008	0·008	0·992
5·0	0·0			0·006	0·006	0·994
10·0	0·0			0·005	0·005	0·995

Visual (V) absorption for a clear atmosphere [1, 5]

$$= 0\cdot20 \quad \text{mag/air mass}$$

Photographic (B) absorption for a clear atmosphere

$$= 0\cdot34 - 0\cdot03\,(B-V) \quad \text{mag/air mass}$$

Ultra-violet (U) absorption for clear atmosphere

$$= 0\cdot65 - 0\cdot03\,(B-V) \quad \text{mag/air mass}$$

[1] *A.Q.* **1**, § 54.
[2] H. C. van de Hulst, *Atmosphere of the Earth and Planets*, ed. Kuiper, p. 49, 1948.
[3] F. E. Fowle, *Ap. J.*, **38**, 392, 1913.
[4] E. Vigroux, *Contr. Inst. d'Ap. Paris*, A No. 152, 1953.
[5] S. C. B. Gascoigne, Private Communication.

§ 56. Ultra-violet Absorption of Atmospheric Gases

The table gives $\log k_\lambda$, where k_λ is the exponential absorption coefficient per atmo-cm (i.e. per cm at S.T.P. $=$ per $2 \cdot 687\ 0 \times 10^{19}$ molecules in a cm^2 column). In order to determine the atmospheric absorption from the data it is necessary to introduce the atomic and molecular composition of the atmosphere which is not well known, § 53. However it will be noticed that for $\lambda < 800$ Å the absorption per N or O atom is much the same in all four columns.

The column h_1 gives the height representing unit optical depth in the atmosphere.

   i = irregular with λ as a result of lines and bands. Values at specified wavelengths
         may differ by ± 1 dex

   e = absorption edge. λ given in notes

   M = absorption maximum. λ and $\log k_\lambda$ given in notes

   m = absorption minimum. λ and $\log k_\lambda$ given in notes.

For absorption at Lα, see [6].

Ultra-violet absorption

λ	log k_λ [2, 3, 4, 7, 8]					h_1 [4, 5]	Notes λ at edges, etc. maxima and minima
	O_2	O	N_2	N	H_2O		
Å	in atmo-cm					km	λ in Å, log $k\lambda$
0·01		−4·38		−4·46			
0·02		−4·25		−4·31			
0·05		−4·13		−4·14			
0·1	−3·69	−4·00	−3·74	−4·05			
0·2	−3·57	−3·85	−3·64	−3·91			
0·5	−3·08	−3·37	−3·27	−3·52			
1	−3·32	−2·67	−2·57	−2·89			
2	−1·46	−1·76	−1·70	−2·03			
5	−0·29	−0·58	−0·52	−0·82			
10	+0·56	+0·28	+0·34	+0·06		100	
20	+0·8	+1·01	+1·3	+0·85^e		120	O 23; N 31
50	+1·2	+0·73^e	+0·5	+0·48^e		105	
100	+1·79	+1·48	+1·73	+1·28		120	
150	+2·20	+1·85	+2·36	+1·6		130	
200	+2·42	+2·04	+2·30	+1·90	+2·11	135	
300	+2·68	+2·42^e	+2·48	+2·08	+2·73	145	O 310
400	+2·76	+2·53^e	+2·58	+2·28	+2·83	150	O 435
500	+2·79	+2·56^e	+2·70	+2·45	+2·60	160	
600	+2·78	+2·54	+2·75	+2·48	+2·66	165	O 664
700	+2·7 i	+2·32^e	+2·76	+2·43	+2·60	165	O 732
800	+2·5 i	+1·92^e	+2·64	+2·34	+2·54	140	
900	+2·2 i	+1·89			+2·60^e	120	O 910; H_2O 984
1000	+1·7 i				+2·4 i^e	105	
1100	+0·9 i		0·0		+2·2 i	95	
1200	+1·0 i	O_3			+2·2 i$_M$	90	H_2O 1280, 2·34
1300	+1·1 i				+2·3	100	
1400	+2·58	↓			+1·38	110	
1500	+2·50^M	+1·10			+1·46^m	110	O 1430, 2·60; H_2O 1440, 1·14
1600	+2·18	+1·46			+1·98$_M$	110	H_2O 1650, 2·09
1700	+1·43	+1·34			+2·03^M	100	
1800	0·0 i	+1·30			+1·32	90	
1900	−3·0	+1·14			−1·1	65	
2000	−3·3	+0·89				45	
2200	−3·7	+1·70				35	
2400	−4·3	+2·36				40	
2600		+2·46				42	
2800		+2·06				35	
3000		+1·03				20	

[1] A.Q. 1, § 55.
[2] M. NICOLET, Spectra in Far Ultra-violet, p. 319, Liège Symp., 1961.
[3] G. HERZBERG, MONFILS, and ROSEN, Spectra in Far Ultra-violet, p. 146, Liège Symp, 1961.
[4] R. W. DITCHBURN, Proc. Roy. Soc., A 236, 216, 1956.
[5] H. FRIEDMAN, J. Geoph. Res., 64, 1751, 1959.
[6] R. W. DITCHBURN, et al., Rocket Expl. of Upper Atm., 327, Pergamon, 1954.
[7] R. W. DITCHBURN and P. A. YOUNG, J.A.T.P., 24, 127, 1962.
[8] K. WATANABE and H. G. HINTEREGGER, J. Geoph. Res., 67, 999, 1962.

§ 57. Long-wave Absorption of Atmospheric Gases

Bands made up of discrete lines do not obey the Lambert law of exponential absorption and the absorption coefficient must be replaced by its analogue b_λ such that the transmission is $f(b_\lambda l)$ where l is the layer thickness.

For the function f we adopt the relation [1]

$\log(b_\lambda l)$	$f(b_\lambda l)$	$\log(b_\lambda l)$	$f(b_\lambda l)$	$\log(b_\lambda l)$	$f(b_\lambda l)$	$\log(b_\lambda l)$	$f(b_\lambda l)$
$-3\cdot0$	$1\cdot000$	$-1\cdot2$	$0\cdot877$	$0\cdot0$	$0\cdot500$	$+1\cdot2$	$0\cdot072$
$-2\cdot5$	$0\cdot990$	$-1\cdot0$	$0\cdot836$	$+0\cdot2$	$0\cdot412$	$+1\cdot4$	$0\cdot033$
$-2\cdot0$	$0\cdot971$	$-0\cdot8$	$0\cdot782$	$+0\cdot4$	$0\cdot332$	$+1\cdot6$	$0\cdot011$
$-1\cdot8$	$0\cdot958$	$-0\cdot6$	$0\cdot721$	$+0\cdot6$	$0\cdot258$	$+1\cdot8$	$0\cdot001$
$-1\cdot6$	$0\cdot940$	$-0\cdot4$	$0\cdot651$	$+0\cdot8$	$0\cdot187$	$+2\cdot0$	$0\cdot000$
$-1\cdot4$	$0\cdot914$	$-0\cdot2$	$0\cdot578$	$+1\cdot0$	$0\cdot124$		

The quantity b_λ is the reciprocal of the thickness (in the chosen units) that would give 50% absorption. Values of $\log b_\lambda$ for individual atmospheric gases are given in the diagrams. The unit chosen for l is an amount normally found in 1 air mass, as follows:

$$
\begin{aligned}
\text{for } H_2O \text{ unit of } l &= \quad 1\ 245 \quad \text{atmo-cm} \equiv 1 \text{ cm precipitable water} \\
O_2 \quad &,, \quad = 167\ 600 \qquad ,, \\
O_3 \quad &,, \quad = \quad\ \ 0\cdot3 \qquad ,, \\
CO_2 \quad &,, \quad = \quad 220 \qquad ,, \\
N_2O \quad &,, \quad = \quad\ \ 0\cdot4 \qquad ,, \\
CH_4 \quad &,, \quad = \quad\ \ 1\cdot2 \qquad ,,
\end{aligned}
$$

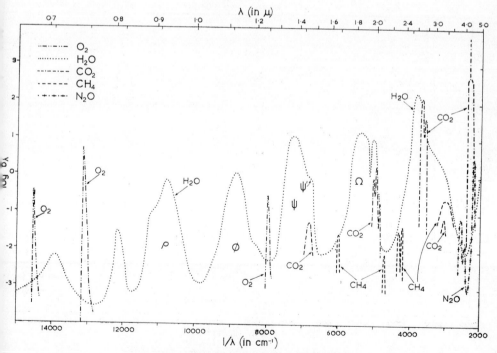

Infra-red band absorption of atmospheric gases

Absorption at the short-wave end of the radio window. The table gives exponential absorption coefficient k_λ [2, 3].

for 167 600 atmo-cm of O_2

and 1 245 atmo-cm of H_2O = 1 cm ppt. water.

λ	ν	k_ν [2, 3]	
		O_2	H_2O
cm	Mc/s		
0·3	100 000	0·1	0·03
0·4	75 000	0·4	0·02
0·5	60 000	25	0·01
0·6	50 000	0·4	0·01
0·8	37 500	0·05	0·01
1·0	30 000	0·03	0·02
1·2	25 000	0·02	0·06
1·5	20 000	0·02	0·02
2·0	15 000	0·015	0·003
3·0	10 000	0·013	0·000 9

[1] *A.Q.* **1**, § 56.
[2] J. L. Pawsey and R. N. Bracewell, *Radio Astronomy*, p. 341, Oxford, 1955.
[3] M. L. Meeks, *J. Geoph. Res.*, **66**, 3749, 1961.
[4] J. N. Howard, Burch and Williams, *J.O.S.A.*, **46**, 186, 237, 242, 334, 452, 1956.

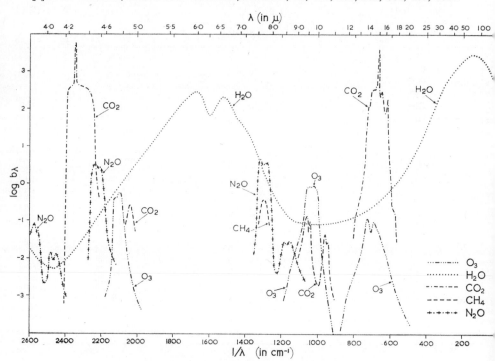

Infra-red band absorption of atmospheric gases

§ 58. Transmission of Atmosphere to Solar Radiation

The table gives the fractional transmission of the atmosphere to total solar radiation in clear (dust-free) air.

Air mass	Water-vapour in cm of precipitable water per unit air mass					
	0·0	0·5	1·0	2·0	3·0	4·0
0·5	0·902	0·852	0·837	0·821	0·812	0·805
1·0	0·859	0·794	0·778	0·762	0·752	0·745
2·0	0·796	0·715	0·699	0·682	0·671	0·644
3·0	0·743	0·652	0·636	0·618	0·609	0·604
4·0	0·704	0·607	0·590	0·572	0·565	0·560

[1] *A.Q.* **1**, § 57.

§ 59. Atmospheric Ozone

Height of maximum ozone density [1, 2, 3]

$$= 24 \text{ km}$$

Ozone layer (to 0·25 maximum density) [1, 2, 3]

between 15 and 36 km.

Maximum ozone density [1, 2, 3] $= 0·016 \text{ cm (S.T.P.) km}^{-1}$

Sea-level density $= 0·001\ 5 \text{ cm (S.T.P.) km}^{-1}$

Total amount of ozone [1]

Latitude	Jan.	March	May	July	Sept.	Nov.	Year
				Atmo-cm			
60° N	0·305	0·350	0·330	0·285	0·250	0·255	0·296
40° N	0·260	0·280	0·270	0·250	0·225	0·220	0·251
20° N	0·205	0·220	0·225	0·220	0·205	0·200	0·213
0°	0·190	0·195	0·200	0·205	0·205	0·200	0·199
20° S	0·210	0·205	0·210	0·215	0·220	0·220	0·213
40° S	0·240	0·230	0·250	0·290	0·310	0·280	0·267

Ozone absorption with λ; see § 55, § 56, and § 57. Negative correlation of ozone with the sunspot cycle; see [5].

[1] *A.Q.* **1**, § 58.
[2] R. H. KAY, *Rocket Exploration of the Upper Atmosphere*, J.A.T.P. Supp., p. 208, 1954.
[3] S. V. VENKATESWARAN, MOORE, and KRUEGER, *J. Geoph. Res.*, **66**, 1751, 1961.
[4] A. W. BREWER, et al., *Ann. de Geoph.*, **16**, 196, 1960.
[5] H. C. WILLETT, *J. Geoph. Res.*, **67**, 661, 1962.

§ 60. Atmospheric Electricity

The values quoted for atmospheric electrical quantities are intended to represent mean fine weather conditions. Land and sea results are quoted separately only if there are large differences in the mean values. Usually observations over the oceans are less dependent on local conditions than those on land and consequently the former are more suitable for providing mean values.

The normal fine weather gradient drives positive ions towards the earth; i.e. the field is downward, and the upward potential gradient is positive. Insulated objects above the earth therefore tend to acquire a free positive charge.

Atmospheric electrical quantities

Quantity	Unit	Altitude above sea-level in km							
		0	1	2	5	10	15	20	50
Potential gradient [1, 2, 9]	volt/m	130	75	45	15	5	2	1	0
Potential [1,3]	kv	0	100	156	240	270	290	300	300
Total conductivity [1, 3, 4, 5], $\lambda = \lambda_+ + \lambda_-$	10^{-4} E.S.U. $= 1 \cdot 1 \times 10^{-16}$ $\mho$/cm	2·8	5	7	18	55	130	300	30 000
Conductivity ratio [1, 4, 5, 8], λ_+/λ_-		1·2	1·2	1·1	0·9	0·9	0·9	1·0	0·5
Small ion density n_+ [1, 6] n_-	ion cm^{-3} ion cm^{-3}	600 500	900 800	1 200 1 100	2000 2000	3 800 3 800	4 600 4 600	4 400 4 400	1 000? 1 000?
Mean life of small ions [1]	sec	70	130	200	200	100	100	150	
Density of nuclei and heavy ions [1] $N_0 + N_+ + N_-$	cm^{-3}	10 000	3 000	1 000	50	3			
Mobility of small ions k_+ k_-	(cm/s)/ (volt/cm)	1·3 1·5 }	varies inversely with air density						
Positive space charge [1, 3]	e/cm^3 $= 4 \cdot 8 \times 10^{-10}$ E.S.U.	2	2	1	0·2	0·1			
Rate of formation of ion pairs Cosmic rays at equator [1] All sources over land [1]	ion pair cm^{-3} s^{-1}	1·6 9·5	2·1 6	2·7 5	7 11	40	45	24	
Resistance of air column [1]	10^{20} Ω cm^2	0	3	5	8	9·5	9·9	10·2	
Atmospheric radium emanation [1]	10^{-18} curie cm^{-3}	100	49	25	3	0·5			

Variations with location [1, 3]

Quantity (sea-level)	Unit	City	Country	Sea
Air–earth current	10^{-7} E.S.U. $= 33 \times 10^{-18}$ amp cm^{-2}	4	7	9
Total conductivity $\lambda = \lambda_+ + \lambda_-$	10^{-4} E.S.U. $= 1.1 \times 10^{-16}$ ℧/cm	0.3	2.5	2.8
Large ion density N_+ and N_-	ion pairs cm^{-3}	30 000	1 000	200
Neutral nuclei (Aitken) N_0	nuclei cm^{-3}	100 000	5 000	500
Life of small ions	sec	10	50	200

Rate of ion production at sea-level [1]

Results vary within 1 metre of the ground

	On land				At sea
	Ionizing rays			Total	
	α	β	γ		
	Ion pairs per cm^3 per sec				
Radio-active matter in the earth	0	0.2	3.0	3.2	⎫
Radio-active matter in the air	4.3	0.4	0.15	4.8	⎬ 0.6
Cosmic radiation (equator)				1.6	1.6
Total	4.3	0.6	3.1	9.6	2.2

World variation of potential gradient and potential with season and universal time [1]

	U.T.											
	0	2	4	6	8	10	12	14	16	18	20	22
	Percentage of mean											
Jan, Feb., Nov., Dec.	94	85	84	87	90	90	100	110	116	121	118	105
Mar., Apr., Sept., Oct.	98	88	84	86	90	91	97	106	113	118	118	109
May, June, July, Aug.	102	92	86	89	94	94	94	100	107	113	118	112
Year	98	88	85	88	92	92	97	105	112	118	118	109

Recombination rate for small ions $= \alpha n_+ n_-$　　[1]

coefficient $\alpha = 1.6 \times 10^{-6}$ cm^3 s^{-1}

where n_+ and n_- are small ion concentrations per cm^3.

Combination and attachment rates of small ions with large ions of opposite sign or with neutral nuclei are $\eta_{+-}n_+N_-$, $\eta_{+0}n_+N_0$, etc. The various coefficients η are approximately equal [1], and

$$\eta \simeq 3 \times 10^{-6} \text{ cm}^3 \text{ s}^{-1}.$$

Recombination rate for large ions $= \gamma N_+ N_-$

$$\gamma = 10^{-8} \text{ cm}^3 \text{ s}^{-1}$$

Mobility of electrons $= 20\,000$ (cm/s)/(volt/cm)

       small ions $= 1\cdot4$ (cm/s)/(volt/cm)

       intermediate ions $= 0\cdot003$ to $0\cdot1$ (cm/s)/(volt/cm)

       large ions $= 0\cdot000\,1$ to $0\cdot003$ (cm/s)/(volt/cm)

Earth negative surface charge $= 3\cdot5 \times 10^{-4}$ E.S.U. $= 1\cdot2 \times 10^{-3}$ coulomb km^{-2}

Fine weather air–earth current for whole earth ($+$ downwards)

$$= 1\,500 \text{ amp}$$

Resistance between whole earth surface and conducting layer above 20 km

$$= 200 \text{ ohm}$$

Time required to neutralize surface charge (in absence of thunderstorms)

$$= 56 \text{ minutes}$$

Mean upward current in single thunderstorm

$$= 0\cdot9 \text{ amp}$$

Mean world population of thunderstorms

$$= 2\,200$$

Mean total thunderstorm area [7] $= 800\,000$ km$^2 = 0\cdot001\,6$ earth surface

Mean charge in a lightning flash $= 16$ coulombs

Energy of flash $= 2 \times 10^{17}$ erg

Break-down electric field in thunderstorm

$$\simeq 10^4 \text{ volt/cm}$$

Mean thunderstorm field (required for zero earth charge [7])

$$= 800 \text{ volt/cm}$$

Potential difference in lightning flash

$$\simeq 4 \times 10^9 \text{ volts}$$

Mean height of thundercloud striking to earth [1]

$$= 5\cdot2 \text{ km}$$

Radium content of terrestrial surface rocks [1]

$$= 2\cdot3 \times 10^{-12} \text{ g-radium/g-rock}$$
$$\equiv 7 \times 10^{-6} \text{ g-uranium/g-rock}$$

Thorium content $= 15 \times 10^{-6}$ g-thorium/g-rock

Radium content of sea water $= 2 \times 10^{-15}$ g-radium cm^{-3}

Radio-active matter in air

       over land at sea-level $= 130 \times 10^{-18}$ curie cm^{-3}

       over sea at sea-level $= 2\cdot6 \times 10^{-18}$ curie cm^{-3}

       (1 curie $\rightarrow$ about $3\cdot7 \times 10^{10}$ disintegrations per sec).

[1] A.Q. 1, § 59.
[2] C. G. STERGIS, REIN, and KANGAS, J.A.T.P., 11, 77, 1959.
[3] J. H. KRAAKEVIK, J. Geoph. Res., 63, 161, 1958; 66, 3735, 1961.
[4] C. G. STERGIS, et al., J.A.T.P., 6, 233, 1955.

[5] R. H. WOESSNER, COBB, and GUNN, *J. Geoph. Res.*, **63**, 171, 1958.
[6] J. L. KROENING, *J. Geoph. Res.*, **65**, 145, 1960.
[7] J. F. CLARK and J. H. KRAAKEVIK, *J.A.T.P.*, **6**, 344, 1955.
[8] R. E. BOURDEAU, WHIPPLE, and CLARK, *J. Geoph. Res.*, **64**, 1363, 1959.
[9] R. MÜHLEISEN and H. J. FISCHER, *Naturwiss.*, **47**, 36, 1960.

§ 61. Ionosphere

f_0 = ordinary critical frequency

f_x = extra-ordinary critical frequency

f_H = gyro-frequency for magnetic field H

ν_{ei} = collision frequency of electrons with ions

ν_{en} = collision frequency of electrons with neutral particles

$\nu_{in}(\simeq \nu_{nn})$ = collision frequency of ions with neutral particles

N_e = electron concentration

N_{max} = maximum electron concentration in an ionospheric layer

$N_{max} = (\pi m/e^2)f_0^2 = 1{\cdot}240\ 4 \times 10^4 f_0^2\ \mathrm{cm}^{-3}$　$[f$ in Mc/s]

$\qquad\ = (\pi m/e^2)(f_x^2 - f_x f_H) = 1{\cdot}240\ 4 \times 10^4 (f_x^2 - f_x f_H)$　$[f_x, f_H$ in Mc/s]

$f_H = (e/2\pi mc)H = 2{\cdot}799\ 4\ H$ Mc/s　$[H$ in gauss]

In this equation H is strictly the magnetic flux density (generally denoted B) in gauss but in free space it is numerically equal to the magnetic field in oersted.

α = recombination coefficient in recombination rate = $\alpha N_i N_e$ where $_i$ = ion, $_e$ = electron, and normally $N_i = N_e$

β = attachment-like coefficient in electron attachment rate = βN_e

q = ionizing rate (derived, e.g. from sun's spectrum and absorption coefficients [20]), then

$$dN_e/dt = q - \alpha N_e^2 - \beta N_e \quad \text{[usually either α or β]}$$

R = sunspot number, h = altitude

$$\phi = \text{Faraday rotation} = \frac{e^3}{2\pi m^2 c^2}\cdot\frac{1}{f^2}\int_0^\infty NH\cos\theta\,dz$$

$$= 2{\cdot}36 \times 10^4/f^2 \times \int NH\cos\theta\,dz$$

with ϕ in radian, e in E.S.U., f in c/s, H in gauss, angle θ between field and ray, and integration along path. The rotation is in a corkscrew sense when the magnetic field is in the *same* direction as the radiation.

Ionospheric layers

Quantity	Unit	D [21]	E	F$_1$	F$_2$
Altitude of N_{max} [1, 2, 3, 4]	km	80	115	170	300
Molecular and atomic density	cm^{-3}	10^{15}	10^{12}	2×10^{10}	10^9
Behaviour		Regular	Simple theory		Anomalous
f_0 ($R = 0$, zenith sun) [1] f_0 ($R = 100$, zenith sun)	Mc/s	0·2	3·29 3·90	4·40 5·38	6·9 11·9
N_{max} ($R = 0$, zenith sun) [1] N_{max} ($R = 100$, zenith sun)	cm^{-3}	600	$1·34 \times 10^5$ $1·88 \times 10^5$	$2·40 \times 10^5$ $3·59 \times 10^5$	$5·9 \times 10^5$ $17·7 \times 10^5$
q ($R = 0$) [6, 20] ($R = 100$)	cm^{-3} s^{-1}		500 1 000	700 1 500	100 300
Equivalent layer thickness	km	15	25	60	300
$\int_0^\infty q\, dh$ ($R = 0$) ($R = 100$)	cm^{-2} s^{-1}		12×10^8 25×10^8	40×10^8 90×10^8	30×10^8 90×10^8
Equivalent photon emis-sson at sun surface ($R = 0$) ($R = 100$)	photon cm^{-2} s^{-1}		5×10^{13} 12×10^{13}	18×10^{13} 40×10^{13}	14×10^{13} 40×10^{13}
α [1, 7, 16] β (day) [1, 6] β (night) [1]	cm^3 s^{-1} s^{-1} s^{-1}	3×10^{-8}	$1·6 \times 10^{-8}$ 10^{-3}	8×10^{-9} 10^{-3}	8×10^{-11} $1·5 \times 10^{-4}$ 3×10^{-5}
ν_{el} [5] ν_{en}	s^{-1} s^{-1}	10^7	1 000 30 000	1 000 12 000	1 000 12

Variations with height

h	$\log N_e$ (day) [19]	$\log \alpha$ [3, 8, 9, 16]	$\log \beta$ [1, 6, 8, 9]	$\log \nu_{ei}$	$\log \nu_{en}$ [5, 10, 11, 12]	$\log \nu_{in}$ = $\log \nu_{nn}$
	in cm^{-3}	in cm^3 s^{-1}	in s^{-1}	in s^{-1}	in s^{-1}	in s^{-1}
60	1·8	−5·2				
70	2·3	−5·7			7·5	
80	2·8	−6·3			6·5	
90	4·0	−6·9			5·7	
100	5·0	−7·8			5·1	4·5
110	5·1	−7·9			4·7	3·9
120	5·1	−7·95	−3	3·0	4·3	3·3
150	5·35	−8·05	−3	3·0	3·5	2·2
200	5·35	−8·4	−3·2	3·0	2·6	1·0
250	5·7	−9·3	−3·6	3·0	1·8	0·4
300	6·0	−10·2	−4·1	3·0	1·1	−0·1
400	5·8	−11·3	−5·1	3·0	0·0	−0·9
500	5·6	−11·8	−5·9		−1·0	−1·6
600	5·4	−12·0	−6·1		−2·5	
1 000	4·7	−12	−7			
3 000	3·7	−12	−8			
10 000	2·9	−12	−9			
20 000	2·2	−12	−10			
30 000	1·5	−12	−11			

The ionosphere as a whole

Equivalent thickness below maximum $B = 120$ km

Equivalent thickness above maximum [13, 15] $A = 320$ km

   Total electron content

$$\int_0^\infty N_e \, dh = N_{max}(A+B) \simeq 5 \times 10^{13} \text{ cm}^{-2}$$

Energy required to maintain ionization [14]

$$\simeq 1\cdot5 \text{ erg cm}^{-2} \text{s}^{-1}$$

$$\simeq 4 \times 10^{10} \text{ photons cm}^{-2} \text{ s}^{-1}$$

Height of q_{max} $\simeq 180$ km

Integrated conductivity, $K = \int_0^\infty k \, dh$

where k = electrical conductivity. As a result of the magnetic field there are three forms of conductivity considered to be significant in particular cases [5, 17]

		height km	thickness km
K_1 (transverse)	8×10^{-9} E.M.U.	140	40
K_2 (Hall effect)	12×10^{-9} ,,	120	50
K_3 (related to equatorial values)	180×10^{-9} ,,	105	20

Allowance for earth curvature in formulae for ionization and absorption. The factor sec χ in such formulae should be replaced by Ch (x, χ) [18], where χ is sun's zenith distance, $x = Q + (h - h_0)/H_s$, $Q = (a + h_0)/H_s$, H_s = scale height, a = earth radius, h = height, h_0 = height of maximum ionization rate.

Ch (x, χ)

χ:		30°	45°	60°	75°	80°	85°	90°	95°
Q	sec χ:	1·155	1·414	2·000	3·864	5·76	11·47	∞	
50		1·148	1·389	1·908	3·232	4·10	5·82	8·93	16
100		1·151	1·401	1·946	3·512	4·61	7·07	12·58	30
200		1·153	1·407	1·972	3·646	5·01	8·28	17·76	68
400		1·154	1·411	1·985	3·742	5·38	9·33	25·09	220
800		1·154	1·412	1·993	3·800	5·55	10·15	35·46	1 476

[1] *A.Q.* **1**, § 60.
[2] K. RAWER, *The Ionosphere*, p. 120, American ed., 1956.
[3] A. H. WAYNICK, *Phys. of Ionosphere*, p. 1, Phys. Soc., 1955.
[4] H. R. PEIFFER and A. P. MITRA, *J.A.T.P.*, **6**, 291, 1955.
[5] S. CHAPMAN, *High Alt. Ob. Boulder, Misc. Repr.* No., 82, 1956.
[6] J. A. RATCLIFFE (et al.), *Phil. Trans.*, A **248**, 621, 1956; *Phys. Soc. Year B.*, 1, 1959.
[7] S. A. BOWHILL, *J.A.T.P.*, **20**, 19, 1961.
[8] M. E. SZENDREI and W. M. McELHINNY, *J.A.T.P.*, **8**, 108, 1956; **9**, 118, 1956.
[9] A. P. MITRA (and R. E. JONES), *J. Geoph. Res.*, **59**, 391, 1954; **64**, 733, 1959.
[10] J. A. KANE, *J. Geoph. Res.*, **64**, 133, 1959.
[11] J. D. WHITEHEAD, *J.A.T.P.*, **16**, 283, 1959.
[12] D. F. MARTYN, *Proc. I.R.E.*, **47**, 147, 1959.
[13] O. K. GARRIOTT, *I.G.Y. Satellite Rep.*, **10**, 1, 1960.
[14] D. C. HUNT and T. E. VAN ZANDT, *J. Geoph. Res.*, **66**, 1673, 1961.
[15] J. W. WRIGHT, *J. Geoph. Res.*, **65**, 185, 1960.
[16] J. HUNAERT and M. NICOLET, *J. Geoph. Res.*, **60**, 537, 1955.
[17] L. J. CAHILL and J. A. VAN ALLEN, *J. Geoph. Res.*, **63**, 270, 1958.
[18] S. CHAPMAN, *Proc. Phys. Soc.*, **43**, 26, 483, 1931; B **66**, 710, 1953.
[19] R. A. HELLIWELL, *Ann. de Geoph.*, **17**, 76, 1961.
[20] K. WATANABE and H. E. HINTEREGGER, *J. Geoph. Res.*, **67**, 999, 1962.
[21] J. E. TITHERIDGE, *J.A.T.P.*, **24**, 259, 1962.

§ 62. Night Sky and Aurorae

The units used for expressing the night sky brightness of spectroscopic features (lines, or bands of restricted extent in wavelength) [5]:

1 rayleigh = R $\qquad = 10^6$ photons emitted in all directions per cm^2 vertical column per sec

$\qquad = 1 \cdot 581 \times 10^{-3}/\lambda$ (in Å) erg cm^{-2} s^{-1} sterad^{-1} at zenith

1 photon $\qquad = (1 \cdot 986 \times 10^{-8})/\lambda$ (in Å) ergs

1 $(m_v = 10)$ star deg^{-2} through clear atmosphere near 5500 Å

$\qquad = 0 \cdot 003\ 6$ R/Å

Oblique columns are often used for defining the kilo-rayleigh (= 1 000 R) in aurorae. All terrestrial night sky illumination factors (night glow, airglow) are variable; $\pm 0 \cdot 2$ dex

Night sky brightness [1, 2, 3]

Source	Photographic	Visual	Photometry
	10th mag stars deg^{-2}		10^{-9} stilb
Atomic lines (near zenith)	0	50	3
Resolved bands (near zenith)	30	60	4
Continuum (near zenith)	70	150	10
Zodiacal light (away from zodiac)	20	30	2
Faint stars, $m > 6$ (gal. pole)	16	30	2·5
Faint stars, $m > 6$ (mean sky)	48	95	7
Faint stars, $m > 6$ (gal. equator)	140	320	22
Non-star galactic light	20 ?	40 ?	2 ?
Total brightness (zenith, mean sky)	200	400	30
Total brightness (15° alt, mean sky)	300	700	50

Spectral distribution of night sky light omitting atomic lines [1, 4]

λ in Å	3200	3600	4000	4500	5000	5500	6000	8000	10000
Intensity in 10^{-7} erg cm^{-2} s^{-1} sterad^{-1} Å^{-1}	1·4	1·1	1·3	2·0	2·0	3	5	20	60

Spectral emissions in the night sky

Source	λ, etc.	Intensity			Height [8, 9, 10, 11, 12]
		Night	Twilight [1, 5, 6, 9]	Aurora	
	Å	R		kR	km
[O I]	5577	260	180	100	96
"	6300–64	80	1 000	50	160
"	2972			3	
[O II]	7319–20			5	
"	2470			1	
"	3727			0·5	
[N I]	10400			100	
"	3466			7	High
"	5199		10	1	High
[N II]	Visible			1	
O I	Photogr. I.R.			25	
"	Far U.V.			25	
O II	Visible			5	
"	Far U.V.			5	
N I	Photogr. I.R.			5	
"	Far U.V.			5	
N II	Visible			25	
"	Far U.V.			20	
Na I	5890–96, summer	30	1 000	1	90
"	5890–96, winter	200	5 000	1	
H I	Hα 6563, Balmer	10		10	
"	Lα, 1216, Lyman	2 500		100	
Ca II	3933–67		150		
Li I	6708		200		
N_2	I.R. 1st positive			2 000	
"	U.V. 2nd positive			100	
"	Blue, Vegard-Kaplan			150	
"	2000 Lyman				
N^+	U.V.-vis. 1st neg.		1 000	170	
"	6300–8900 Meinel			2 500	
O_2	1500 Schumann-Runge				
"	3000–4000 Herzberg	430			90
"	8645 Atm. (0, 1)	1 500		400	90
"	15800 Atm. I.R.		20 000	1 000	
OH	15800 (4, 2)	175 000			
"	Total spectrum	4×10^6			
"	vis (5, 0)(7, 1)(8, 2)(9, 3) [7]	130			75

Colour index of night sky [1]　　　　　　= +0·5

Night sky intensity increase with latitude [1]
　　　ratio (lat. 70°)/(lat. 20°)　　　　≃ 2

Night sky intensity increase with sunspot number [1]. The increase is due chiefly to 5577 Å for which the intensity ratio $(R = 100)/(R = 0) \simeq 1·6$, where $R =$ sunspot number.

Number of Na atoms above 70 km [1, 13]

$$= 7 \times 10^9 \text{ atoms cm}^{-2}$$

Zone of maximum auroral activity
geomag. lat. $= 68°$

Auroral heights [1]

Sharp lower boundary	90 km	
Normal upper extremity	300 km	
Sunlit upper extremity	700 km (1 000 km in extreme cases)	

Auroral International Coefficients of Brightness [5]

I.C.B. I	5577 brightness =	1 kR $\simeq 10^{-8}$ stilb	
II	,,	=	10 kR $\simeq 10^{-7}$,,
III	,,	=	100 kR $\simeq 10^{-6}$,,
IV	,,	=	1 000 kR $\simeq 10^{-5}$,,

Temperature measurements from auroral emissions [7, 8] are in approximate agreement with the model temperatures (§ 53) at the appropriate heights.

Flux of monoenergetic protons required to produce 10 kR of Hα in the zenith [9].

Initial energy	Minimum penetration height	$\dfrac{\text{H}\alpha \text{ photons}}{\text{protons}}$	Proton flux	Total incident energy flux
kev	km		cm^{-2} s^{-1}	ev cm^{-2} s^{-1}
130	100	60	$1\cdot6 \times 10^8$	$2\cdot1 \times 10^{13}$
27	110	20	5×10^8	$1\cdot4 \times 10^{13}$
8·5	120	7	14×10^8	$1\cdot2 \times 10^{13}$

For energy, rigidity, velocity, geomagnetic latitude, and penetration level of incoming auroral particles, see § 128.

[1] A.Q. 1, § 61.
[2] F. E. ROACH and L. R. MEGILL, Ap. J., 133, 228, 1961.
[3] N. C. GERSON, J.A.T.P., 5, 67, 1954.
[4] E. N. PAVOLVA, RODIONOV, and SOLOHOVA, Astr. N.L., No. 85, 18, 1957.
[5] D. M. HUNTEN, ROACH, and CHAMBERLAIN, J.A.T.P., 8, 345, 1956.
[6] J. E. KUPPERIAN, et al., I.G.Y. Rocket Rep. Ser., 1, 186, 1958.
[7] D. E. BLACKWELL, INGHAM, and RUNDLE, Ap. J., 131, 15, 1960.
[8] E. B. ARMSTRONG, J.A.T.P., 13, 205, 1959.
[9] J. W. CHAMBERLAIN, Ann. de Geoph., 17, 90, 1961.
[10] D. M. PACKER, Ann. de Geoph., 17, 67, 1961.
[11] F. E. ROACH, Ann. de Geoph., 11, 214, 1955.
[12] J. P. HEPPNER and L. H. MEREDITH, J. Geoph. Res., 63, 51, 1958.
[13] G. I. GALPERIN, A. Zh., 33, 173, 1956.

§ 63. Geomagnetism

Earth magnetic dipole moment (1955) [1, 2]

$$= 8\cdot07 \times 10^{25} \text{ E.M.U.}$$

Direction of dipole N (1955) [2]

$$\text{lat} = 78°\cdot3 \text{ N} \quad \text{long} = 69°\cdot0 \text{ W}$$

Eccentric dipole (1955) [3]

Displacement from earth centre
$$= 436 \text{ km} = 0.068 \ 5 \ \mathcal{R}_{\oplus}$$

towards   15°·6 N,   150°·9 E

Poles of eccentric dipole
81°·0 N	84°·7 W
75°·0 S	120°·4 E

Location of 90° dip for eccentric dipole
82°·4 N	137°·3 W
67°·9 S	130°·6 E

Geomagnetic poles [4]

N pole (90° dip) 76° N   101° W

S pole (90° dip) 67° S   144° E

Horizontal magnetic field H at geomagnetic equator [1]
$$= 0.32 \text{ gauss } (0.29 \text{ to } 0.40)$$

Vertical magnetic field Z at geomagnetic N pole
$$= 0.62 \text{ gauss}$$

Vertical magnetic field Z at geomagnetic S pole
$$= 0.70 \text{ gauss}$$

Dipole magnetic field
$$H = 0.312 \cos \phi \text{ gauss } \quad [\phi = \text{geomagnetic latitude}]$$
$$Z = 0.624 \sin \phi \text{ gauss}$$

Zone of maximum geomagnetic activity
$$\text{geomag. lat} = 68°$$

Sq overhead current system

Node of EW currents   lat $= 38°$

Current between node and either pole or equator (at equinox and zero sunspots)
$$= 59 \ 000 \text{ ampere}$$

Relation between K_p index, a_p index and γ change in a 3-hour period for mid-latitude stations (lat $\simeq 45°$) [1, 6, 7]

K_p index	0	1	2	3	4	5	6	7	8	9
a_p index	0	3	7	15	27	48	80	140	240	400
$\gamma (= 10^{-5} \text{gauss})$	0	5	10	20	40	70	120	200	330	500	∞

The factors by which the γ figures are to be multiplied ranged from 0·6 at low latitudes (although higher at the geomagnetic equator itself) to 5·0 in the auroral zone.

Relation between various daily indices [1, 6, 7, 8]

$C9$	0	1	2	3	4	5	6	7	8	9
$C_p \simeq C_i$	0·05	0·25	0·45	0·65	0·85	1·05	1·30	1·60	1·90	2·20
$A_p = \text{mean } a_p$	3	5	8	11	15	20	31	52	109	240
K_p sum	6	10	15	18	22	26	33	39	49	64
max K_p	$1\frac{1}{2}$	$2\frac{1}{2}$	$3\frac{1}{2}$	4	$4\frac{1}{2}$	5	6	7	8	9

Atom density of cloud of particles causing a geomagnetic storm of intensity A_p (still very uncertain) [1]

$$\simeq 2A_p \text{ atoms cm}^{-3}$$

Velocity of geomagnetic particles in transit from the sun [1]

Great storms (sudden commencements)	$v =$	1 600 km/s
Minor sunspot storms (main stream)	$v =$	600 km/s
Recurrent storms	$v =$	500 km/s

Van Allen radiation belts [5]

Distance from earth centre

Inner belt	$1\cdot6\ \mathscr{R}_{\oplus}$
Outer belt	$3\cdot5\ \mathscr{R}_{\oplus}$

Interpretation in terms of number density and energy of electrons and protons is still uncertain.

[1] *A.Q.* **1**, § 62.
[2] H. F. Finch and B. R. Leaton, *Geoph. Supp. R.A.S.*, **7**, 314, 1957.
[3] W. D. Parkinson and J. Cleary, *Geoph. J.*, **1**, 346, 1958.
[4] E. R. Hope, *J. Geoph. Res.*, **62**, 19, 1957.
[5] J. A. van Allen, *J. Geoph. Res.*, **64**, 1683, 1959.
[6] J. Bartels, *Cp and Kp tabulations and diagrams*, Göttingen, Ak. Wiss., 1884 to 1950, 1951; 1937 to 1958, 1958.
[7] J. Bartels, *I.G.Y. Instructions*, 1957.
[8] Tabulations in *Solar-Geophysical Data* (B) and *J. Geoph. Res.*

§ 64. Meteorites and Craters

Occurrence of stone and iron meteorites

	Meteorites seen falling [8]	Meteorite finds
Irons	6%	66 %
Stony-irons	2%	$7\frac{1}{2}$%
Stones	92%	$26\frac{1}{2}$%

The figures represent the relative difficulty of *finding* stony meteorites; the 'seen falling' column should represent relative abundance. Meteorites are from sporadic meteors. The higher percentage of stones in meteorites as compared with meteors (see § 73) is probably related to their larger size.

Density of meteorites [4]

Irons	7·5 to 8·0 g cm^{-3}
Stony-irons	5·5 to 6·0 ,,
Stones	3·0 to 3·5 ,,

Fall of meteors large enough to be seen and found [1, 8]

$$= 2 \text{ meteorites day}^{-1} \text{ over whole earth.}$$

For total mass of meteor falls, see § 73.

Most probable size of found meteorites [8]

Irons	15 kg
Stones	3 kg

Meteorite mass before entry to earth atmosphere

$$\simeq 10^2 \text{ kg}$$

Mass of greatest known meteorite

$$\text{original mass} = 8 \times 10^4 \text{ kg}$$

The Siberian meteorite of 1908 was probably greater than this.

Crater volume ratio

   (material displaced in meteorite crater)/(meteorite)

$$= 60\,000$$

Meteor energy required to produce terrestrial or lunar crater of diameter d [2, 3]

$$= 4 \times 10^{13}\, d^3 \text{ erg} \quad [d \text{ in metres}]$$

The constant quoted is 20 times greater than in [2] and 3 times less than in [3].

Energy of 1 kiloton of TNT [3] $= 4 \cdot 2 \times 10^{19}$ erg

Meteorite crater diameter and depth. The following relation applies approximately to *new* meteorite craters, bomb craters, and lunar craters [2]

Diameter	in m	1	10	100	1 000	10 000	100 000
Depth from rim	in m	0·12	2·7	27	180	1 000	4 700
Rim above outer plane	in m		0·5	7	70	370	1 200

Terrestrial meteorite craters

Crater name, location	Discovery year	Lat.	Long.	Number of craters	Diam. of largest crater	Rim height above outer plane	Rim height above crater floor
					m	m	m
Barringer, Arizona, U.S.A.	1891	35° N	111° W	1	1 240	39	190
Tunguska, Siberia, U.S.S.R.	1908	61° N	102° E	10+	52		
Odessa, U.S.A.	1921			4	170	3	4
Dalgaranga, Australia	1923	27° 45′ S	117° 05′ E	1	70		5
Ösel, Estonia	1927			6	100		15
Campo del Cielo, Argentina		28° S	62° W	Many	75	1	
Henbury, Australia	1931	25° S	133° E	13	200 × 110		15
Wabar, Arabia	1932			2	100		12
Haviland, Kansas, U.S.A.	1933	30° N	96° W	1	17 × 11		3
Boxhole, Australia	1937	22° 37′ S	132° 12′ E	1	175		15
Wolf Creek, Australia	1947			1	820	30	60
Le Clot, Béziers, France	1950	43° N	3° E	6	230	0	50
Chubb, Quebec, Canada	1950	61° 17′ N	73° 41′ W	1	3 400	100	380
Brent, Ontario, Canada [5]	1951	46° 04′ N	78° 30′ W	1	3 200		70
E. Pamir, Tadzhik, S.S.R.	1952	38° 06′ N	74° 17′ E	2	80		15
Deep Bay, Sask., Canada[6]	1956	56° 24′ N	103° O′ W	1	13 000		340

[1] *A.Q.* **1**, § 90.
[2] R. B. Baldwin, *The Face of the Moon*, Chicago, 1949.
[3] J. E. Hill and J. J. Gilvarry, *J. Geoph. Res.*, **61**, 501, 1956.
[4] F. C. Leonard, *Sky and Tel.*, **16**, 370, 1957.
[5] C. S. Beals, Ferguson, and Landau, *J.R.A.S. Canada*, **50**, 203, 1956.
[6] M. J. S. Innes, *J.R.A.S. Canada*, **51**, 235, 1957.
[7] F. G. Watson, *Between the Planets*, Revised, Harvard, 1956.
[8] H. Brown, *J. Geoph. Res.*, **65**, 1679, 1960; **66**, 1316, 1961.

CHAPTER 7

PLANETS AND SATELLITES

§ 65. Planetary System

Total mass of planets		$= 447 \cdot 9 \, \mathcal{M}_{\oplus}$	$[\mathcal{M}_{\oplus} = 5 \cdot 977 \times 10^{27} \text{ g}]$
,,	,, ,, satellites	$= 0 \cdot 12 \, \mathcal{M}_{\oplus}$
,,	,, ,, minor planets	$= 0 \cdot 000 \, 3 \, \mathcal{M}_{\oplus}$
,,	,, ,, meteoric matter	$= 5 \times 10^{-10} \, \mathcal{M}_{\oplus}$
,,	,, ,, planetary system	$= 448 \cdot 0 \, \mathcal{M}_{\oplus} = 2 \cdot 678 \times 10^{30} \text{ g}$
		$= \mathcal{M}_{\odot}/743$

Total angular momentum of planetary system [1, 2]
$$= 3 \cdot 148 \times 10^{50} \text{ g cm}^2 \text{ s}^{-1}$$

Total kinetic energy of planetary system (translational)
$$= 1 \cdot 99 \times 10^{42} \text{ erg}$$

Total rotational energy of planets $\quad = 0 \cdot 7 \times 10^{42} \text{ erg}$

Invariable plane of the solar system [2]

longitude of ascending node $\Omega = 106° \, 44' + 59' \, T$

inclination $\qquad\qquad\qquad I = 1° \, 38' \, 58'' - 18'' \, T$

where T is epoch in centuries from 1900·0.

Period of comet or asteroid $\qquad = 1 \cdot 000 \, 040 \, 27 \, a^{3/2}$ tropical years

where a is semi-major axis of orbit in AU.

Bode's law. Distance of planets from sun in AU $= 0 \cdot 4 + 0 \cdot 3 \times 2^n$ where n is $-\infty$ for Mercury, 0 for Venus, 1 for Earth, etc.

Planet	n	Bode's law	Planetary distance
		AU	AU
Mercury	$-\infty$	0·4	0·39
Venus	0	0·7	0·72
Earth	1	1·0	1·00
Mars	2	1·6	1·52
Asteroids	3	2·8	2·8
Jupiter	4	5·2	5·20
Saturn	5	10·0	9·55
Uranus	6	19·6	19·2
Neptune	7	38·8	30·1
Pluto	8	77·2	39·5

[1] *A.Q.* **1**, § 82.
[2] G. M. CLEMENCE and D. BROUWER, *A.J.*, **60**, 118, 1955.

§ 66. Planetary Orbits and Physical Elements

The orbital elements are not tabulated with full precision normally required for ephemeris work since this would entail an elaborate definition of certain elements.

The epoch (except for L) is $1900 + T$ centuries. The longitude of perihelion $\tilde{\omega}$ is measured from ♈, whence $\tilde{\omega} = \Omega + \omega$ where ω is the longitude of perihelion measured from the ascending node along the orbit. ☊ and L are also measured from ♈.

In the semi-diameter column of the table of physical elements, C = inferior conjunction (Mercury and Venus only), and O = opposition. In the second last column an inclination of the equator to the orbit greater than 90° indicates that the rotation is retrograde with respect to the orbit.

For secular variations of planetary orbits: see [13].

Planetar

Planet		Semi-major axis of orbit [1, 3, 4]		Sidereal period [1, 3, 4]		Synodic period [1]	Mean daily motion [1, 4]	Mean orbita vel. [1]
		AU	10^6 km	Tropical years	Days	Days	″	km/s
Mercury	☿	0·387 099	57·91	0·240 85	87·968 6	115·88	14 732·420 2	47·90
Venus [2]	♀	0·723 332	108·21	0·615 21	224·700	583·92	5 767·671	35·05
Earth	⊕	1·000 000	149·60	1·000 04	365·257		3 548·192 6	29·80
Mars	♂	1·523 69	227·94	1·880 89	686·980	779·94	1 886·518 6	24·14
Jupiter	♃	5·202 8	778·3	11·862 23	4 332·587	398·88	299·127 8	13·06
Saturn	♄	9·540	1 427	29·457 72	10 759·20	378·09	120·456	9·65
Uranus	♅	19·18	2 869	84·013	30 685	369·66	42·234	6·80
Neptune	♆	30·07	4 498	164·79	60 188	367·49	21·53	5·43
Pluto	♇	39·44	5 900	248·4	90 700	366·74	14·29	4·74

Physi

Planet		Semi-diameter (equatorial) at 1 AU [1, 4]	Semi-diameter (equatorial) at mean C or O [1, 4]	Radius (equatorial) R_e [1, 3, 4, 8]		Ellipticity $\frac{R_e - R_p}{R_e}$ [1]	Volume	Reciprocal mass (including satellites) [1, 8, 9, 13]
		″	″	km	⊕ = 1		⊕ = 1	1/☉ = 1
Mercury	☿	3·34	5·45	2 420	0·38	0·0	0·055	6 050 000
Venus [5, 6]	♀	8·43	30·5	6 100	0·96	0·0	0·88	408 600
Earth	⊕	8·80		6 378	1·00	0·003 4	1·000	328 700
Mars	♂	4·68	8·94	3 380	0·53	0·005 2	0·150	3 089 000
Jupiter	♃	98·47	23·43	71 350	11·19	0·062	1 318	1 047·38
Saturn	♄	83·33	9·76	60 400	9·47	0·096	769	3 497·6
Uranus	♅	32·8	1·80	23 800	3·73	0·06	50	22 930
Neptune [9]	♆	30·7	1·06	22 200	3·49	0·02	42	19 100
Pluto	♇	4·1	0·11	3 000	0·47		0·1	400 000 ?

[1] *A.Q.* **1**, § 83.
[2] R. L. Duncombe, *Astron. Papers Am. Ephem.*, **16**, part 1, 1958.
[3] G. H. Herbig and C. E. Worley, *A.S.P. Leaflet*, No. 325 revised, 1960.
[4] *B.A.A. Handbook* (Annual).
[5] G. de Vaucouleurs and D. H. Menzel, *Nature*, **188**, 28, 1960.
[6] D. Ya. Martynov, *A. Zh.*, **37**, 848, 1960; *Sov. A.*, **4**, 798.
[7] H. Camichel, *Ann. d'Ap.*, **21**, 217, 1958.
[8] G. M. Clemence and D. Brouwer, *A.J.*, **60**, 118, 1955.
[9] G. van Biesbroeck, *A.J.*, **62**, 272, 1957.
[10] M. F. Walker and R. Hardie, *P.A.S.P.*, **67**, 224, 1955.
[11] R. S. Richardson, *P.A.S.P.*, **67**, 304, 1955; **70**, 251, 1958.
[12] W. C. De Marcus, *Handb. der Phys.*, **52**, 431, 1959.
[13] D. Brouwer and G. M. Clemence, *Planets and Satellites*, ed. Kuiper and Middlehurst, p. 31, Chicago. 1961.

orbits

Eccentricity e [1, 3, 4]	Inclination to ecliptic i [1, 4]		Mean longitude of ascending node Ω [1, 4]		perihelion ϖ [1, 4]		Planet at 1950 Jan0·5 L [1]
	° ′ ″	″	° ′ ″	″	° ′ ″	″	° ′ ″
0·205 615 +0·000 020 T	7 00 10·6	+6·3 T	47 08 43	+4266 T	75 53 54	+5596 T	33 10 06
0·006 820 −0·000 048 T	3 23 37·1	+3·6 T	75 46 50	+3240 T	130 09 51	+5063 T	81 34 19
0·016 750 −0·000 042 T					101 13 11	+6180 T	99 35 18
0·093 312 +0·000 094 T	1 51 01·1	−2·3 T	48 47 12	+2786 T	334 13 6	+6626 T	144 20 07
0·048 332 +0·000 164 T	1 18 31·4	−20·5 T	99 26 20	+3640 T	12 43	+5800 T	316 09 34
0·055 890 −0·000 345 T	2 29 33·1	−14 T	112 47 10	+3140 T	91 05	+7050 T	158 18 13
0·047 1	0 46 21	+ 3 T	73 28 50	+1800 T	169 03	+5800 T	98 18 31
0·008 5	1 46 45	−34 T	130 40 50	+3950 T	43 52	+2400 T	194 57 08
0·249 4	17 10		109 00	+5000 T	224		165 36 09

elements

Mass (excluding satellites) ℳ	Density ρ	Surface gravity		Escape velocity [1]	Rotation period (equatorial) [1, 4]	Inclination of equator to orbit [1, 4]		Moment of inertia (C) [1, 12]
		attract-ive	equator centrifugal [1]					
⊕ = 1	g cm⁻³	cm s⁻²		km/s		°	′	ℳa²⊕
0·054	5·4	360	−0·0	4·2	88ᵈ			
0·815	5·1	870	−0·0	10·3		23 ?	[11]	
1·000	5·52	982	−3·39	11·2	23ʰ 56ᵐ 4ˢ·1	23	27	0·333 5
0·108	3·97	376	−1·71	5·0	24ʰ 37ᵐ 22ˢ·6	23	59	0·389
317·8	1·334	2 600	−225	61	9ʰ 50ᵐ·5**	3	05	0·25
95·2	0·684	1 120	−176	37	10ʰ 14ᵐ***	26	44	0·22
14·5	1·60	940	− 62	22	10ʰ 49ᵐ	97	55	0·23
17·2	2·25	1 500	− 28	25	15ʰ	28	48	0·29
0·8 ?	*				6ᵈ·39 [10]			

* Density of Pluto uncertain because of apparent discrepancy between radius and mass
** 9ʰ 55ᵐ·4 for latitude >12°
*** 10ʰ 38ᵐ for temperate zones

§ 67. Photometry of Planets and Satellites

$A = pq = $ Bond albedo = ratio of total light reflected from a sphere to total light incident on it.

$r = $ sun-planet distance in AU.

$\Delta = $ earth-planet distance in AU.

$\mathscr{R} = $ planet radius also in AU = unit distance semi-diameter in $''/206\ 265$.

$\alpha = $ phase angle = angle between sun and earth seen from planet.

$\phi(\alpha) = $ phase law = change of planet brightness with α, putting $\phi(0) = 1$.

$p = $ ratio of planet brightness at $\alpha = 0$ to brightness of perfectly diffusing disk with same position and apparent size as the planet. Then

$$\log p + \log \phi(\alpha) = 0\cdot4(m_\odot - m_{\text{planet}}) + 2 \log (r\Delta/\mathscr{R})$$

When q is unknown because the α range is small p is sometimes called the albedo.

$q = 2 \int_0^\pi \phi(\alpha) \sin \alpha \, d\alpha$ is a factor that represents the phase law. We have the following special cases

Lambert law (perfect diffusion)	$q = 1\cdot50$
Lommel-Seeliger law	$q = 1\cdot64$
Metallic reflection	$q = 4\cdot00$
$\phi(\alpha) = \frac{1}{2}(1 + \cos \alpha)$ (i.e. $\propto$ illuminated area)	$q = 2\cdot00$

$E = $ at maximum elongation ($\alpha = 90°$); for Mercury $18°$ to $28°$, for Venus $47°$ to $48°$.

$S = $ seen from the sun.

$O = $ at mean opposition   ($\alpha = 0°$).

$L = $ Saturnicentric ring longitude difference of sun and earth; i.e. the positive value of $(U' + \omega - U)$ in the *Nautical Almanac* prior to 1960; $0° < L < 6°$.

$B = $ Saturnicentric latitude of earth regarded as positive; $0° < B < 27°$.

$OM = $ at opposition, with L and $B = 0$.

$c = $ angle between polar axis of Eros and line of sight (the brightness of Eros becomes variable as c increases from zero; for minimum brightness add c term in parenthesis).

$B - V = $ colour index.

Photometry of planets and satellites

Planet Satellite	p	q [1,11]	A	m_v [1,11]	at	rΔ AU²	B − V [1,6,7,11]	Variation of magnitude m_v with phase, etc. [1] $m_v =$
								α, c, and L in degrees; r and Δ in AU
Mercury	0·096	0·61	0·059	− 0·2	E	0·357	+ 0·93	$-0{\cdot}21 + 5\log r\Delta + 0{\cdot}038\,\alpha - 0{\cdot}000\,34\,\alpha^2 + 0{\cdot}000\,002\,\alpha^3$
Venus [12]	0·85	1·0	0·85	− 4·22	E	0·500	+ 0·79	$-4{\cdot}3 + 5\log r\Delta + 0{\cdot}000\,9\,\alpha + 0{\cdot}000\,24\,\alpha^2 - 0{\cdot}000\,000\,6\,\alpha^3$
Earth [2]	0·38	1·07	0·40	− 3·80	S	1·000	+ 0·2	
Mars [3]	0·14	1·07	0·15	− 1·98	O	0·798	+ 1·41	$-1{\cdot}41 + 5\log r\Delta + 0{\cdot}014\,2\,\alpha \quad [0° < \alpha < 47°]$
Jupiter	0·41	1·4	0·58	− 2·50	O	21·9	+ 0·6	$-9{\cdot}1 + 5\log r\Delta + 0{\cdot}015\,\alpha$
Saturn [4, 8, 9]	0·44	1·3	0·57	+ 0·70	OM	81·6	+ 0·9	$-8{\cdot}8 + 5\log r\Delta + 0{\cdot}044\,L - 2{\cdot}6\sin B + 1{\cdot}2\sin^2 B$
Uranus [4]	0·56	1·4	0·80	+ 5·51	O	349	+ 0·55	$-7{\cdot}2 + 5\log r\Delta + 0{\cdot}001\,0\,\alpha,\ \text{variable}$
Neptune [4]	0·51	1·4	0·71	+ 7·85	O	876	+ 0·43	$-6{\cdot}9 + 5\log r\Delta + 0{\cdot}001\,\alpha$
Pluto [5]	0·14	1·1	0·15	+ 14·87	O	1 521	+ 0·80	$-1{\cdot}2 + 5\log r\Delta$
Ceres	0·11	0·26	0·028	+ 7·0	O	4·89	+ 0·6	$+3{\cdot}6 + 5\log r\Delta + 0{\cdot}05\,\alpha \pm 0{\cdot}02$
Pallas	0·13	0·39	0·053	+ 7·9	O	4·90	+ 0·2	$+4{\cdot}5 + 5\log r\Delta + 0{\cdot}04\,\alpha \pm 0{\cdot}07$
Juno	0·30	0·48	0·145	+ 8·7	O	4·46	+ 0·5	$+5{\cdot}4 + 5\log r\Delta + 0{\cdot}03\,\alpha \pm 0{\cdot}08$
Vesta	0·42	0·65	0·27	+ 6·2	O	3·21	+ 0·7	$+3{\cdot}7 + 5\log r\Delta + 0{\cdot}03\,\alpha \pm 0{\cdot}08$
Eros	0·30	0·76	0·23	+ 9·9	O	0·668	+ 1·0	$+10{\cdot}8 + 5\log r\Delta + 0{\cdot}02\,\alpha + 0{\cdot}004c + (0{\cdot}010c)$
Moon [10]	0·110	0·62	0·068	− 12·70	O	0·002 58	+ 0·88	$+0{\cdot}25 + 5\log r\Delta + 0{\cdot}027\,\alpha \quad [\text{for } \alpha < 70°]$
Io [10]	0·92	0·8	0·73	+ 5·52	O	21·9	+ 1·0	$-1{\cdot}18 + 5\log r\Delta + 0{\cdot}016\,\alpha$
Europa ,,	0·85	0·8	0·68	+ 5·67	O	21·9	+ 0·85	$-1{\cdot}03 + 5\log r\Delta + 0{\cdot}019\,\alpha$
Ganymede ,,	0·49	0·7	0·34	+ 5·18	O	21·9	+ 0·78	$-1{\cdot}52 + 5\log r\Delta + 0{\cdot}023\,\alpha$
Callisto ,,	0·26	0·5	0·13	+ 6·20	O	21·9	+ 0·75	$-0{\cdot}50 + 5\log r\Delta + 0{\cdot}046\,\alpha$

Moon's phase law [1]

α	$m_\alpha - m_0$	$\phi(\alpha)$	α	$m_\alpha - m_0$	$\phi(\alpha)$	α	$m_\alpha - m_0$	$\phi(\alpha)$
0°	0·00	1·000	50°	1·35	0·288	110°	3·48	0·041
5	0·08	0·929	60	1·62	0·225	120	3·93	0·027
10	0·23	0·809	70	1·91	0·172	130	4·44	0·017
20	0·51	0·625	80	2·24	0·127	140	5·07	0·009
30	0·79	0·483	90	2·63	0·089	150	5·9	0·004
40	1·06	0·377	100	3·04	0·061	160	7·5	0·001

[1] *A.Q.* **1**, § 84.
[2] E. K. DZHASYBEKOVA, et al., *A. Zh.*, **37**, 131, 1960; *Sov. A.*, **4**, 125.
[3] R. v. D. R. WOOLLEY (et al.), *M.N.*, **113**, 531, 1953; **115**, 57, 1955.
[4] W. M. SINTON, *Lowell Obs.*, IV, Bull. 95, p. 93, 1959.
[5] M. F. WALKER and R. HARDIE, *P.A.S.P.*, **67**, 224, 1955.
[6] I. GROENEVELD, et al., *Ap. J.*, **120**, 529, 547, 551, 1954.
[7] U. V. SHARNOV, *A. Zh.*, **30**, 532, 1953.
[8] A. V. NIELSEN, F. M. HOLBORN, and J. H. ROBINSON, *J.B.A.A.*, **65**, 283, 284, 1955; **66**, 24, 1956.
[9] H. L. GICLAS, *A.J.*, **59**, 128, 1954.
[10] E. A. MOISEENKO, *A. News. Let.*, No. 81, 40, 1956.
[11] D. L. HARRIS, *Planets and Satellites*, ed. Kuiper and Middlehurst, p. 272, Chicago, 1961.
[12] C. F. KNUCKLES, M. K. and W. M. SINTON, *Lowell Ob. Bull.*, No. 115, **5**, 153, 1961.

§ 68. Satellites

The inclinations of satellite orbits are complicated by precession around the 'proper plane' which is normally close to the planet's equator. Because of the variations only approximate values can be quoted. Inclinations are measured from the planet's equator. R = retrograde with respect to the planet's rotation and equatorial plane (the satellites of Uranus are retrograde with respect to the ecliptic).

Saturn ring system [1, 2]

Radius (limiting values quoted)

	137×10^3 km
Outer A ring: moderately bright	
	120×10^3 km
Cassini division: dark	
	116×10^3 km
Main B ring: very bright	
	90×10^3 km
Gap: dark	
	89×10^3 km
Crape or C ring: faint	
	72×10^3 km
Planet radius (equatorial)	60×10^3 km

Thickness of rings [3] $\simeq 10$ km

Mass of rings [1, 4] $\simeq 5 \times 10^{-5} \times$ mass of Saturn
     or perhaps much less [3].

Reciprocal mass of total satellites

     Jupiter   5 110 (Jupiter)$^{-1}$
     Saturn   4 020 (Saturn)$^{-1}$
     Uranus   9 900 (Uranus)$^{-1}$

Total mass of all satellites $= 7·35 \times 10^{26}$ g

Planet	Satellites	Distance from planet [1, 2, 5] 10³ km	Distance from planet [1, 2, 5] 10⁻³ AU	Distance from planet [1, 2, 5] at mean opp'n (° ′ ″)	Sidereal period [1, 2, 6] days	Synodic period (d h m)	Orbit incl. [1, 2, 7] °	Orbit eccentricity [1, 2, 7]	Radius [1, 5, 8, 9] km	Reciprocal mass [1, 2, 9] 1/planet	Mass 10²⁴ g	m_v at mean opp'n [1, 2, 5]
Earth	Moon	384	2·571		27·321 661	29 12 44		0·054 9	1 738	81·33	73·5	−12·7
Mars	1 Phobos	9	0·062 7	25	0·318 910	7 39	1·1	0·021	6	—		+11·5
	2 Deimos	23	0·157 0	1 02	1·262 441	1 06 21	1·6	0·002 8	3			+12·5
Jupiter	1 Io	422	2·819 6	2 18	1·769 138	1 18 29	0	small and vari-able	1 670	26 000	73	+5·5
	2 Europa	671	4·486 2	3 40	3·551 181	3 13 18	0		1 460	40 000	47·5	+5·8
	3 Ganymede	1 070	7·155 9	5 51	7·154 553	7 04 00	0		2 550	12 300	154	+5·1
	4 Callisto	1 883	12·586 5	10 18	16·689 018	16 18 05			2 360	20 000	95	+6·3
	5	181	1·207	59	0·498 179	11 57	0·4	0·003	70			+13
	6	11 470	76·70	1 02 43	250·59	264	28	0·158	50			+14
	7	11 740	78·47	1 04 11	259·7	276 10	26	0·206	10			+18
	8	23 500	157·20	2 08 35	737	630	33 R	0·40	10			+18·5
	9	23 700	158·5	2 09 30	758	645	25 R	0·27	8			+19
	10	11 850	79·21	1 04 40	255	272	28·5	0·135	7			+19
	11	22 560	150·83	2 03 24	692	596	16·5 R	0·207	8			+19
	12	21 200	141·7	1 55 50	631	551	33 R	0·16	6			+19
Saturn	1 Mimas	186	1·240 4	30	0·942 422	22 37	1·5	0·020 1	300	15 000 000	0·04	+12·1
	2 Enceladus	238	1·591 3	38	1·370 218	1 08 53	0·0	0·004 4	300	8 000 000	0·07	+11·7
	3 Tethys	295	1·970 0	48	1·887 802	1 21 19	1·1	0·0	500	870 000	0·65	+10·6
	4 Dione	377	2·523 0	1 01	2·736 915	2 17 42	0·0	0·002 2	500	550 000	1·0	+10·7
	5 Rhea	527	3·523	1 25	4·517 50	4 12 28	0·3	0·001 0	700	250 000	2·3	+10·0
	6 Titan	1 222	8·166 4	3 17	15·945 452	15 23 15	0·3	0·029 0	2 440	4 150	137	+8·3
	7 Hyperion	1 481	9·893	3 59	21·276 66	21 07 39	0·5	0·104	200		0·31	+14·5
	8 Iapetus	3 560	23·798	9 35	79·330 82	79 22 05	14·7	0·028 3	500	5 000 000	1	+11
	9 Phoebe	12 950	86·58	34 52	550·41	523 15 36	30 R	0·163 3	100	500 000		+14
Uranus	1 Ariel	192	1·282 0	14	2·520 38	2 12 30	0	0·003	300	70 000	1·2	+14
	2 Umbriel	267	1·785 9	20	4·144 18	4 03 28	0	0·004	200	170 000	0·5	+15
	3 Titania	438	2·930 3	33	8·705 88	8 17 00	0	0·002 4	500	20 000	4	+13·8
	4 Oberon	586	3·918 7	44	13·463 26	13 11 16	0	0·000 7	400	34 000	2·6	+14·0
	5 Miranda	128	0·85	10	1·414			< 0·01	100	1 000 000	0·1	+16·9
Neptune	1 Triton	353	2·363 5	17	5·876 83	5 21 03	20·1 R	0·0	2 000	750	140	+13·6
	2 Nereid	5 600	37	4 30	360		27·5	0·76	100	3 000 000	0·03	+19·5

[1] *A.Q.* **1**, § 85.
[2] *Handbook B.A.A.*, 1960+.
[3] M. S. BOBROV, *A. Zh.*, **33**, 161, 904, 1956.
[4] Y. KOZAI, *P.A.S. Jap.*, **9**, 1, 1957.
[5] G. H. HERBIG and C. E. WORLEY, *A.S.P. Leaflet*, No. 325 revised, 1960.
[6] *Astronomical Ephemeris.*
[7] O. GINGERICH, *Sky and Tel.*, **18**, 376, 1959.
[8] A. DOLLFUS, *C.R.*, **238**, 1475, 1954.
[9] D. BROUWER and G. M. CLEMENCE, *Planets and Satellites*, ed. Kuiper and Middlehurst, p. 31, Chicago, 1961.

§ 69. Moon

Mean distance from earth $\qquad$ = 384 404 ± 2 km

  Extreme range $\qquad$ = 356 400 to 406 700 km

Mean equatorial horizontal parallax, $\pi_{\mathbb{C}}$ [1, 2, 3]

$\qquad\qquad\qquad\qquad$ = 3 422″·62

$\qquad$ 206 264·8 sin $\pi_{\mathbb{C}}$ = 3 422·46

Eccentricity of orbit $\qquad$ = 0·054 90

Inclination of orbit to ecliptic [4] $\qquad$ = 5° 8′ 43″

  oscillating ± 9′ with period of 173 d.

Sidereal period (fixed stars) [5] $\qquad$ = (27·321 661 40 + 0·000 000 16 T) ephem. days

  where T is in centuries from 1900·0.

Synodical month (new moon to new moon) [1]

$\qquad\qquad\qquad\qquad$ = (29·530 588 2 + 0·000 000 16 T) ephem. days

Tropical month (equinox to equinox) [5]

$\qquad\qquad\qquad\qquad$ = (27·321 582 14 + 0·000 000 13 T) ephem. days

Anomalistic month (perigee to perigee) [1]

$\qquad\qquad\qquad\qquad$ = (27·554 550 5 − 0·000 000 4 T) days

Nodical month (node to node) $\qquad$ = 27·212 220 days

Period of moon's node (nutation period) (retrograde)

$\qquad\qquad\qquad\qquad$ = 18·61 tropical years

Period of rotation of moon's perigee (direct) [7]

$\qquad\qquad\qquad\qquad$ = 8·85 years

Moon's sidereal mean daily motion [5]

$\qquad\qquad\qquad\qquad$ = 47 434″·889 871 − 0″·000 284 T

Mean transit interval $\qquad$ = $24^{\text{h}}50^{\text{m}}·47$

Main periodic terms in the moon's motion [7]

  Principal elliptic term in longitude = 22 639″ sin g

  Principal elliptic term in latitude = 18 461″ sin u

  Evection $\qquad\qquad\qquad\qquad$ = 4 586″ sin $(2D-g)$

  Variation $\qquad\qquad\qquad\qquad$ = 2 370″ sin $2D$

  Annual inequality $\qquad\qquad$ = − 669″ sin g'

  Parallactic inequality $\qquad\quad$ = − 125″ sin D

$\qquad$ where $\quad g$ = moon's mean anomalie

$\qquad\qquad\qquad g'$ = sun's mean anomalie

$\qquad\qquad\qquad D$ = moon's age

$\qquad\qquad\qquad u$ = distance of mean moon from ascending node

Physical libration [6]	in longitude	in latitude
Displacement (selenocentric)	$\pm 0°\cdot02$	$\pm 0°\cdot04$
Period	1 y	6 y

Optical libration [6]		
Displacement (selenocentric)	$\pm 7°\cdot6$	$\pm 6°\cdot7$
Period	approximately sidereal lunar	

Surface area of moon at some time visible from earth

$$= 59\%$$

Moon radius, $(b+c)/2$

$$= 1\ 737\cdot9 \text{ km}$$
$$= 0\cdot272\ 5 \text{ earth equatorial radius}$$

Moon mass

$$\mathscr{M}_{\mathbb{C}} = (7\cdot349 \pm 0\cdot007) \times 10^{25} \text{ g}$$
$$= \mathscr{M}_{\oplus}/81\cdot33$$

Moon semi-diameter at mean distance

   (geocentric) $= 15'\ 32''\cdot6$

   (topocentric, zenith) $= 15'\ 48''\cdot3$

Moon volume $= 2\cdot199 \times 10^{25} \text{ cm}^3$

Moon mean density $= 3\cdot34 \text{ g cm}^{-3}$

Surface gravity $= 162\cdot0 \text{ cm s}^{-2}$

Surface escape velocity $= 2\cdot38 \text{ km/s}$

Inclination of lunar equator [4]

   to ecliptic $= 1°\ 32'\ 40''$

   to orbit $= 6°\ 41'$

(Radius directed towards earth) − (polar radius) [8, 13]

$$a - c = 1\cdot09 \text{ km}$$

(Radius directed towards earth) − (radius in direction of orbit) [8, 13]

$$a - b = 0\cdot36 \text{ km}$$

Moment of inertia (about rotation axis)

$$C = 0\cdot397\ \mathscr{M}_{\mathbb{C}} b^2$$

Moment of inertia differences [4, 13], $(\alpha + \gamma = \beta)$

$$\alpha = \frac{C-B}{A} = 0\cdot000\ 420$$

$$\beta = \frac{C-A}{B} = 0\cdot000\ 628$$

$$\gamma = \frac{B-A}{C} = 0\cdot000\ 208$$

where A axis is towards earth, B along orbit, C towards pole.

11—A.Q.

Brightness temperature T of moon at infra-red and radio wavelengths λ [8, 9, 10].
T_0 = mean T at centre of disk. $T_1/(1+2\delta+2\delta^2)^{1/2}$ = variation of T with lunar cycle. T_1 is intended to represent surface temperature variation which is not actually measured by radio methods. δ depends on thermal and electrical properties of the lunar surface [9].

ϕ = phase lag between T and reflected light.

λ	$10\ \mu$	1 cm	10 cm	100 cm
T_0	$260\ °K$	$220\ °K$	$280\ °K$	$240\ °K$
$T_1/(1+2\delta+2\delta^2)^{1/2}$	$130\ °K$	$44\ °K$	$2\ °K$	$0\ °K$
ϕ [11, 12]	$0°$	$43°$	–	–
δ [9]	0	2	20	–

Flow of heat through moon's surface [9]
$$= 2 \times 10^{-7}\ \text{cal cm}^{-2}\ \text{s}^{-1}$$

Lunar photometric data: see § 67 [14].

Moon's atmospheric density [8] $< 10^{-12}$ earth sea-level atmosphere.

Number of maria and craters on the lunar hemisphere (readily visible part) with diameters greater than d km [8] $= 250\ 000/d^{1\cdot 8}$
This rule extends from the largest mare ($d \simeq 1\ 000$ km) to the smallest completely identifiable craters ($d \simeq 3$ km)

[1] *A.Q.* **1**, § 86.
[2] R. H. BRUTON, CRAIG, and YAPLEE, *A.J.*, **64**, 325, 1959.
[3] S. HERRICK, BAKER, and HILTON, *U.C.L.A. Paper*, No. 24, 1958.
[4] H. JEFFREYS, *M.N.*, **122**, 421, 1961.
[5] G. M. CLEMENCE, *A.J.*, **53**, 169, 1948.
[6] *Astronomical Ephemeris.*
[7] *Landolt-Börnstein Tables*, **3**, p. 83, 1962.
[8] G. FIELDER, *Structure of the Moon's Surface*, Pergamon, 1961; and private communications.
[9] J. E. BALDWIN, *M.N.*, **122**, 513, 1961.
[10] R. H. GARSTANG, *J.B.A.A.*, **68**, 155, 1958.
[11] A. E. SALOMONOVICH, *A.Zh.*, **35**, 129, 1958; *Sov. A.*, **2**, 112.
[12] J. L. PAWSEY and R. N. BRACEWELL, *Radio Astronomy*, p. 280, Oxford, 1955.
[13] R. M. L. BAKER and M. W. MAKEMSON, *Astrodynamics*, p. 96, Academic Press, 1960.
[14] V. G. FESSENKOV, *Physics and Astronomy of the Moon*, ed. Kopal, p. 99, Academic Press, 1962.

§ 70. Surface Condition of Planets

T_S = temperature at the visible surface near the subsolar point of the illuminated hemisphere (mainly from infra-red measurements).

T_D = temperature of dark side.

T_R = radio temperature of illuminated hemisphere (cm range).

T_b = equilibrium temperature of an insulated black surface with normal directed towards the sun. This is the highest temperature that a solid black or grey body can attain as a result of solar radiation. The equilibrium temperature of a perfectly conducting black sphere is $T_b/\sqrt{2}$.

P = atmosphere pressure at lowest visible level.

Surface temperature and pressure

Planet or satellite	Lowest visible surface	T_S [1, 4, 14]	T_D	T_R [6, 13, 14]	T_b [1]	P
		°K	°K	°K	°K	mm-Hg
Mercury	Solid	611			633	
Venus [2, 3, 12, 16]	Cloud	250	240	610	464	70
Earth	Solid	295			394	760
Mars [5]	Solid	270		220	319	70
Jupiter	Cloud	135		150	173	
Saturn	Cloud	125		110	127	
Uranus	Cloud	103			90	
Neptune	Cloud	108			72	
Pluto					63	
Moon	Solid	380	120	230	394	0
Jupiter, 1 to 4	Solid				173	
Titan					127	

Components of planet atmospheres

The amounts are expressed in cm at S.T.P. gas above the visible surface.

D means undetectable gas is probably a dominating component.

P means present but with no quantitative estimate.

Planet or satellite	H_2	Ar	N_2	O_2	CO_2	CH_4	NH_3	H_2O	N_2O_4 [10]	Total
	atmo-cm ($\equiv 2 \cdot 69 \times 10^{19}$ molecules cm^{-2})									
Mercury										2 000
Venus [12]			?	< 200	50 000	< 20	< 4	< 100		200 000
Earth	< 1	7 400	625 000	168 000	200	2	0	2 000	< 1	799 000
Mars [7, 8, 9]			2 000	178 000	< 200	420	< 10	< 2	10	< 1	180 000
Jupiter [11]	D[15]					15 000	700		P	
Saturn	D					35 000	< 250			
Uranus	2×10^6					150 000				
Neptune	D					250 000				
Pluto										
Moon										0
J. 1 to 4						< 200	< 40			
Titan						20 000	< 300			

[1] *A.Q.* **1**, § 87.
[2] E. PETTIT and S. B. NICHOLSON, *P.A.S.P.*, **67**, 293, 1955.
[3] J. W. CHAMBERLAIN and G. P. KUIPER, *Ap. J.*, **124**, 399, 1956.
[4] W. M. SINTON, *P.A.S. Leaflet* No. 345, 1958.
[5] F. GIFFORD, *Ap. J.*, **123**, 154, 1956.
[6] C. H. MAYER, McCULLOUGH, and SLOANAKER, *Ap. J.*, **127**, 1, 11, 1958.
[7] G. DE VAUCOULEURS, Liege Symp. on *Molecules*, p. 161, 1957.
[8] E. J. ÖPIK, *J. Geoph. Res.*, **65**, 3057, 1960.
[9] C. SAGAN, *A.J.*, **66**, 52, 1961.

[10] W. M. SINTON, *P.A.S.P.*, **73**, 125, 1961.
[11] C. C. KIESS, CORLISS, and KIESS, *Ap. J.*, **132**, 221, 1960.
[12] L. D. KAPLAN, *Planet Space Sci.*, **8**, 23, 1961.
[13] G. B. FIELD, *J. Geoph. Res.*, **64**, 1169, 1959
[14] C. H. MAYER, *Planets and Satellites*, ed. Kuiper and Middlehurst, p. 442, Chicago, 1961.
[15] W. A. BAUM and A. D. CODE, *A.J.*, **58**, 108, 1953.
[16] F. D. DRAKE, *Pub. Nat. Radio A. Ob.*, **1**, 165, 1962.

§ 71. Asteroids or Minor Planets

Number of minor planets with determined orbits (numbered planets) [4]
$$= 1\ 647 \text{ (in 1962)}$$
Median semi-major axis of orbits [1]
$$\bar{a} = 2 \cdot 77 \text{ AU}$$
99·8% are between $a = 1 \cdot 524$ (Mars) and $a = 5 \cdot 203$ (Jupiter).

Median eccentricity $\qquad \bar{e} = 0 \cdot 14$

Median inclination to the ecliptic $\quad \bar{i} = 8° \cdot 6$

Median period $\qquad = 4 \cdot 6$ years

94% between 3·3 and 6·0 years with conspicuous gaps at 4·0, 4·8, and 5·9 years, i.e. $\frac{1}{3}$, $\frac{2}{5}$, and $\frac{1}{2}$ Jupiter's period.

Photographic magnitudes are used for statistical studies of asteroids [5].

Median asteroid colour index [6, 7]
$$\overline{B-V} = 0 \cdot 86$$

The absolute magnitude of an asteroid (denoted g in [4]) is the observed magnitude m_{pg} adjusted to unit solar and terrestrial distance (r and $\Delta = 1$)[5].

Relation between magnitude, number, radius, and mass of asteroids [4, 10]

Range in m_{pg} at $r\Delta = 1$	4 5	5 6	6 7	7 8	8 9	9 10	10 11	11 12	12 13	13 14	14 15	15 16	16 17	17 18
% of numbered planets	0·1	0·1	0·4	1·5	5·3	13	20	23	19	12	4·7	0·7	0·3	0·1
log (actual number)	0·3	0·0	0·8	1·4	1·9									
log (estimated number)						2·3	2·7	3·1	3·5	3·8	4·2	4·6	5·0	5·3
Radius in km	265	220	140	70	44	28	18	11	7	4·4	2·8	1·8	1·1	0·7
Total mass in 10^{22} g	68	16	28	16	13	8·3	5·0	3·0	1·8	1·1	0·6	0·4	0·2	0·1

Total mass of asteroids $\qquad = 1 \cdot 7 \times 10^{24}$ g
Density (probable) $\qquad = 3 \cdot 5$ g cm^{-3}

Selected minor planets

Number and name [4]	Radius [1, 3, 8]	Mass [1, 3, 8]	m_{pg} at $r\Delta=1$ [4]	Rot. period [2, 6, 9]		Orbital data Period $\quad a \quad\mid\quad e \quad\mid\quad i$ [4]			
	km	g		h	m	d	AU		°
1 Ceres	350	60×10^{22}	4·0	9	05	1 681	2·767	0·079	10·6
2 Pallas	230	18×10^{22}	5·1			1 684	2·767	0·235	34·8
3 Juno	110	2×10^{22}	6·3	7	13	1 594	2·670	0·256	13·0
4 Vesta	190	10×10^{22}	4·2	5	20	1 325	2·361	0·088	7·1
6 Hebe	110	20×10^{21}	6·6	7	17	1 380	2·426	0·203	14·8
7 Iris	100	15×10^{21}	6·7	7	07	1 344	2·385	0·230	5·5
10 Hygiea	160	60×10^{21}	6·4	18?		2 042	3·151	0·099	3·8
15 Eunomia	140	40×10^{21}	6·2	6	05	1 569	2·645	0·185	11·8
16 Psyche	140	40×10^{21}	6·8	4	18	1 826	2·923	0·135	3·1
51 Nemausa	40	9×10^{20}	8·6			1 330	2·366	0·065	9·9
433 Eros	7	5×10^{18}	12·3	5	16	642	1·458	0·223	10·8
511 Davida	130	3×10^{22}	7·0			2 072	3·182	0·177	15·7
1566 Icarus	0·7	5×10^{15}	17·7			408	1·077	0·827	23·0
1620 Geographos	1·5	5×10^{16}	15·9			507	1·244	0·335	13·3
Apollo	0·5	2×10^{15}	18			662	1·486	0·566	6·4
Adonis	0·15	5×10^{13}	21			1 008	1·969	0·779	1·5
Hermes	0·3	4×10^{14}	19			535	1·290	0·475	4·7

Radius of planet $\mathscr{R}$ $\qquad\log \mathscr{R} = 2\cdot95 - \tfrac{1}{2}\log p - 0\cdot2 m_{pg} \quad$ (at $r\Delta = 1$)

$$[\mathscr{R} \text{ in km}, \ p = \text{albedo factor}, \ \S 67]$$

The table is based on $p = 0\cdot16$.

[1] *A.Q.* **1**, § 88.
[2] G. H. Herbig and C. E. Worley, *A.S.P. Leaflet*, No. 325 Revised, 1960.
[3] J. Ashbrook, *Sky and Tel.*, **17**, 74, 1957.
[4] *Ephemeris of Minor Planets*, Acad. U.S.S.R., Annual.
[5] T. Gehrels, *Ap. J.*, **125**, 550, 1957.
[6] I. van Houten-Groeneveld and C. J. van Houten, *Ap. J.*, **127**, 253, 1958.
[7] M. Kitamura, *P.A.S. Jap.*, **11**, 79, 1959.
[8] K. Stumpff, *A.N.*, **276**, 118, 1948.
[9] I. I. Ahmed, *Ap. J.*, **120**, 551, 1954.
[10] T. Kiang, *M.N.*, **123**, 509, 1962.

CHAPTER 8

INTERPLANETARY MATTER

§ 72. Comets

RATE of discovery of comets [1, 2]:

New nearly parabolic	3 per year
New periodic	1·0 per year
Periodic, predicted, and recovered	2·5 per year
Comets visible annually	2

Periodic comets

The table gives the periodic comets that have appeared at least three times and are expected to be recovered on next appearance. The orbital elements are for the equinox 1950·0 [2]. P = period, ω = angle from ascending node to perihelion, Ω = longitude of ascending node, i = inclination, e = eccentricity, q = perihelion distance, and a = semi-major axis. Name abbreviations are: Skj. = Skjellerup, W. = Wachmann, Z. = Zinner, Schwass. = Schwassmann.

Comet	Recent perihelion date, and return number		P	ω	Ω	i	e	q	a
			y	°	°	°		AU	AU
Encke	1961·10	46	3·30	185	335	12·4	0·847	0·339	2·21
Grigg-Skj.	1957·09	9	4·90	356	215	17·6	0·704	0·855	2·89
Temple (2)	1957·10	12	5·28	191	119	12·5	0·545	1·38	3·0
Kopff	1958·05	8	6·3	160	120	5	0·556	1·51	3·4
Giacobini-Z.	1959·82	7	6·5	172	196	30·8	0·72	0·94	3·5
Schwass.-W. (2)	1961·68	6	6·53	358	126	3·7	0·384	2·155	3·50
Wirtanen	1961·29	3	6·67	343	86	13·4	0·543	1·62	3·55
Reinmuth (2)	1960·90	3	6·7	45	296	7·0	0·46	1·93	3·6
Brooks (2)	1960·46	10	6·75	197	177	5·6	0·50	1·76	3·6
Finlay	1960·67	7	6·85	321	42	3·5	0·705	1·07	3·6
Borrelly	1960·45	7	7·01	351	76	31·1	0·604	1·450	3·67
Faye	1955·17	14	7·42	201	206	10·6	0·565	1·655	3·80
Whipple	1955·91	4	7·42	190	189	10·2	0·356	2·450	3·80
Reinmuth (1)	1958·23	4	7·67	13	124	8·4	0·478	2·03	3·90
Oterma	1958·44	Annual	7·89	355	155	4·0	0·144	3·39	3·96
Schaumasse	1960·29	6	8·18	52	86	12·0	0·705	1·195	4·05
Wolf (1)	1959·22	10	8·42	161	204	27·3	0·396	2·505	4·15
Comas Solá	1961·26	5	8·57	40	63	13·5	0·577	1·775	4·19
Väisälä (1)	1960·35	3	10·5	44	135	11·3	0·635	1·745	4·79
Schwass.-W. (1)	1957·36	Annual	16·1	356	322	9·5	0·132	5·53	6·4
Neujmin (1)	1948·96	3	17·9	347	347	15·0	0·774	1·54	6·8
Crommelin	1956·80	6	27·9	196	250	28·9	0·919	0·744	9·2
Olbers	1956·45	3	69·6	65	85	44·6	0·930	1·18	16·8
Pons-Brooks	1954·39	3	70·9	199	255	74·1	0·955	0·775	17·2
Halley	1910·30	29	76·2	112	57	162·3	0·967	0·587	17·8

Short period comets. Period, $P < 100$ y. At any epoch about 40 such comets are bright enough to be detectable as they come to perihelion.

Median period	$= 7$ y
Median semi-major axis	$= 3 \cdot 6$ AU
Median perihelion distance (influenced by visibility)	
	$= 1 \cdot 3$ AU
Median eccentricity	$= 0 \cdot 56$ (lowest $= 0 \cdot 135$)
Median inclination	$= 15°$ ($11°$ for $P < 10$ y)

Median absolute magnitude m_0 of *observed* periodic comets (i.e. m at $r = 1$, $\Delta = 1$ where r and Δ are the sun and earth distances from the comet in AU)

First appearance	$m_0 = 9$
Last appearance	$m_0 = 10$

Orbital direction. Nearly all periodic comets are direct, i.e. $i < 90°$ (Halley's comet is an exception).

Mean number of apparitions $= 7$

However very few well established and regular periodic comets have finally disappeared.

Nearly parabolic comets. Period, $P > 100$ y.

Median perihelion distance (influenced by comet visibility)
$$= 1 \cdot 0 \text{ AU}$$

Median absolute magnitude for observed near-parabolic comets (i.e. m at $r = 1$, $\Delta = 1$) $= 7$

Orbital orientation is random.

Decrease in $1/a$ between distant comet referred to centre of gravity of the solar system and total mass, and near-perihelion comet referred to the sun
$$= 0 \cdot 000 \ 63 \text{ AU}^{-1}$$

Near-perihelion orbits referred to the sun are sometimes hyperbolic, i.e. $1/a$ is negative.

Physical elements

Diameter of head or coma (varies irregularly with r) [9]

r in AU	$0 \cdot 3$	$0 \cdot 5$	$1 \cdot 0$	$2 \cdot 0$	$3 \cdot 0$
Diameter in 10^3 km	20	100	200	100	30

Diameter of central condensation	$\simeq 2 \ 000$ km
Diameter of nucleus	$\simeq 10$ km
Length of tail visible to eye	$\simeq 10 \times 10^6$ km,
	up to 150×10^6 km in special cases
Solar distance at which tail appears	$\simeq 1 \cdot 7$ AU

Mass $\mathcal{M}$ of comet of absolute magnitude m_0 [3, 4]
$$\log (\mathcal{M} \text{ in g}) = 21 - 0 \cdot 4 \, m_0$$

Absolute magnitudes of comets m_0 are listed in [5] (where $H_{10} \simeq m_0$).

Change of magnitude with solar and terrestrial distances r and Δ [1, 6]

$$m = m_0 + 5 \log \Delta + 2 \cdot 5\, n \log r$$
$$n = 4 \cdot 2 \pm 1 \cdot 5$$

n is not necessarily constant for any comet.

Atoms, molecules and ions observed in comets [7]

Comet heads	Comet tails
Na	
C_2, C_3, CN, CH, NH, OH, NH_2	CN
OH^+, CH^+	N_2^+, CO^+, OH^+, CO_2^+

Diameter of dust particles in comet tail (probably metallic) [3]

$$\simeq 0 \cdot 6\,\mu$$

[1] A.Q. **1**, § 89.
[2] J. G. PORTER, Catalogue of Cometary Orbits, Mem. B.A.A., **39**, No. 3, 1961.
[3] W. LILLER, Ap. J., **132**, 867, 1960.
[4] B. VORONTSOV-VELYAMINOV, Ap. J., **104**, 226, 1946.
[5] S. K. VSESSVIATSKY, A. Zh., **33**, 516, 1956.
[6] A. HRUŠKA, B.A. Czech., 8, 10, 1957.
[7] P. SWINGS and L. HASER, Atlas of Representative Cometary Spectra, Liège.

§ 73. Meteors and Space Particles

The absolute visual magnitude of a meteor, M_v, is the observed magnitude corrected to the zenith and to a height of 100 km. This magnitude is often used as an index relating to mass and size of particles that are too small to form visible meteors.

Relation between M_v and number α of electrons per cm in meteor trail (faint meteors) [2, 3]

$$M_v = 35 \cdot 5 - 2 \cdot 5 \log \alpha_z - \delta M$$

where $\alpha_z = \alpha$ corrected to vertical fall, and δM is a correction depending on meteor velocity v as follows:

$$v = 20 \qquad 40 \qquad 60 \qquad \text{km/s}$$
$$\delta M = 1 \cdot 9 \qquad 0 \cdot 7 \qquad 0 \cdot 0$$

$\mathcal{M}, a$ = mass and radius of particles
N = space density of particles at 1 AU from sun;
       subscripts $_b$ = larger or brighter than given value,
              $_m$ = per magnitude range,
              $_s$ = extra component of slow particles near to the earth [12].

$n \simeq \frac{1}{4} vN$ = rate of fall of same particles onto a horizontal surface.

$$n = 1 \cdot 10 \times 10^{28} vN \quad [N \text{ in cm}^{-3}, n \text{ in particles per day over}$$
$$\text{whole earth, } v \text{ in km/s}]$$

Density of meteoric material ρ

ρ (meteorites)	= 3 to 8 g cm^{-3} (see § 64)
ρ (meteoroids)	= 0·05 g cm^{-3} [4].

The argument for the low density of meteoroids is strong [4], nevertheless a compromise $\rho = 1$ has been used for conversion of the data in the table.

Mean geocentric velocity of observed meteors

$$\bar{v} = 40 \text{ km/s}.$$

However a value of 30 km/s has been used for data conversion to allow for less visible slow meteors.

Relations between M, 𝓜, a, α, N, and n

The data quoted are an attempt at a compromise between studies of the corona [5, 6], zodiacal light [6, 9], meteors [2, 4, 7, 8], spherule deposits [2, 13], and artificial satellite observations [2, 10, 12, 14].

	M_v	−10	−5	0	5	10	15	20	25	30
log M	in g	+3·9	+1·9	−0·1	−2·1	−4·1	−6·1	−8·1	−10·1	−12·1
log a	in cm	+0·9	+0·3	−0·3	−0·9	−1·5	−2·2	−2·9	−3·5	−4·2
log α	in cm⁻¹				12·0	10·0	8·0	6·0	4·0	2·0
log N_b	in cm⁻³	−29·0	−26·5	−24·0	−21·6	−19·2	−16·8	−14·9	−13·7	−13·0
log n_b	in d⁻¹ earth⁻¹	0·5	3·0	5·5	7·9	10·3	12·7	14·6	15·8	16·5
log n_{bs}	in d⁻¹ earth⁻¹							16·2	18·3	20
log n_m	in d⁻¹ earth⁻¹ m⁻¹	0·5	3·0	5·5	7·9	10·4	12·7	14·4	15·5	15·9
log n_{ms}	in d⁻¹ earth⁻¹							16·2	18·3	20
log $n_m\mathcal{M}$	in g d⁻¹ earth⁻¹ m⁻¹	4·4	4·9	5·4	5·8	6·3	6·6	6·3	5·4	3·8
log $n_{ms}\mathcal{M}$								8·1	8·2	8

Ratio (solar gravitational force)/(force of solar radiation pressure) for small black spheres [1]
$$= 1·7 \times 10^4 a\rho \quad [a \text{ in cm}, \rho \text{ in g cm}^{-3}]$$
where a is the radius and ρ the density of the spheres.

Poynting-Robertson effect [1]. Time taken for particles to move into sun
$$t = 7·0 \times 10^6 a\rho A q \text{ years}$$
$$[a \text{ in cm}, \rho \text{ in g cm}^{-3}, A \text{ and } q \text{ in AU}]$$
where A and q are the semi-major axis and perihelion distance of the initial particle orbit.

Hourly rate of meteors seen by one visual observer (mean non-shower night) [1]
$$\text{H.R.} = 10$$

Effective surface area visible to one observer
$$= 5\,000 \text{ km}^2 = 10^{-5} \text{ earth surface.}$$

Daily mass of meteoric (high speed) material reaching earth
$$= 9 \times 10^6 \text{ g} = 9 \text{ tons}$$

Daily mass of low-speed micrometeorite material reaching earth
$$= 1\,200 \times 10^6 \text{ g} = 1\,200 \text{ tons}$$

It is uncertain whether the data can be interpreted as a high speed and a low speed component [4].

Space density of small particles some distance from the earth (i.e. excluding slow particles orbiting the earth) $= 3 \times 10^{-23} \text{ g cm}^{-3}$

Meteor surface temperature at maximum [1]
$$= 3\,000 \text{ °K}$$

Colour index of meteors [15, 16]
$$C = -1·3$$

$C \simeq -1·8$ for $M_v > 0$ and $\simeq -1·0$ for $M_v < 0$ but this difference may be due to eye sensitivity characteristics.

Principal meteor streams [17, 18]

H.R. = hourly rate visible by a single observer for a zenith radiant in non-display years of the present century. v_G = geocentric velocity. The velocity v_E on entering the earth's atmosphere is given by $v_E = \sqrt{v_G^2 + 125}$ (in km/s). The orbital elements are Ω = longitude of ascending node, ω = angle from ascending node to perihelion, i = inclination of orbit to ecliptic, e = eccentricity, q = solar distance at perihelion = $(1-e) \times$ semi-major axis.

Stream	Maximum	Normal period of visibility	Radiant α (°)	Radiant δ (°)	Transit (h U.T.)	H.R.	v_G (km/s)	Ω (°)	ω (°)	i (°)	e	q (AU)	Associated comet
Quadrantids	Jan. 3	J. 2–4	231	+49	8.5	30	43	283	168	76	0.72	0.97	
Lyrids	Apr. 21	A. 20–22	271	+33	4.1	8	48	31	214	80	0.97	0.92	1861 I
η Aquarids	May 4	M. 2–7	336	0	7.6	10	64	44	85	161	0.93	0.49	Halley?
δ Aquarids	July 30	J. 20–A. 14	339	–10	2.2	15	42			30	0.98	0.06	
Perseids	Aug. 12	J. 29–A. 18	46	+58	5.7	40	60	138	152	115	0.96	0.94	1862 III
Draconids	Oct. 10	O. 10	265	+54	16.3		23	196	173	31	0.72	1.00	1933 III, G.–Z.
Orionids	Oct. 21	O. 16–26	95	+15	4.3	15	66	29		162	0.93	0.54	Halley?
Taurids	Nov. 4	O. 20–N. 25	53	+16	0.6	8	30			4	0.85	0.34	Encke
Andromedids	Nov. 10		23	+35	22.3		20	224	242		0.77	0.77	Biela
Leonids	Nov. 16	N. 14–19	152	+22	6.4	6	72	234	175	163	0.92	0.97	1866 I Temp.
Geminids	Dec. 13	D. 8–15	112	+32	2.0	50	36	260	325	26	0.90	0.14	
Ursids	Dec. 22	D. 19–23	210	+78	8.2	12	36	265	212	52	0.84	0.92	Tuttle
Permanent daytime streams [1]													
Arietids	June 8	M. 29–J. 17	44	+23	9.9	40	39	77		20	0.94	0.09	
ξ Perseids	June 9	J. 1–15	61	+23	11.0	30	29	78		1	0.79	0.34	
β Taurids	June 30	J. 23–J. 7	86	+19	11.2	20	31	277		6	0.85	0.34	Encke

Heights of meteors [1]

	Magnitude	Sporadic meteors	Shower meteors
Appearance	−4 to +4	98 km	114 km
Disappearance	−4	62 ,,	
	0	76 ,,	90 km
	+4	86 ,,	92 ,,

Composition of sporadic meteors   50% iron   50% stone

Composition of shower meteors   100% stone

Heliocentric velocity of a parabolic meteor at unit distance
$$= 42 \cdot 12 \text{ km/s}$$

Earth escape velocity (corresponding energy is added to that of a falling meteor)
$$= 11 \cdot 19 \text{ km/s}$$

[1] *A.Q.* **1**, §§ 90 and 91.
[2] T. R. KAISER, *Ann. de Geoph.*, **17**, 50, 1961.
[3] G. S. HAWKINS, *Ap. J.*, **124**, 311, 1956.
[4] F. L. WHIPPLE, *Harv. Repr.*, Nos. 494 and 495, 1958.
[5] H. C. VAN DE HULST, *Ap. J.*, **105**, 471, 1947.
[6] M. MINNAERT, Liège Symp. on *Solid Particles*, 15, 1955.
[7] F. G. WATSON, *Between the planets*, Harvard, 1956.
[8] A. C. B. LOVELL, *Meteor Astronomy*, Oxford, 1954.
[9] M. F. INGHAM, *M.N.*, **122**, 157, 1961.
[10] H. E. LA GOW and W. M. ALEXANDER, *I.G.Y. Bull.*, No. 38, 12, 1960.
[11] H. BROWN, *J. Geoph. Res.*, **65**, 1679, 1960; **66**, 1316, 1961.
[12] A. R. HIBBS, *J. Geoph. Res.*, **66**, 361, 1961.
[13] E. THIEL and R. A. SCHMIDT, *J. Geoph. Res.*, **66**, 307, 1961.
[14] M. DUBIN, *Planet and Space Sci.*, **2**, 121, 1960; *I.G.Y. Sat. Rep.*, No. 14, 157, 1961.
[15] L. G. JACCHIA, *A.J.*, **62**, 358, 1957.
[16] ZD. CEPLECHA, *B.A. Czech.*, **10**, 39, 1959.
[17] F. L. WHIPPLE and G. L. HAWKINS, *Handb. der Phys.*, **52**, 519, 1959.
[18] *B.A.A. Handbook*, p. 52, 1961.

§ 74. Zodiacal Light

Surface brightness and polarization of zodiacal light on its ecliptic axis

Elongation	Surface brightness [1, 2, 3]		Polarization [1, 2]
°	$10^{-14} \bar{B}_{\odot}$	$(m_v = 10) \text{ deg}^{-2}$	%
10	1 300	30 000	4
20	240	5 500	10
30	80	1 900	21
40	38	900	27
50	24	560	30
60	17	400	31
70	13	300	30
90	8·6	200	20
110	7·7	180	
130	7·0	160	
150	7·0	160	
170	7·7	180	
180 = Gegenschein	9·0	210	

Excess brightness of gegenschein above the zodiacal light bridge [4]
$$= 37 \ (m_{\mathrm{v}} = 10 \ \mathrm{stars})/\mathrm{deg}^2$$
Whole-$\frac{1}{2}$-width of gegenschein [4] $= 13°$

Colour of zodiacal light [2, 3, 4] is close to that of the sun. Detected differences do not appear systematic.

Whole-$\frac{1}{2}$-width of zodiacal light band [1, 3]

Elongation	30°	40°	60°	90°	180°
Whole-$\frac{1}{2}$-width	25°	28°	31°	42°	40°

Position of minimum sky intensity [1]
$$\mathrm{Elongation} = 180° \qquad \mathrm{Ecliptic \ latitude} = \pm 75°$$

Brightness near minimum [1]

Distance from minimum point	0°	10°	20°	30°	40°	50°
Brightness in $(m_{\mathrm{v}} = 10) \ \mathrm{deg}^{-2}$	40	44	55	68	82	100

There is some doubt whether this radiation is true zodiacal light.

Distribution of zodiacal light scattering material with solar distance [1, 5]

Radial distance from sun in AU	0·3	0·5	0·8	1·0	1·5
Relative density of material	3	2·3	1·4	1·0	0·3

Axis ratio of scattering material spheroid [1]
$$= 3·5$$

[1] *A.Q.* **1**, § 91.
[2] D. E. BLACKWELL and M. F. INGRAM, *M.N.*, **122**, 133, 1961.
[3] N. B. DIVARI and A. S. ASAAD, *A. Zh.*, **36**, 856, 1959; *Sov. A.*, **3**, 832.
[4] H. ELSÄSSER and H. SIEDENTOPF, *Z. Ap.*, **43**, 132, 1957.
[5] M. F. INGHAM, *M.N.*, **122**, 157, 1961.

CHAPTER 9

SUN

§ 75. Sun Dimensions

Sun radius $\qquad \mathscr{R}_\odot = (6{\cdot}959\ 8 \pm 0{\cdot}000\ 7) \times 10^{10}$ cm

Volume $\qquad V_\odot = 1{\cdot}412\ 2 \times 10^{33}$ cm^3

Surface area $\qquad = 6{\cdot}087 \times 10^{22}$ cm^2

Sun mass $\qquad \mathscr{M}_\odot = (1{\cdot}989 \pm 0{\cdot}002) \times 10^{33}$ g

Mean density $\qquad \bar{\rho}_\odot = 1{\cdot}409$ g cm^{-3}

Gravity at surface $\qquad = (2{\cdot}739\ 8 \pm 0{\cdot}000\ 4) \times 10^4$ cm s^{-2}

Centrifugal acceleration at equator $\quad = -0{\cdot}587$ cm s^{-2}

Radiation emitted $\qquad \mathscr{L}_\odot = (3{\cdot}90 \pm 0{\cdot}04) \times 10^{33}$ erg s^{-1}

Radiation emitted at surface $\qquad = 6{\cdot}41 \times 10^{10}$ erg cm^{-2} s^{-1}

Angular rotation velocity (at lat. $= 16°$)

$\qquad = 2{\cdot}87 \times 10^{-6}$ radian s^{-1}

Moment of inertia [7] $\qquad = 6{\cdot}0 \times 10^{53}$ g

Angular-momentum $\qquad = 1{\cdot}7 \times 10^{48}$ g cm^{-2} s^{-1}

Rotational energy $\qquad = 2{\cdot}5 \times 10^{42}$ erg

Work required to dissipate solar matter to infinity

$\qquad = 7{\cdot}4 \times 10^{48}$ erg

Sun's total internal radiant energy [1]

$\qquad = 2{\cdot}8 \times 10^{47}$ erg

Translational energy (atoms and electrons) [1]

$\qquad = 2{\cdot}7 \times 10^{48}$ erg

Escape velocity at sun's surface $\qquad = 617{\cdot}7$ km/s

General magnetic field near sun's pole (at spot minimum) [2]

$\qquad \simeq 1$ or 2 gauss

Magnetic flux from polar area at spot min. [2]

$\qquad \simeq 8 \times 10^{21}$ maxwell.

Viewed from the earth (Pray tell where else ?)

Mean equatorial horizontal parallax [1, 3, 4]

$\qquad = 8''{\cdot}794\ 15 \pm 0''{\cdot}000\ 05$

$\qquad = 4{\cdot}263\ 52 \times 10^{-5}$ radian

Mean distance from earth = astronomical unit [1, 3, 4] §10

$\qquad$ AU $=$ A $= (1{\cdot}495\ 985 \pm 0{\cdot}000\ 005) \times 10^{13}$ cm

$\qquad = 92{\cdot}956 \times 10^6$ miles

Distance at perihelion $\qquad = 1{\cdot}471\ 0 \times 10^{13}$ cm

Distance at aphelion $\qquad = 1{\cdot}521\ 0 \times 10^{13}$ cm

Semi-diameter of sun at mean earth distance
$$= 959''\cdot63 = 0\cdot004\ 652\ 4\ \text{radian}$$
   circular to $\pm 0''\cdot01$.

Semi-diameter plus irradiation (for observing limb)
$$= 961''\cdot2$$

Solid angle at mean distance $= 6\cdot800\ 0 \times 10^{-5}$ sterad
$$A/\mathscr{R}_\odot = 214\cdot94$$
$$(A/\mathscr{R}_\odot)^2 = 46\ 200$$

Surface area of sphere of unit radius
$$4\pi A^2 = 2\cdot812 \times 10^{27}\ \text{cm}^2$$

At mean distance A
$$1'\ \text{of arc} = 4\cdot352 \times 10^4\ \text{km}$$
$$1''\ \text{of arc} = 725\cdot3\ \text{km}$$

Sun as a star

Magnitude [5, 6]

	Apparent	Modulus	Absolute
Visual	$m_v = V = -26\cdot78$	$31\cdot57$	$M_v = +4\cdot79$
Blue	$B = -26\cdot16$		$M_B = +5\cdot41$
Ultra-violet	$U = -26\cdot06$		$M_U = +5\cdot51$
Bolometric	$m_{bol} = -26\cdot85$		$M_{bol} = +4\cdot72$

Colour indices
$$B - V = +0\cdot62\quad [6]$$
$$U - B = +0\cdot10\quad \text{from } Sp. \text{ Class.}$$

Bolometric correction   B.C. $= 0\cdot07$ from $Sp.$ Class.

Spectral type $=$ G2 v

Effective temperature $= 5\ 800\ °\text{K} \pm 15\ °\text{K}$
   Other temperatures quoted in § 82.

Velocity relative to near stars $= 20\cdot0 \pm 0\cdot5$ km/s
   Solar apex $A = 271°$ $D = 30°$ (1900)
                $L^{\text{II}} = 57°$ $B^{\text{II}} = 22°$

Relative solar motion is dependent on stars selected, § 119.

[1] *A.Q.* **1**, § 63.
[2] H. W. Babcock, *Ap. J.*, **133**, 572, 1961.
[3] J. H. Thomson, et al., *Nature*, **190**, 519, 1961.
[4] The Lincoln Lab., *Nature*, **190**, 592, 1961.
[5] D. Yu. Martinov, *A. Zh.*, **36**, 648, 1959; *Sov. A.*, **3**, 633.
[6] J. Stebbins and G. E. Kron, *Ap. J.*, **126**, 266, 1957.
[7] I. Epstein and L. Motz, *Ap. J.*, **120**, 353, 1954.

§ 76. Internal Constitution of Sun

The data tabulated are averaged and smoothed from a number of models [1–10] which represent a wide range of assumptions. Indications of error are obtained from the interagreement of these models.

Central values
   Temperature $T_c = (13\cdot6 \pm 1\cdot2) \times 10^6\ °\text{K}$
   Density $\rho_c = 98 \pm 15\ \text{g cm}^{-3}$
   Pressure $P_c = 2\cdot0 \times 10^{17}\ \text{dyn cm}^{-2}$

Internal distribution

T = temperature, ρ = density, P = pressure, $\mathscr{M}_r$ = mass within radius r, $\mathscr{L}_r$ = energy generation within radius r, $\mathscr{R}_\odot$, $\mathscr{M}_\odot$, $\mathscr{L}_\odot$ = radius, mass, energy generation of whole sun.

r		T	ρ	$\mathscr{M}_r$	$\mathscr{L}_r$	$\log P$
$\mathscr{R}_\odot$	10^3 km	10^6 °K	g cm^{-3}	$\mathscr{M}_\odot$	$\mathscr{L}_\odot$	in dyn cm^{-2}
0·00	0	13·6	98	0·000	0·00	17·3
0·04	28	13·1	95	0·006	0·08	17·2
0·1	70	11·6	78	0·062	0·40	17·1
0·2	139	8·5	42	0·35	0·91	16·8
0·3	209	6·0	14	0·64	0·99	16·0
0·4	278	4·2	4·0	0·84	1·00	15·4
0·5	348	2·8	1·1	0·942	1·00	14·6
0·6	418	1·9	0·35	0·984	1·00	14·0
0·7	487	1·2	0·08	0·995	1·00	13·1
0·8	557	0·68	0·018	0·999	1·00	12·2
0·9	627	0·31	0·002 0	1·000	1·00	10·9
0·95	661	0·16	0·000 4	1·000	1·00	9·9
0·99	$\mathscr{R}_\odot - 7·0$	0·042	0·000 05	1·000	1·00	8·4
0·995	$\mathscr{R}_\odot - 3·5$	0·027	0·000 02	1·000	1·00	7·8

[1] *A.Q.* **1**, § 64.
[2] A. G. MASEVICH and T. G. VOLKONSKAYA, *A. Zh.*, **37**, 42, 1960; *Sov. A.*, **4**, 40.
[3] A. N. COX and R. R. BROWNLEE, *Stellar Models and Evolution*, Liège Symp., p. 469, 1959.
[4] M. SCHWARZSCHILD, *Structure and Evolution of Stars*, Princeton, 1958.
[5] P. NAUR, *Ap. J.*, **119**, 365, 1954.
[6] I. EPSTEIN and L. MOTZ, *Ap. J.*, **120**, 156, 353, 1954.
[7] G. O. ABELL, *Ap. J.*, **121**, 430, 1955.
[8] M. SCHWARZSCHILD, HOWARD, and HÄRM, *Ap. J.*, **125**, 233, 1957.
[9] R. WEYMANN, *Ap. J.*, **126**, 208, 1957.
[10] S.-M. KUNG, *Budapest*, No. 42, p. 109, 1957.

§ 77. Distribution of Photosphere with Height

Heights are measured from the *base of the chromosphere* taken as $\tau_5 = 0.004$ and representing the solar limb. τ_5 = optical depth at 5000 Å, T = temperature (electron temperature for $\tau_5 < 0.05$), $\Theta = 5\,040\,°K/T$, P_g = gas pressure, P_e = electron pressure, h = height, ρ = density, κ_5 = mass absorption coefficient at 5000 Å, N = number of atoms (neutral or ionized) per unit volume, and $\int N\,dh$ = total number of atoms in column above level. Lower temperatures, down to 3 700 °K [2, 3], are needed near $\tau_5 = 0.004$ if one is to represent the central intensities of strong Fraunhofer lines.

Distribution of photosphere

τ_5	Θ	T	$\log P_g$	$\log P_e$	h	$\log \rho$	$\log \kappa_5$	$\log N$	$\log \int N dh$
		°K	in dyn cm^{-2}		km	in g cm^{-3}	in g^{-1} cm^4	in cm^{-3}	in cm^{-3}
0·004	1·14	4 400	3·7	−0·22	0	−7·7	−1·35	15·9	22·9
0·01	1·13	4 450	3·97	−0·06	−40	−7·48	−1·22	16·17	23·2
0·02	1·10	4 600	4·14	+0·09	−80	−7·31	−1·10	16·34	23·38
0·05	1·04	4 850	4·37	+0·33	−125	−7·11	−0·92	16·54	23·59
0·1	0·99	5 090	4·53	0·55	−160	−6·97	−0·78	16·68	23·74
0·2	0·94	5 380	4·71	0·80	−200	−6·81	−0·61	16·84	23·94
0·5	0·85	5 900	4·88	1·22	−260	−6·68	−0·34	16·97	24·12
1	0·79	6 360	5·02	+1·70	−300	−6·57	−0·04	17·08	24·26
2	0·72	7 000	5·1	2·23	−320	−6·5	+0·35	17·1	24·3
5	0·61	8 300	5·2	3·05	−360	−6·4	+1·00	17·2	24·4
10	0·52	9 700	5·4	3·4	−380	−6·3	+1·4	17·3	24·5
	0·36	14 000	6·1		−1 000	−5·8		17·8	
	0·25	20 000	7·0		−2 000	−5·1		18·6	
	0·15	34 000	8·1		−5 000	−4·3		19·4	

[1] *A.Q.* **1**, § 65.
[2] E. Böhm-Vitense, *Z. Ap.*, **34**, 209, 1954; **46**, 108, 1958.
[3] H. Neckel, *Z. Ap.*, **44**, 153, 160, 1958.
[4] B. E. J. Pagel, *Ap. J.*, **132**, 790, 1960; **133**, 924, 1961.
[5] B. E. J. Pagel, *M.N.*, **115**, 493, 1955; **116**, 608, 1956.
[6] R. Cayrel and G. Traving, *Z. Ap.*, **50**, 239, 1960.
[7] A. Przybylski, *M.N.*, **117**, 600, 1957; **120**, 3, 1960.
[8] C. de Jager, *Handb. der. Phys.*, **52**, pp. 92, 105, 1959.
[9] D. Mugglestone, *M.N.*, **118**, 432, 1958.
[10] E. Lamla and H. Scheffler, *Z. Ap.*, **40**, 93, 1956.
[11] Z. Hitotuyanagi and H. Inaba, *Sendai A.R.*, No. 39, 1954.
[12] H. Hubenet, *Utrecht Reprints*, Quarto No. 10, 1956; No. 13, 1957.

§ 78. Fraunhofer Line Intensities

R = Rowland intensity = visual estimate of intensity [2, 3]

r = intensity within spectrum line relative to continuum.

W = equivalent width. In wavelength units $W_\lambda = \int (1 - r)\,d\lambda$.

W_λ/λ = equivalent width in dimensionless units. $10^6 W_\lambda/\lambda = 1$ fraunhofer.

r_c = value of r for line centre corrected for instrumental distortion.

NH = number of atoms per cm^2 column (in lower energy level) above photosphere; i.e. $H \simeq$ scale height, N = atom density at photospheric level.

f = absorption oscillator strength.

X = scattering optical depth at line centre for fictitious case of zero damping = $1.497 \times 10^{-15} NHf\lambda/v$ with λ in Å and v = most probable random speed in km/s.

η_c = ratio (line absorption or scattering)/(continuous absorption) for the line centre and for the fictitious case of zero damping (as in X).

τ, τ_5 = optical depth in continuum. Subscript $_5$ represents standard λ at 5000 Å.

g' = weighting function expressed in τ_5 as depth variable.

κ, κ_5 = continuum mass absorption coefficient ($_5 \equiv 5000$ Å).

Curve of growth for Fraunhofer lines [1, 17]

The number of atoms in the reversing layer is expressed by X, η_c, and NHf.

$\log X$	$\log \eta_c$	$\log NHf(\lambda/5000 \text{ Å})$	$\log W_\lambda/\lambda$
		in cm^{-2}	
-1.0	-0.6	10·42	-6.05
-0.5	-0.1	10·92	-5.55
0.0	$+0.4$	11·42	-5.13
$+0.5$	$+0.9$	11·92	-4.86
$+1.0$	$+1.4$	12·42	-4.72
$+1.5$	$+1.9$	12·92	-4.64
$+2.0$	$+2.4$	13·42	-4.53
$+2.5$	$+2.9$	13·92	-4.35
$+3.0$	$+3.4$	14·42	-4.10
$+3.5$	$+3.9$	14·92	-3.85
$+4.0$	$+4.4$	15·42	-3.59

Intensity within faint Fraunhofer lines [4, 6]

$$1 - r = \int_0^\infty g'(\tau_5) \frac{\kappa}{\kappa_5} d\tau_5$$

Equivalent width of faint Fraunhofer lines [4]

$$\frac{W_\lambda}{\lambda} = 3.4 \times 10^3 \lambda f \int \frac{g'(\tau_5)}{\kappa_5} \frac{N}{N_H} d\tau_5$$

where N_H is H atom density, and we have used $\rho = 1.60 \, m_H \, N_H$

Mean relation between W_λ (centre of disk) and R

R	W_λ		R	W_λ		R	W_λ	
	Visible [2]	Infra-red [3]		Visible [2]	Infra-red [3]		Visible [2]	Infra-red [3]
	milli-angstroms			milli-angstroms			milli-angstroms	
-3	3		3	80	50	9	370	150
-2	6		4	105	65	10	470	180
-1	11	20	5	130	80	15	700	
0	20	20	6	170	95	20	1300	
1	37	28	7	220	110	30	2000	
2	58	40	8	290	130	40	3000	

The Rowland intensities for the infra-red ($\lambda > 6600$ Å) are from [3] and differ considerably from the earlier values given in [2].

Weighting functions g′ for the centre of sun's disk [5, 6, 8]

τ_5	λ in Å				
	4000	5000	6000	8000	20000
0·0	0·92	0·90	0·87	0·75	0·39
0·01	0·90	0·83	0·77	0·65	0·38
0·03	0·85	0·77	0·69	0·58	0·35
0·1	0·80	0·69	0·58	0·46	0·29
0·3	0·68	0·54	0·44	0·31	0·18
0·5	0·57	0·43	0·33	0·22	0·12
1·0	0·37	0·23	0·17	0·11	0·04
1·5	0·24	0·14	0·08	0·05	0·01
2·0	0·17	0·09	0·05	0·026	0·001
3	0·07	0·03	0·014	0·009	
4	0·03	0·011	0·005	0·002	
6	0·003	0·001	0·000 5	0·000 2	

Variation of absorption coefficient with wavelength [1, 16, 18]

λ	κ/κ_5
3000 Å	1·5
3500	1·00
4000	0·88
4500	0·91
5000	1·00

λ	κ/κ_5
6000 Å	1·14
7000	1·25
8000	1·37
9000	1·41
10000	1·31

λ	κ/κ_5
15000Å	0·57
17000	0·41
20000	0·48
30000	1·0
40000	1·5

Limb, disk, and centre ratios of W [10, 11, 12, 13]
Subscripts L = limb (cos θ ≃ 0·3), D = disk, C = centre.

$10^6 W_C/\lambda$	0	1	10	100	1 000
W_L/W_C	1·55	1·50	1·19	0·90	0·77
W_D/W_C	1·31	1·28	1·11	0·94	0·83

Total light loss ratios by Fraunhofer lines

$$\sum W_L/\sum W_C = 1\cdot13$$
$$\sum W_D/\sum W_C = 1\cdot08$$
$$\sum W(\theta)/\sum W_C \simeq 1+0\cdot18(1-\cos\theta)$$

For integrated loss of light by Fraunhofer lines in various parts of the spectrum: see §§ 80, 82.

Doppler velocity for curve of growth $= [(2kT/m_a)+v_s^2]^{1/2}$ [1]
$$= 1\cdot9 \text{ km/s}$$

where m_a is atomic mass and v_s is small scale turbulent velocity.

Doppler velocity for line breadths $= [(2kT/m_a)+v^2]^{1/2}$
  at centre of disk $= 2\cdot2$ km/s
  at limb $= 3\cdot1$ km/s
    where v = large or small scale turbulent velocity.

Atomic thermal velocity $= (2kT/m_a)^{1/2}$
                        $= 1\cdot4$ km/s   (heavier atoms)

Small scale turbulent velocity [7]
                    $v_s = 1\cdot3$ km/s

Large and small scale turbulent velocity $= v$
  at centre of disk $= 1\cdot7$ km/s
  at limb $= 2\cdot8$ km/s

Damping constant for Fraunhofer lines $= \gamma$ ($\gamma/2\pi$ = whole-$\frac{1}{2}$-damping width in c/s)
                    γ_{cl} = classical radiation damping
                    $= 0\cdot222\ 3 \times \lambda^{-2}\ s^{-1}$ [λ in cm] $= 0\cdot000742$ Å

  γ/γ_{cl} ranges from 10 to 1 000 [5, 14, 15]

Normally the quantum calculated radiation damping is of the same order as the classical value, the calculated collision damping (§33) is about 20 times greater, and the damping observed in line wings 5 times greater than the collision calculations [5].

[1] *A.Q.* **1**, § 66, 67.
[2] C. E. St John, et al., *Revised Rowland Table*, Carnegie Pub. 396, 1928.
[3] H. D. Babcock and C. E. Moore, *The Solar Spectrum* λ 6600 *to* λ 13495, Carnegie Pub., 379, 1947.
[4] W. J. Claas, *Rech. Ob. Utrecht*, **12**, 1, 1951.
[5] V. Weidemann, *Z. Ap.*, **36**, 101, 1955.
[6] M. Minnaert, *B.A.N.*, **10**, 339, 399, 1948.
[7] R. B. Teplitskaya, *A. Zh.*, **37**, 51, 1960; *Sov. A.*, **4**, 49.
[8] L. Goldberg and A. K. Pierce, *Handb. der Phys.*, **52**, 1, 1959.
[9] H. Inaba, *Repr. Tôhoku*, Sendai A.R., No. 37, 1954.
[10] C. W. Allen, *M.N.*, **109**, 343, 1949.
[11] J. Houtgast, *Dissertation*, Utrecht, 1942.
[12] M. Bretz, *Z. Ap.*, **38**, 259, 1956.
[13] B. E. J. Pagel, *M.N.*, **115**, 493, 1955.
[14] G. Godoli, *Contr. Dom. Ob. Ottawa*, **2**, No. 24, 1958.
[15] J. B. Rogerson, *Ap. J.*, **125**, 275, 1957.
[16] F. Saiedy, *M.N.*, **121**, 483, 1960.
[17] L. H. Aller, *Astrophysics: Atm. of Sun and Stars*, p. 292, Ronald Press, 1953.
[18] E. Vitense, *Z. Ap.*, **28**, 81, 1951.

§ 79. The Strong Fraunhofer Lines

W = equivalent width, r_0 = central intensity corrected for instrumental distortion, c = a measure of wing intensity defined by $c = \Delta\lambda^2(1-r)/r$ [1] where r is the intensity relative to the continuum at $\Delta\lambda$ from the line centre. The limb is represented by $\cos\theta = 0\cdot3$ where θ is the angular distance from the disk centre. At this position errors are small but the primary limb effects are demonstrated. Between $\cos\theta = 0\cdot3$ and $0\cdot0$ most features change rapidly. R = Rowland number.

λ	Name	Atom	R	Centre of disk			Limb ($\cos\theta = 0\cdot3$)	
				W	r_0	c	W	r_0
Å				Å	%	Å^2	Å	%
2795·4		Mg II	1 000	} 22				
2802·3		Mg II	700					
2851·6		Mg I	200	9·6				
2881·1		Si I	80	2·6				
3581·209	N	Fe I	30	2·3	3			
3734·875	M	Fe I	40	3·1	1			
3820·437	L	Fe I	25	1·8	2			
3933·682	K	Ca II	1 000	19·1	6	39	16	11
3968·492	H	Ca II	700	14·4	6	26	12	11
4045·825		Fe I	30	1·25	2	0·22	1·4	5
4101·748	h, Hδ	H I	40N	3·00	21		1·4	29
4226·740	g	Ca I	20	1·41	2	0·23	1·4	3
4340·475	G', Hγ	H I	20N	2·89	16		1·4	23
4383·557	d	Fe I	15	1·05	3			
4861·342	F, Hβ	H I	30	3·75	15		1·9	22
5167·328	b₄	Mg I	15	0·88	13	0·09	0·74	18
5172·698	b₂	Mg I	20	1·27	10	0·24	1·3	14
5183·619	b₁	Mg I	30	1·62	9	0·37	1·5	14
5889·973	D₂	Na I	30	0·83	4	0·091	0·85	6
5895·940	D₁	Na I	20	0·60	5	0·045	0·59	6
6562·808	C, Hα	H I	40	4·1	16		1·9	20
8498·062		Ca II	20	1·29	29	0·27	0·95	34
8542·144		Ca II	25	3·3	21	1·86	2·6	21
8662·170		Ca II	23	2·5	23	1·05	2·0	25
10049·27		H I	50N	1·6	79			
10938·10		H I	50N	2·3	74			84
12818·23		H I	20	4·2	63			

[1] *A.Q.* **1**, § 68.
[2] *Rech. Astrom. Ob. Utrecht*, **15**, 1, 1960.
[3] W. PRIESTER, *Z. Ap.*, **32**, 200, 1953.
[4] R. J. BRAY, *M.N.*, **116**, 395, 1956.
[5] O. R. WHITE, *Thesis*, Colorado, 1962.

§ 80. Total Solar Radiation

Solar constant = flux of total radiation received outside earth's atmosphere per unit area at mean sun-earth distance [1, 2, 3]

$$f = 1\cdot99 \pm 0\cdot02 \text{ cal cm}^{-2} \text{ min}^{-1} \text{ (or langley/min)}$$
$$= 1\cdot388 \times 10^6 \text{ erg cm}^{-2} \text{ s}^{-1}$$

Mean radiation intensity of sun's disk
$$F = 2 \cdot 04 \times 10^{10} \text{ erg cm}^{-2} \text{ s}^{-1} \text{ sterad}^{-1}$$

Radiation intensity at centre of disk
$$I(0) = 2 \cdot 49 \times 10^{10} \text{ erg cm}^{-2} \text{ s}^{-1} \text{ sterad}^{-1}$$

Radiation emittance of sun's surface
$$\mathscr{F} = \pi F = 6 \cdot 41 \times 10^{10} \text{ erg cm}^{-2} \text{ s}^{-1}$$

Continuous background radiation emittance of sun's surface (smoothing the continuum near 3650 Å)
$$\mathscr{F}' = 7 \cdot 08 \times 10^{10} \text{ erg cm}^{-2} \text{ s}^{-1}$$

Fraction of continuous radiation absorbed in Fraunhofer lines
$$\eta = 0 \cdot 094$$

Radiation from the whole sun $\mathscr{L}_\odot = (3 \cdot 90 \pm 0 \cdot 04) \times 10^{33} \text{ erg s}^{-1}$

Radiation per unit mass $= 1 \cdot 96 \text{ erg s}^{-1} \text{ g}^{-1}$

Sun's effective temperature
$$T_e = (\mathscr{F}/\sigma)^{1/4} = 5\,800 \text{ °K}$$

Centre disk temperature $\{\pi I(0)/\sigma\}^{1/4} = 6\,110$ °K.

Mean brightness of sun's disk outside atmosphere [1, 4, 5]
$$= 2 \cdot 02 \times 10^5 \text{ stilb} = 6 \cdot 33 \times 10^5 \text{ lambert}$$

Brightness of centre of disk outside atmosphere [1, 4]
$$= 2 \cdot 53 \times 10^5 \text{ stilb} = 7 \cdot 94 \times 10^5 \text{ lambert}$$

Candle power of sun $= 3 \cdot 07 \times 10^{27} \text{ cd}$

Light flux outside earth atmosphere at mean solar distance [1, 2, 4, 5, 6]
$$= 13 \cdot 7 \text{ phot} = 137\,000 \text{ lux}$$

[1] *A.Q.* **1**, § 69.
[2] F. S. JOHNSON, 9th *Rep. Sol. Terr. Rel.*, p. 53, 1957.
[3] C. W. ALLEN, *Q.J.R. Met. Soc.*, **84**, 307, 1958.
[4] R. V. KARANDIKAR, *J.O.S.A.*, **45**, 483, 1955.
[5] L. DUNKELMAN and R. SCOLNIK, *J.O.S.A.*, **49**, 356, 1959.
[6] *I.G.Y. Annals*, **5**, 374, 1958.

§ 81. Solar Limb Darkening

$I'_\lambda(\theta)$ = intensity of solar radiation at angle θ from the centre of the disk; θ = angle between the sun's radius vector and the line of sight.

$I'_\lambda(0)$ = intensity at centre of disk.

The ratio $I'_\lambda(\theta)/I'_\lambda(0)$, which varies with wavelength λ defines *limb darkening*. As far as possible measurements are made in the continuum between the spectrum lines (hence primes ' in the notation).

The results may be fitted to the following expressions

$$I'_\lambda(\theta)/I'_\lambda(0) = 1-u-v+u\cos\theta+v\cos^2\theta$$

or

$$I'_\lambda(\theta)/I'_\lambda(0) = a+b\cos\theta+c[1-\cos\theta\ln(1+1/\cos\theta)]$$
$$\text{where } a+b+(1-\ln 2)c = 1$$

or less accurately

$$I'_\lambda(\theta)/I'_\lambda(0) = 1-u_1+u_1\cos\theta$$

For determining u_1 it is preferable to make a fit at $\cos\theta = 0.5$, whence $u_1 = u+\tfrac{3}{2}v$.

Ratio mean/central intensity

$$F'_\lambda/I'_\lambda(0) = 1-\tfrac{1}{3}u-\tfrac{1}{2}v$$

or

$$= a+c+\tfrac{2}{3}b-2c(\tfrac{2}{3}\ln 2-\tfrac{1}{6})$$
$$= a+0.667b+0.409c$$

or

$$= 1-\tfrac{1}{3}u_1$$

Ratio limb/central intensity

$$I'_\lambda(90°)/I'_\lambda(0) = 1-u-v$$

or

$$= a+c$$

or

$$= 1-u_1$$

No consistent difference between pole and equator has been detected [9].

The new analysis [10] giving smaller $I'_\lambda(\theta)/I_\lambda(0)$ in the blue has not been included.

The change of the Balmer discontinuity D_θ with θ is given in the table, where

$$D_\theta = \log\{[I'_{\lambda=0.37+}(\theta)]/[I'_{\lambda=0.37-}(\theta)]\}$$

$$I'_\lambda(\theta)/I'_\lambda(0)$$

λ	Cos θ	1·0	0·8	0·6	0·5	0·4	0·3	0·2	0·1	0·05	0·02
	Sin θ	0·000	0·600	0·800	0·866	0·916	0·954	0·980	0·995	0·9987	0·9998 [7, 8, 11]
μ											
0·32		1·00	0·809	0·623	0·532	0·438	0·347	0·262	0·17		
0·35		1·00	0·837	0·665	0·579	0·487	0·397	0·306	0·213		
0·37		1·00	0·851	0·687	0·603	0·513	0·421	0·332	0·233		
0·40		1·00	0·835	0·663	0·585	0·494	0·408	0·320	0·228		
0·45		1·00	0·860	0·713	0·636	0·554	0·466	0·375	0·271	0·20	0·14
0·50		1·00	0·877	0·744	0·675	0·597	0·513	0·421	0·323	0·26	0·19
0·60		1·00	0·900	0·788	0·727	0·660	0·586	0·504	0·410	0·35	0·28
0·80		1·00	0·924	0·843	0·793	0·742	0·678	0·610	0·53		
1·0		1·00	0·941	0·870	0·828	0·783	0·731	0·672	0·57		
1·5		1·00	0·958	0·902	0·875	0·830	0·789	0·735	0·65		
2·0 [4]		1·00	0·965	0·921	0·895	0·863	0·825	0·780	0·70		
3·0		1·00	0·971	0·934	0·917	0·899	0·870	0·832	0·78		
5·0		1·00	0·980	0·954	0·943	0·928	0·914	0·890			
10·0 [6]		1·00	0·993	0·982	0·973	0·964	0·953	0·935			
Total radiation		1·00	0·898	0·787	0·731	0·669	0·602	0·525	0·448	0·39	0·32
D_θ [5]		0·125	0·107	0·086	0·075	0·061	0·047	0·031	0·013		

The limb darkening constants

λ	u	v	a	b [2]	c	u_1	$\beta = \dfrac{u_1}{1-u_1}$	$\dfrac{F'_\lambda}{I'_\lambda(0)}$	$\dfrac{I'_\lambda(90°)}{I'_\lambda(0)}$
μ									
0·32	0·86	+0·05	−0·05	+0·99	+0·18	0·94	16	0·687	0·11
0·35	0·96	−0·08	+0·17	+0·84	−0·06	0·84	5·2	0·720	0·11
0·37	1·01	−0·15	+0·39	+0·71	−0·32	0·79	3·8	0·737	0·11
0·40	0·93	−0·06	+0·17	+0·84	−0·04	0·84	5·2	0·720	0·13
0·45	0·99	−0·17	+0·54	+0·59	−0·43	0·73	2·7	0·757	0·15
0·50	0·95	−0·20	+0·69	+0·48	−0·55	0·65	1·86	0·783	0·20
0·60	0·86	−0·21	+0·78	+0·38	−0·54	0·55	1·22	0·817	0·30
0·80	0·71	−0·20	+0·92	+0·25	−0·55	0·41	0·70	0·863	0·43
1·0	0·63	−0·19	+0·95	+0·20	−0·50	0·34	0·51	0·887	0·51
1·5	0·56	−0·21	+1·10	+0·08	−0·60	0·26	0·33	0·913	0·58
2·0	0·48	−0·18	+1·10	+0·05	−0·48	0·21	0·27	0·930	0·66
3·0	0·36	−0·13	+1·05	+0·05	−0·35	0·16	0·19	0·947	0·74
5·0	0·23	−0·08	+1·04	+0·04	−0·25	0·11	0·12	0·963	0·82
10·0	0·14	−0·04	+1·07	+0·00	−0·23	0·05	0·05	0·983	0·88
Total	0·84	−0·20	+0·72	+0·42	−0·45	0·54	1·16	0·820	0·32

[1] *A.Q.* **1**, § 70.
[2] A. K. PIERCE and J. H. WADDELL, *Mem. R.A.S.*, **68**, 89, 1961.
[3] W. E. MITCHELL, *Ap. J.*, **129**, 93, 1959.
[4] N. I. KOZHEVNIKOV, *A. Zh.*, **34**, 883, 1957; *Sov. A.*, **1**, 856.
[5] R. PEYTURAUX, *Contr. I.A. Paris*, A Nos. 168, 176, 1954; *C.R.*, **238**, 1867; **239**, 1460, 1954.
[6] F. SAIEDY, *M.N.*, **121**, 483, 1960.
[7] B. E. J. PAGEL, *Ap. J.*, **132**, 790, 1960.
[8] K. SAITO and S. HATA, *P.A.S. Jap.*, **12**, 143, 1960.
[9] P. MALTBY, *Ap. Norvegica*, **7**, 89, 1960.
[10] K.-H. DAVID and G. ELSTE, *Z. Ap.*, **54**, 12, 1962.
[11] T. DE GROOT, *B.A.N.*, **16**, 181, 1962.

§ 82. Distribution of Radiation in Solar Spectrum

F_λ = intensity of mean solar disk per unit wavelength with spectrum lines smoothed.

$\mathscr{F}_\lambda = \pi F_\lambda$ = emittance of solar surface per unit wavelength range.

$f_\lambda = \mathscr{F}_\lambda (\mathscr{R}_\odot/A)^2 = 6·80 \times 10^{-5} F_\lambda$ = solar flux outside earth atmosphere per unit area and wavelength range. A = astronomical unit.

F'_λ = as for F_λ but referring to the continuum between the spectrum lines. The curve joining the most intense windows between the lines is regarded as the continuum. This may differ appreciably from the intensity level in the entire absence of absorption lines, and does not allow for sudden changes (e.g. at the Balmer limit *).

$I_\lambda(0)$ = intensity at centre of sun's disk with spectrum lines smoothed.

$I'_\lambda(0)$ = intensity at centre of sun's disk between spectrum lines.

Solar spectral distribution

λ	F_λ	F'_λ	$I_\lambda(0)$	$I'_\lambda(0)$ [4, 5, 6, 7]	f_λ [2, 3, 13]	$\dfrac{I_\lambda(0)}{I'_\lambda(0)}$ [1, 12]	$\dfrac{F'_\lambda}{I'_\lambda(0)}$ [1, 11, 12]	$\dfrac{F_\lambda}{I'_\lambda(0)}$
μ	10^{10} erg sterad^{-1} cm^{-2} μ^{-1} s^{-1}				erg cm^{-2} Å^{-1} s^{-1}			
0·20	0·018	0·04	0·03	0·06	1·2	0·5	0·60	0·30
0·22	0·066	0·13	0·10	0·21	4·5	0·5	0·62	0·31
0·24	0·094	0·19	0·14	0·29	6·4	0·5	0·63	0·32
0·26	0·19	0·39	0·30	0·60	13	0·5	0·64	0·32
0·23	0·37	0·85	0·66	1·30	25	0·51	0·66	0·29
0·30	0·87	1·65	1·30	2·45	59	0·53	0·67	0·36
0·32	1·25	2·24	1·88	3·25	85	0·58	0·687	0·39
0·34	1·68	2·68	2·37	3·77	114	0·63	0·710	0·44
0·36	1·69	3·03	2·56	4·13	115	0·62	0·730	0·42
0·37	1·87	3·15	2·45	4·23*	127	0·58	0·737	0·43
0·38	1·78	3·35	2·59	4·63	121	0·56	0·710	0·39
0·39	1·69	3·54	2·62	4·95	115	0·53	0·711	0·34
0·40	2·35	3·71	3·24	5·15	160	0·63	0·720	0·46
0·41	2·75	3·82	3·68	5·26	187	0·70	0·728	0·52
0·42	2·78	3·90	3·85	5·28	189	0·73	0·736	0·53
0·43	2·69	3·91	3·73	5·24	183	0·71	0·743	0·51
0·44	2·95	3·90	4·14	5·19	201	0·80	0·750	0·57
0·45	3·13	3·87	4·38	5·10	213	0·86	0·757	0·61
0·46	3·16	3·82	4·35	5·00	215	0·87	0·763	0·63
0·48	3·13	3·71	4·16	4·79	213	0·87	0·774	0·65
0·50	3·00	3·57	3·96	4·55	204	0·87	0·783	0·66
0·55	2·90	3·25	3·72	4·02	198	0·92	0·803	0·72
0·60	2·75	2·86	3·42	3·52	187	0·97	0·817	0·78
0·65	2·46	2·54	3·00	3·06	167	0·98	0·832	0·80
0·70	2·19	2·25	2·65	2·69	149	0·985	0·843	0·82
0·75	1·90	1·93	2·25	2·28	129	0·986	0·853	0·83
0·8	1·68	1·73	2·01	2·03	114	0·987	0·863	0·83
0·9	1·32	1·35	1·54	1·57	90	0·98	0·878	0·85
1·0	1·08	1·11	1·25	1·26	74	0·99	0·887	0·87
1·1	0·90	0·91	1·00	1·01	61	0·99	0·895	0·89
1·2	0·73	0·74	0·80	0·81	50	0·99	0·900	0·90
1·4	0·48	0·48	0·52	0·53	33	0·99	0·910	0·91
1·6	0·328	0·33	0·36	0·36	22·3	0·993	0·918	0·92
1·8	0·218	0·220	0·235	0·238	14·8	0·994	0·925	0·92
2·0	0·150	0·151	0·159	0·160	10·2	0·996	0·930	0·93
2·5	0·073	0·073	0·078	0·078	4·97	0·998	0·940	0·94
3·0	0·039		0·041		2·63	1·0	0·947	0·95
4	0·013 7		0·014 2		0·93	1·0	0·957	0·96
5	0·006 0		0·006 2		0·41	1·0	0·963	0·96
6	0·003 1		0·003 2		0·21	1·0	0·968	0·97
8	0·000 93		0·000 95		0·063	1·0	0·976	0·98
10	0·000 34		0·000 35		0·023	1·0	0·983	0·98
12	0·000 18		0·000 18		0·012	1·0	0·985	0·98

* Hypothetical continuum between Balmer lines = 5·6.

Colour temperature

$$\mathscr{F}_\lambda \quad \text{in visible (4400–5500 Å)} \quad = 5\,900\ ^\circ\text{K}$$
$$\mathscr{F}'_\lambda \quad \text{in visible (4400–5500 Å)} \quad = 7\,200\ ^\circ\text{K}$$
$$I'_\lambda(0) \text{ in visible (4400–5500 Å)} \quad = 8\,000\ ^\circ\text{K}$$
$$I'_\lambda(0) \text{ in ultra-violet (3300–4400 Å)} = 6\,000\ ^\circ\text{K}$$

Brightness temperatures

	4400 Å	5500 Å
$\mathscr{F}_\lambda$	5 910 °K	5 910 °K
$\mathscr{F}'_\lambda$	6 220 °K	6 090 °K
$I_\lambda(0)$	6 300 °K	6 270 °K
$I'_\lambda(0)$	6 620 °K	6 390 °K

For ultra-violet and soft x-ray regions

The radiations for $\lambda < 1600$ Å are mainly from emission lines and may vary with solar activity. Radiation from the dominating resonance lines are excluded from f_λ and tabulated separately. Other lines are smoothed [6, 9, 10, 14, 15].

λ	$\log f_\lambda$	λ	$\log f_\lambda$
Å	in erg cm^{-2} Å^{-1} s^{-1}	Å	in erg cm^{-2} Å^{-1} s^{-1}
10	-4	900	$-2\cdot4$
20	$-3\cdot2$	1000	$-2\cdot3$
50	$-2\cdot6$	1100	$-2\cdot8$
100	$-2\cdot5$	1200	$-2\cdot7$
200	$-2\cdot4$	1400	$-2\cdot3$
400	$-2\cdot8$	1600	$-1\cdot3$
600	$-2\cdot8$	1800	$-0\cdot6$
800	$-2\cdot8$	2000	$+0\cdot1$

For ultra-violet resonance lines

H I	Lα at 1216 Å	6	erg cm^{-2} s^{-1} at earth.
He I	584 Å	0·1	,, ,,
He II	304 Å	0·3	,, ,,

[1] *A.Q.* **1**, § 71.
[2] C. W. Allen, *Q.J.R. Met. Soc.*, **84**, 307, 1958.
[3] L. Dunkelman and R. Scolnik, *J.O.S.A.*, **49**, 356, 1958.
[4] G. F. Sitnik, *Astr. In. Sternberg*, No. 113, 19, 1961.
[5] R. Peyturaux, *Contr. I. Ap. Paris*, No. A 267, 1961.
[6] F. Saiedy, *M.N.*, **121**, 483, 1960.
[7] D. Labs, *Z. Ap.*, **44**, 37, 1957.
[8] C. R. Detwiler, Purcell, and Tousey, *A.J.*, **66**, 281, 1961; also manuscript of March 1961, *Ann. de Geoph.*, **17**, 263, 1961.
[9] H. E. Hinteregger, *Ap. J.*, **132**, 801, 1960.
[10] C. W. Allen, *Comm. London Ob.*, No. 42, 1961; Liège Symp. p. 241, 1961.
[11] H. C. McAllister, *Prelim. Photometric Atlas*, 1800–2956 Å, Univ. Colorado, 1960.
[12] G. Brückner, *Photometric Atlas*, 2988–3629 Å, Univ. Göttingen, 1960.
[13] R. Stair and R. G. Johnson, *N.B.S. J. Res.*, **57**, 205, 1956.
[14] H. Friedman, *Phys. of Upper Atm.*, ed. Ratcliffe, Academic Press, p. 133, 1960.
[15] K. Watanabe and H. E. Hinteregger, *J. Geoph. Res.*, **67**, 999, 1962.

§ 83. Chromosphere

The distribution in the chromosphere quoted in the table is smoothed and averaged from [1, 2, 3, 4, 5, 6, 7, 8, 11]. The uncertainties are too great to quote 'active' or 'undisturbed' regions separately, or to quote the various types of temperature T. Heights are measured from the *base of the chromosphere* at $\tau_5 = 0 \cdot 004$ as in § 77.

$$N = \text{number of atoms} + \text{atomic ions per cm}^3$$
$$N_0 = \text{number of electrons per cm}^3$$
$$h = \text{height above } \tau_5 = 0 \cdot 004$$
$$r = \text{radial distance from sun's centre}$$
$$H_N = \text{scale height in number of atoms.}$$

Distribution in chromosphere

h	r	$\log \tau_5$	T	$\log T$	$\log N$	$\log N_e$	H_N	$dh/d(\log T)$
10^8 cm	$\mathscr{R}_\odot$		°K	in °K	in cm^{-3}	in cm^{-3}	km	10^8 cm/dex
0	1·000 0	−2·4	4 400	3·65	15·9	12·1	140	
0·2	1·000 3	−3·5	4 700	3·67	15·3	11·8	160	
0·5	1·000 7	−4·5	4 900	3·69	14·5	11·5	190	
1	1·001 4		5 200	3·72	13·6	11·1	310	
2	1·002 9		5 800	3·77	12·6	10·7	500	
3	1·004 3		6 300	3·80	11·9	10·4	640	
4	1·005 7		7 400	3·87	11·3	10·3	740	7·6
5	1·007 2		13 000	4·10	10·7	10·2	820	3·3
6	1·008 6		30 000	4·48	10·2	10·0	950	2·4
7	1·010 1		75 000	4·88	9·8	9·7	1 100	2·6
8	1·011 5		160 000	5·20	9·4	9·4	1 400	3·6
10	1·014 4		400 000	5·60	8·9	8·9	2 500	6·6
15	1·021 5		10^6	6·00	8·5	8·5		
20	1·029		10^6	6·00	8·4	8·4		
30	1·043		10^6	6·00	8·3	8·3		
40	1·057		10^6	6·00	8·2	8·2		

Chromospheric kinetic temperature [1, 9]
$$= 8\ 000\ °K$$

Excitation temperature at low levels and low E.P. [1]
$$= 4\ 500\ °K$$

but is increased for higher levels and E.P.'s.

Height of chromosphere seen on limb [10]
$$= 7\ 000\ km$$

Spectroheliogram heights [6]

Centre Hα	4 500 km	Centre K of Ca$^+$	(K3)	4 000 km
Centre Hβ	2 800 km	$\Delta\lambda = 0 \cdot 3$ Å	(K2)	2 000 km
Centre Mg, 5184	300 km	$\Delta\lambda = 0 \cdot 6$ Å	(K1)	600 km
Centre Ca, 4227	800 km	$\Delta\lambda = 1 \cdot 0$ Å	(K1)	200 km

Most probable turbulent velocity ξ [6]

h in km	0	1 000	2 000	3 000
ξ in km/s	2	7	12	16

The number of atoms and electrons within temperature ranges may be derived from the column $dh/d(\log T)$, e.g.

$$\int N_e^2 \, dV = 2\pi \mathscr{R}_\odot^2 N_e^2 \, dh/d(\log T) = 3 \cdot 03 \times 10^{22} N_e^2 \, dh/d(\log T)$$

where the integral covers all electrons visible from the earth within unit range in $\log T$, N_e^2 is in cm^{-6} and dh in cm.

[1] *A.Q.* **1**, § 72.
[2] L. Oster, *Z. Ap.*, **40**, 28, 1956.
[3] I. S. Shklovskii and E. V. Kononovich, *A. Zh.*, **35**, 37, 1958; *Sov. A.*, **2**, 32.
[4] G. S. Ivanov, Kholodnya and G. M. Nikolskii, *A. Zh.*, **38**, 45, 1961; *Sov. A.*, **5**, 31.
[5] R. N. Thomas and R. G. Athay, *Physics of Solar Chromosphere*, Interscience Mon. VI, 1961.
[6] C. de Jager, *Handb. der Phys.*, **52**, pp. 115, 125, 142, 1959.
[7] V. E. Stepanov and N. N. Petrova, *Iz. Crimea*, **21**, 152, 1959.
[8] E. Böhm-Vitense, *Z. Ap.*, **36**, 145, 1955.
[9] R. O. Redman and Z. Suemoto, *M.N.*, **114**, 524, 1954.
[10] O. C. Mohler, *Sky and Tel.*, **20**, 124, 1960.
[11] D. Ya. Martynov, *A.Zh.*, **38**, 443, 1961; *Sov. A.*, **5**, 329.

§ 84. Solar Corona

Radiation from the solar corona contains three components, K = continuous spectrum scattered by electrons, F = Fraunhofer spectrum diffracted by interplanetary particles, and L = coronal line emission. L is negligible for coronal photometry (about 1%).

Total coronal light flux beyond $1 \cdot 03 \, \mathscr{R}_\odot$ (for typical lunar disk) [1]

at sunspot maximum	$= 1 \cdot 3 \times 10^6$ solar flux $= 0 \cdot 57$ full moon
at sunspot minimum	$= 0 \cdot 8 \times 10^6$ solar flux $= 0 \cdot 35$ full moon

Total F corona $= 0 \cdot 29 \times 10^{-6}$ solar flux.

Spectral distribution of K component is similar to $\mathscr{F}_\lambda$ for photosphere, § 82.

Spectral distribution of F component is slightly redder than photosphere (reddening factor about $\lambda^{1/2}$).

Temperature of corona. Measurements do not all give consistent results [2]

From line-broadening, kinetic temperature

$$T_k = 2 \cdot 4 \times 10^6 \, °\text{K}$$

From ionization and radio, electron temperature

$$T_e = 0 \cdot 9 \times 10^6 \, °\text{K}$$

Temperature derived from coronal support is intermediate.

Base of corona

Coronal line emission can be detected without diminution down to 8 000 km above chromosphere base [3], i.e. to $r \simeq 1 \cdot 01 \, \mathscr{R}_\odot$. The real coronal base may be lower.

Coronal ellipticity ϵ [6]

$$\epsilon = (A_3 - P_3)/P_3 \simeq (A_1 - P_1)/A_1$$

where A_1 and P_1 are equatorial and polar diameters and for A_3 and P_3 the corresponding diameters are averaged with those oriented 15° on either side.

ϵ at sunspot max.	$\simeq 0 \cdot 05$
ϵ at sunspot min.	$\simeq 0 \cdot 20$ near $r = 1 \cdot 6 \mathscr{R}_\odot$

Change of ellipticity with distance (combining K and F coronas) [2]

$r/\mathscr{R}_\odot$	1·0	1·2	1·4	1·6	1·8	2	3	4	5	10	20
ϵ at sunspot min.	0·06	0·11	0·15	0·20	0·19	0·16	0·08	0·07	0·09	0·18	0·25

Smoothed coronal brightness and electron density [1, 4, 5, 7]

r	$\log r$	log (surface brightness)				log (electron density)		
		K			F	Max.	Min.	
		Max.	Min.					
			Eq.	Pole			Eq.	Pole
$\mathscr{R}_\odot$	in $\mathscr{R}_\odot$	in $10^{-10}F_\lambda$ (see § 82)				in cm^{-3}		
1·01	0·004	4·68	4·43	4·35	3·22	8·55	8·30	8·20
1·03	0·013	4·55	4·30	4·15	3·16	8·46	8·21	8·12
1·06	0·025	4·41	4·16	3·90	3·06	8·36	8·11	7·97
1·10	0·041	4·27	4·02	3·72	3·00	8·24	7·99	7·80
1·2	0·079	3·95	3·70	3·15	2·80	7·92	7·67	7·30
1·4	0·146	3·39	3·14	2·39	2·46	7·45	7·20	6·63
1·6	0·204	2·98	2·73	1·89	2·24	7·08	6·83	6·13
1·8	0·255	2·61	2·38	1·48	2·06	6·78	6·55	5·75
2·0	0·301	2·28	2·09	1·15	1·93	6·51	6·32	5·48
2·2	0·342	2·04	1·85	0·91	1·81	6·30	6·11	5·28
2·5	0·40	1·71	1·52	0·6	1·65	6·00	5·81	5·0
3·0	0·48	1·31	1·11	0·2	1·43	5·65	5·45	4·7
4	0·60	0·78	0·59	−0·3	1·10	5·18	4·99	4·3
5	0·70	0·41	0·25	−0·7	0·85	4·86	4·70	4·0
10	1·00	−0·42	−0·57	−1·7	0·10	4·16	3·93	
20	1·30		−1·3				3·45	
50	1·70						2·65	
215	2·33						1·38	

Polarization of coronal light (K+F) [1, 8]

$r/\mathscr{R}_\odot$	1·0	1·2	1·5	2·0	3·0	5	10	20
Polarization in % equator (sp. max. and min.)	20	35	40	30	20	11	4	2·6
pole (sp. min.)	18	29	25	10	4			

Density irregularities in the corona may be specified approximately by an irregularity factor $x = \overline{N_e^2}/(\overline{N_e})^2$, where N_e is the electron density. Then r.m.s. $N_e = \sqrt{(x)}\,\overline{N_e}$.

In the striated outer corona one might write $x \simeq 1/$(fraction of space occupied by striae). No reliable data exist but the following compromise values are quoted [5].

$r/\mathscr{R}_\odot$	1	1·5	2	3	5	10	215
x	1·1	1·6	2·5	4	8	17	25

Heat conductivity in an electron-ion plasma (approximately coronal conditions) [10]

$$= 1{\cdot}5 \times 10^{-6}\ T^{5/2}$$

Brightness of sky near sun during total eclipse [1]

$$= 1{\cdot}6 \times 10^{-9}\ \text{mean sun brightness.}$$

[1] *A.Q.* **1**, § 73.
[2] C. DE JAGER, *Handb. der Phys.*, **52**, pp. 254, 249, 1959.
[3] R. N. THOMAS and R. G. ATHAY, *Phys. of Chromosphere*, p. 44, Interscience Mon. VI, 1961.
[4] H. C. VAN DE HULST, *B.A.N.*, **11**, 135, 1950.
[5] C. W. ALLEN, I.A.V. Symp. on *Solar Corona*, p. 241, 1961.
[6] H. LUDENDORFF, *Sitz. Preuss. Ak. Wiss.*, 185, 1928; 200, 1934.
[7] M. WALDMEIER, *Z. Ap.*, **53**, 81, 1961.
[8] D. E. BLACKWELL, *M.N.*, **116**, 56, 1956.
[9] G. NEWKIRK, *Ap. J.*, **133**, 983, 1961.
[10] C. DE JAGER and M. KUPERUS, *B.A.N.*, **16**, 71, 1961.

§ 85. Coronal Line Spectrum

The table contains only identified coronal lines for which $\lambda > 3000$ Å. A = transition probability, and W = equivalent width in terms of the K (electron scatter) corona and referring to $r = 1\cdot2\,\mathcal{R}_\odot$ or 3′ from limb.

Identified coronal lines

λ	Ion	Transition Lower − Upper	Upper E.P.	A	W
Å			ev	s^{-1}	Å
3180?	Cr XI	$^3P_1$–$^1D_2$		23	
3329	Ca XII	$^2P_{1\frac12}$–$^2P_{\frac12}$	3·72	488	0·7
3388·0	Fe XIII	$^3P_2$–$^1D_2$	5·96	87	10
3534·0	V x	$^3P_1$–$^1D_2$		17	1
3600·9	Ni XVI	$^2P_{\frac12}$–$^2P_{1\frac12}$	3·44	193	1·3
3642·8	Ni XIII	$^3P_1$–$^1D_2$	5·82	18	0·4
3685	Mn XII	$^3P_2$–$^1D_2$		68	0·2
3800·7	Co XII	$^3P_1$–$^1D_2$		14	0·5
3987·1	Fe XI	$^3P_1$–$^1D_2$	4·68	9	0·7
3998	Cr XI	$^3P_2$–$^1D_2$		53	0·1
4086·5	Ca XIII	$^3P_2$–$^3P_1$	3·03	319	0·4
4232·0	Ni XII	$^2P_{1\frac12}$–$^2P_{\frac12}$	2·93	237	1·1
4256·4	K XI	$^2P_{1\frac12}$–$^2P_{\frac12}$	2·90	250	0·1
4351·0	Co XV	$^2P_{\frac12}$–$^2P_{1\frac12}$	2·78	110	0·1
4412·4	Ar XIV	$^2P_{\frac12}$–$^2P_{1\frac12}$	2·84	108	0·3
4566·6	Cr IX	$^3P_1$–$^1D_2$		8	0·5
5116·0	Ni XIII	$^3P_2$–$^3P_1$	2·42	157	0·8
5302·9	Fe XIV	$^2P_{\frac12}$–$^2P_{1\frac12}$	2·34	60	20
5444·5	Ca XV	$^3P_1$–$^3P_2$	4·46	78	0·2
5536	Ar x	$^2P_{1\frac12}$–$^2P_{\frac12}$	2·24	126	0·3
5694·5	Ca XV	$^3P_0$–$^3P_1$	2·18	95	0·3
5774	Co XVI	$^3P_1$–$^3P_2$		66	
6374·5	Fe x	$^2P_{1\frac12}$–$^2P_{\frac12}$	1·94	69	5
6535·4	Mn XIII	$^2P_{1\frac12}$–$^2P_{1\frac12}$	1·89	33	
6701·9	Ni XV	$^3P_0$–$^3P_1$	1·85	57	1·2
6740	K XIV	$^3P_1$–$^3P_2$		41	0·1
7059·6	Fe XV	$^3P_1$–$^3P_2$	31·7	38	0·8
7891·9	Fe XI	$^3P_2$–$^3P_1$	1·57	44	6
8024·2	Ni XV	$^3P_1$–$^3P_2$	3·39	22	0·3
10746·8	Fe XIII	$^3P_0$–$^3P_1$	1·15	14	50
10797·9	Fe XIII	$^3P_1$–$^3P_2$	2·30	10	30

Change of W with radial distance in terms of K continuum (varies from line to line) [1].

$r/\mathcal{R}_\odot$	1·0	1·1	1·2	1·5	2·0
W	1·3	1·3	1·00	0·38	0·17

[1] A.Q. 1, § 74.
[2] C. Pecker and F. Rohrlich, *Star Spectra in Far Ultra-violet*, Liège Symp., p. 190, 1961.
[3] C. de Jager, *Handb. der Phys.*, **52**, 260, 1959.
[4] M. K. Aly, *Ap. J.*, **122**, 338, 1955.

§ 86. Solar Rotation

Inclination of solar equator to ecliptic
$$= 7° 15'$$

Longitude of ascending node $= 74° 22' + 84' T$
  where T is epoch in centuries from 1900

Sidereal rotation in the sunspot zone (varies with latitude ϕ) [1, 2]
$$= 14°\cdot38 - 2°\cdot7 \sin^2 \phi \text{ per day}$$

Synodic rotation in the sunspot zone $= 13°\cdot39 - 2°\cdot7 \sin^2 \phi$ per day

Sidereal-synodic rotation = earth orbital motion
$$= 0°\cdot985\ 6 \text{ per day}$$

Period of synodic rotation $\simeq 26\cdot90 + 5\cdot2 \sin^2 \phi$ days

Period of sidereal rotation adopted [3] for heliographic longitudes (corresponding to $\phi = 16°$), also used for solar angular momentum, etc.
$$= 25\cdot38 \text{ days}$$

Corresponding synodic period $= 27\cdot275$ days
  A synodic period of $27\cdot00$ days (corresponding to $\phi = 8°$) is used for many statistical studies.

Sun's angular velocity ($\phi = 16°$) $= 2\cdot865 \times 10^{-6}$ radian s^{-1}

Equatorial sidereal rotation ($\phi = 0$) for various features [1]
  Sunspots $14°\cdot38$ per day
  Faculae $14°\cdot52$,,   ,,
  Flocculi $14°\cdot49$,,   ,,
  Prominences $14°\cdot43$,,   ,,
  Metallic reversing layer [3, 4, 5] $13°\cdot6$,,   ,,

Equatorial surface rotation velocity in km/s
$$= 0\cdot140\ 6 \times \text{sidereal rotation in deg. per day}$$
  Surface velocity (sunspots) $= 2\cdot02$ km/s
  Reversing layer velocity [3, 4, 5] $= 1\cdot91$ km/s

  Sidereal rotation per day over the whole range of solar latitude ϕ.

ϕ	0°	15°	30°	45°	60°	75°	90°
Sunspots and faculae [6, 7, 8]	14·4	14·2	13·6	12·6	11·2	9·9	
Prominences and corona [1, 6, 9, 10, 11]	14·2	14·1	13·7	13·2	12·6	11·8	11

[1] A.Q. 1, § 75.
[2] H. W. NEWTON and M. L. NUNN, M.N., 111, 413, 1961.
[3] L. A. HIGGS, M.N., 121, 421, 1960.
[4] A. B. HART, M.N., 114, 17, 1954.
[5] L. HERZBERG, Contr. Dom. Ob., 2, 23, 1957.
[6] A. BRUZEK, Z. Ap., 51, 75, 1961.
[7] M. WALDMEIER, Z. Ap., 38, 37, 1955; 43, 29, 1957.
[8] K. MILOŠEVIĆ, C.R., 240, 731, 1955.
[9] M. TRELLIS, Supp. Ann. d'Ap., No. 5, 1957.
[10] V. BECKER, Z. Ap., 42, 1, 1957.
[11] R. H. COOPER and D. E. BILLINGS, Z. Ap., 55, 24, 1962.

§ 87. Sunspot Activity

Sunspot number $R = k(10g + s)$

where k = observatory reduction constant of order unity, g = number of sunspot groups, s = total number of individual spots. R_z = Zurich sunspot number.

Mean relations between various measures of sunspot activity [1]

Ratio	at sp. min $R \simeq 0$	at sp. max $R \simeq 100$
Number of individual spots/R_z	0·70	0·87
Number of sunspot groups/R_z	0·097	0·083
Umbrae (millionths of hemisphere)/R_z	2·5	2·7
Spot area (millionths of hemisphere)/R_z [9]	14·0	16·5
Faculae (millionths of hemisphere)/R_z	38	25
New groups per year/mean R_z	6·9	5·0
Revival groups per year/mean R_z	0·51	0·56
Individual spots per group	7·3	11·0

The crowding of sunspot groups on the sun's disk should reduce the apparent number of groups at sunspot maximum. When allowance for crowding is made the mean character of spot groups may not change significantly with the sunspot cycle.

Mean ratio (projected spot area in millionths of disk)/(corrected spot area in millionths of hemisphere)   = 1·33

Mean ratio (projected faculae in millionths of disk)/(corrected faculae in millionths of hemisphere)   = 0·84

One parameter sunspots cycle curves [3]

Cycle parameter a	R_{max}	0	1	2	3	4	5	6	7	8	9	10	11	12	13	14
								R (smoothed)								
3·8	155	0	16	82	140	154	133	98	66	41	23	12	6	3	1	0
4·2	138	0	10	61	117	138	125	94	64	40	23	12	6	3	1	0
4·6	124	0	6	46	98	123	116	90	63	39	22	12	6	3	1	0
5·0	112	0	3	32	81	110	107	86	61	38	22	12	6	3	1	0
6·0	89	0	1	15	48	81	88	76	57	36	22	12	6	3	1	0
7·0	73	0	0	8	30	57	72	67	53	34	22	12	6	3	1	0
8·0	60	0	0	4	16	40	57	58	49	33	22	12	6	3	1	0
9·0	51	0	0	1	9	27	44	51	45	32	21	12	6	3	1	0
10·0	44	0	0	0	4	18	33	43	41	31	21	12	6	3	1	0

Characteristics of actual sunspot cycles [1, 4]

a and *s* are parameters fitted to the one parameter curves

Minima m			Intervals		Maxima M			Cycle parameters [7]		
Epoch	R_{min}	Period m to m	m to M	M to m	Epoch	R_{max}	Period M to M	No.	s	a
		y	y	y			y			
1610·8										
		8·2			1615·5		10·5			
1619·0										
		15·0			1626·0		13·5			
1634·0										
		11·0			1639·5		9·5			
1645·0										
		10·0			1649·0		11·0			
1655·0										
		11·0			1660·0		15·0			
1666·0										
		13·5			1675·0		10·0			
1679·5										
		10·0			1685·0		8·0			
1689·0										
		8·5			1693·0		12·5			
1698·0										
		14·0			1705·5	49	12·7			
1712·0										
		11·5			1718·2	53	9·3			
1723·5										
		10·5			1727·5	90	11·2			
1734·0										
		11·0			1738·7	86	11·6			
1745·0										
		10·2	5·3	5·2	1750·3	92·6	11·2	0	1744·7	6·2
1755·2	8·4									
		11·3	6·3	5·0	1761·5	86·5	8·2	1	1755·8	5·8
1766·5	11·2									
		9·0	3·2	5·8	1769·7	115·8	8·7	2	1765·5	5·2
1775·5	7·2									
		9·2	2·9	6·3	1778·4	158·5	9·7	3	1774·6	4·6
1784·7	9·5									
		13·6	3·4	10·2	1788·1	141·2	17·1	4	1784·3	4·2
1798·3	3·2									
		12·3	6·9	5·4	1805·2	49·2	11·2	5	1797·7	8·3
1810·6	0·0									
		12·7	5·8	6·9	1816·4	48·7	13·5	6	1810·6	9·5
1823·3	0·1									
		10·6	6·6	4·0	1829·9	71·7	7·3	7	1823·5	6·6
1833·9	7·3									
		9·6	3·3	6·3	1837·2	146·9	10·9	8	1833·3	4·4
1843·5	10·5									
		12·5	4·6	7·9	1848·1	131·6	12·0	9	1843·9	5·0
1856·0	3·2									
		11·2	4·1	7·1	1860·1	97·9	10·5	10	1855·6	5·6
1867·2	5·2									
		11·7	3·4	8·3	1870·6	140·5	13·3	11	1866·8	4·6
1878·9	2·2									
		10·7	5·0	5·7	1883·9	74·6	10·2	12	1877·9	6·8
1889·6	5·0									
		12·1	4·5	7·6	1894·1	87·9	12·9	13	1888·8	6·2
1901·7	2·6									
		11·9	5·3	6·6	1907·0	64·2	10·6	14	1901·2	6·9
1913·6	1·5									
		10·0	4·0	6·0	1917·6	105·4	10·8	15	1912·7	6·0
1923·6	5·6									
		10·2	4·8	5·4	1928·4	78·1	9·0	16	1922·5	6·4
1933·8	3·4									
		10·4	3·6	6·8	1937·4	119·2	9·9	17	1933·6	4·9
1944·2	7·7									
		10·2	3·3	6·9	1947·5	151·8	10·3	18	1944·2	4·0
1954·4	3·4									
			3·4		1957·8	193		19	1954	3·8

For early solar activity to 649 B.C.: see [2].

Alternation of sunspot cycles may be designated by labelling the cycle number *odd* or *even*; e.g. 1957 is maximum of an *odd* numbered cycle. (It should be noticed that Richardson and Schwarzschild [7] used the terms odd and even in a *reversed* sense.)

Mean sunspot period $= 11 \cdot 04$ year
Mean maximum $\bar{R}_{max} = 103$
Mean minimum $\bar{R}_{min} = 5 \cdot 2$

Magnetic polarity changes in alternate cycles.

For an *even* numbered cycle (e.g. 1947) the *leading* spots in the *northern* solar hemisphere have a *south* (i.e. S seeking) pole *uppermost* on the sun's surface; i.e. the magnetic field is *inwards* through the sun's surface.

Characteristics of a *mean* sunspot group
Sunspot number $R = 12$
Number of individual spots $= 10$
Spot area $= 200$ millionths of hemisphere
        $= 260$ millionths of disk
            (averaged over hemisphere)
Spot radius (if a single spot) $= 0 \cdot 020 \, \mathcal{R}_{\odot}$
Ca^+ plage area $= 1\,800$ millionths of hemisphere

The plage/spot area ratio is taken as 9 which is fairly typical of large plages and spots [8], but the relation is very irregular for small spot groups.

Mean solar characteristics during a sunspot cycle

Year	Min.——	——	——	——	—Max.—	——	——	——	——	——	——	Min.
	0	1	2	3	4	5	6	7	8	9	10	11
Sunspots												
R New cycle	1	10	48	86	100	93	69	47	27	16	9	4
R Old cycle	4	2	0									
Spot latitude	27°	23°	20°	18°	16°	14°	13°	12°	10°	9°	8°	8°
Lat. range Low	19°	13°	7°	3°	1°	0°	0°	0°	0°	0°	1°	2°
[5] High	34°	36°	36°	37°	37°	33°	31°	28°	25°	20°	16°	12°
Prominences												
Relative numbers												
Equatorial	10	10	20	42	60	65	61	52	41	27	15	10
Polar	14	19	32	40	37	31	24	19	15	14	14	14
Latitudes												
Equatorial			30°	29°	28°	27°	25°	24°	23°	23°	22°	
Polar [4]	45°	49°	56°	64°	70°	81°	90°		48°	45°	44°	45°
Corona												
Rel. 5303												
emission	20	40	71	92	100	95	90	83	77	65	55	20
5303 lat. Low	31°	28°	23°	20°	18°	17°	15°	13°	11°	10°	8°	7°
[1] High	50°	55°	65°	78°	90°			45°	50°	56°	52°	48°
Ellipticity, § 84	0·24	0·16	0·07	0·02	0·04	0·11	0·18	0·23	0·25	0·27	0·26	0·24
Magnetically disturbed days per year												
Recurrent	31	23	27	32	38	45	51	60	69	77	73	31
Sporadic	2	4	8	11	13	13	11	9	6	3	2	2
Doubtful	14	18	22	25	27	27	26	24	22	19	17	14
Great storms												
[6]	0·4	0·9	1·7	2·4	2·9	2·7	2·1	1·4	0·9	0·6	0·4	0·4

[1] *A.Q.* 1, § 76.
[2] D. J. Schove, *J. Geoph. Res.*, **60**, 127, 1955.
[3] A. F. Cook, *J. Geoph. Res.*, **54**, 347, 1949.
[4] M. Waldmeier, *A. Mit. Eidg. St. Zurich*, Nos. 201, 208, 215, 221, 229.
[5] W. Gleissberg, *Z. Ap.*, **46**, 219, 1958.
[6] H. W. Newton and A. S. Milsom, *J. Geoph. Res.*, **59**, 203, 1954.
[7] R. S. Richardson and M. Schwarzschild, *Volta Convention*, p. 228, Rome, 1953.
[8] C.R.P.L., *Solar-Geophysical Data*.
[9] J. Xanthakis, *Contr. Athens (Astron.)*, No. 7, 1960.

§ 88. Sunspots

Intensity ratio of total radiation from large spots (ratios are approximately independent of position on disk) [1, 2, 3]

$$\text{Spot umbra/photosphere} = 0\cdot27$$
$$\text{Penumbra/photosphere} = 0\cdot78$$

Effective temperature of large spots (centre of disk)

Umbra	$= 4\ 400\ ^\circ\text{K}$
Penumbra	$= 5\ 700\ ^\circ\text{K}$
Photosphere (for comparison)	$= 6\ 110\ ^\circ\text{K}$

Intensity of large sunspots as a function of wavelength [1, 2, 3] (ratios are approximately independent of position on disk).

λ in μ	0·3	0·4	0·5	0·6	0·8	1·0	1·5	2·0
Umbra/photosphere	0·05	0·09	0·14	0·18	0·30	0·41	0·60	0·66
Penumbra/photosphere			0·70	0·74	0·77			

Reversing layer in sunspots [1]

Excitation temperature	$= 3\ 700\ ^\circ\text{K}$
Electron pressure	$= 0\cdot7\ \text{dyn cm}^{-2}$
Total pressure	$= 4\times10^4\ \text{dyn cm}^{-2}$
Spectral type	$= \text{K0}$

Relation between radius of spot umbra U, penumbra P, and surrounding bright ring R [1, 4, 5, 6]

$$P/U = 2\cdot46 \text{ at sp. max.}$$
$$= 2\cdot29 \text{ at sp. min.}$$

This ratio decreases for spots with area $a < 70$ millionths of the hemisphere or with $P < 0\cdot012\ \mathscr{R}_\odot$

$$P/R = 0\cdot71$$

Magnetic fields at the centre of sunspots [1, 7]

$$H_0 \simeq 1250\ (\log a - 0\cdot2) \quad [H_0 \text{ in gauss or oersted,}$$
$$a \text{ in } 10^{-6} \text{ hemisphere}]$$

a in 10^{-6} hemisphere	0	5	10	50	100	500	1 000	2 000
P in $10^{-3}\ \mathscr{R}_\odot$	0	3	6	10	14	30	45	63
H_0 in gauss or oersted	0	500	1 100	1 700	2 200	3 200	3 600	3 900

Magnetic field distribution in sunspots [1, 8]
$$H = H_0 \exp\left(-2 \cdot 1 r^2 / P^2\right)$$
where r = radial distance from spot centre.

Inclination of magnetic field from solar radius [1, 8]
$$\theta = 70° \times r/P$$

Magnetic flux from a sunspot [1, 8]
$$\phi = 0 \cdot 35\, H_0\, \pi P^2$$

Mean magnetic flux ratio (preceding)/(following) spot [1]
$$\phi_p / \phi_f = 3 \cdot 7$$

Radial velocity outwards from a sunspot in reversing layer, maximum occurring in penumbral region [1, 8, 9]

maximum velocity = $1 \cdot 5$ km/s

measurements are distorted by asymmetry 'flags' in the spectrum lines [8].

Mean life of sunspot groups [1]   = $0 \cdot 12$ day $\times$ (max. a in 10^{-6} hemisphere)

Life of average sunspot group [1] = 6 days, but the life of large groups dominating solar activity variations = $1 \cdot 5$ month [10].

Distribution of life (includes spot groups of all sizes) [1].

Days	1	2	3	5	10	20	30	50	70	100	150
% spots/1 day range	28	12	8	5	2	0·8	0·3	0·05	0·01	0·003	0·001

Life of radial filaments in penumbra [11]
$$= 30 \text{ min}$$

Width of penumbral radial filaments [11]
$$= 300 \text{ km}$$

[1] A.Q. 1, § 77.
[2] P. STUMPFF, Z. Ap., 52, 73, 1961.
[3] M. MAKITA and M. MORIMOTO, P.A.S. Jap., 12, 63, 1960.
[4] E. TANDBERG-HANSSEN, Ap. Norv., 5, 207, 1956.
[5] E. JENSEN, NORDØ, and RINGNES, Ann. d'Ap., 19, 165, 1956.
[6] A. F. W. EDWARDS, Obs., 77, 69, 1957.
[7] T. S. RINGNES and E. JENSEN, Ap. Norv., 7, 99, 1960.
[8] V. BUMBA, Iz. Crimea, 23, 213, 253, 1960.
[9] J. HOLMES, M.N., 122, 301, 1961.
[10] C. W. ALLEN, M.N., 117, 174, 1957.
[11] R. E. DANIELSON, Ap. J., 134, 275, 1961.

§ 89. Faculae

Faculae are too irregular and granular for precise measurements. They are visible only near the limb (i.e. as $\sin\theta \to 1 \cdot 0$). For interpreting smoothed facular intensities it might be assumed that the facular granules occupy about 50% of the nearby surface.

Smoothed brightness of faculae relative to neighbouring photosphere [1]

Sin θ	0	0·5	0·6	0·7	0·8	0·9	0·95
λ 4000	1·00	1·01	1·03	1·05	1·08	1·13	1·16
λ 6000	1·00	1·00	1·01	1·03	1·05	1·08	1·13
Total radiation	1·00	1·00	1·01	1·02	1·03	1·05	1·08

Maximum relative brightness for λ 5500 [2]
grain/intergranular photosphere   = 1·64
occurring at $\sin \theta$ = 0·99

Life of average facula [1] = 15 days, but the life of large faculae dominating solar variations = 2·7 months [3].

Life of granular elements in faculae   = 1 hour ?

Diameter of granular elements in faculae [1, 2]
= 1″·6 = 1 200 km

Excess temperature in facular granules [2]
= 900 °K

Optical depth of facular emission [2] τ range, 0·05 to 0·3.

Area ratio, facula/associated sunspot = 4.

[1] *A.Q.* **1**, § 78.
[2] J. B. Rogerson, *Ap. J.*, **134**, 331, 1961.
[3] C. W. Allen, *M.N.*, **117**, 174, 1957.

§ 90. Granulation and Spicules

Diameter of granules [1, 2]   = 1″·3 = 1 000 km
Range about 0″·5 to 2″·5.

Number of granules on whole photospheric surface [1, 4, 5]
= 3·1 × 10⁶ at sp. max.

Corresponding area occupied per granule
= 2·0 × 10⁶ km²

Perhaps 30% fewer granules at sp. min. [4]

Granula intensity contrast (at about 5000 Å) [1, 2, 3]
brighter granule/intergranule   = 1·3

Corresponding temperature difference
= 300 °K

Root-mean-square variations [2, 3]
Intensity at 5500 Å   ± 0·09 × mean intensity
Temperature   ± 110 °K.

Mean life of granules [1, 2]   = 6 min

Upward velocity of brighter granules [1]
= 0·9 km/s

Life of chromospheric spicules [6, 8]   = 5 min

Number of spicules at height of 3 000 km on the whole sun surface [6, 7, 8, 9]
= 100 000 spicules

Scale height in number of spicules
= 2 000 km

Solar surface occupied by spicules extending to 3 000 km [7]
= 0·8%.

[1] *A.Q.* **1**, § 79.
[2] J. Bahng and M. Schwarzschild, *Ap. J.*, **134**, 312, 337, 1961.
[3] D. E. Blackwell, Dewhirst, and Dollfus, *M.N.*, **119**, 98, 1959.
[4] C. Macris and D. Elias, *Ann. d'Ap.*, **18**, 143, 1965.
[5] J. Rösch, *Ann. d'Ap.*, **22**, 584, 1959.
[6] J. H. Rush and W. O. Roberts, *A.J.*, **58**, 226, 1953.
[7] R. G. Athay, *Ap. J.*, **129**, 164, 1959.
[8] S. L. Lippincott, *A.J.*, **61**, 8, 1956.
[9] L. Woltjer, *B.A.N.*, **12**, 165, 1964.

§ 91. Flocculi, Flares, and Prominences

Flocculus and flare characteristics

Feature	Hα central intensity [1, 2, 3, 4, 6]	Flare Hα line width [1, 2, 3, 6]	Flare area [2]	Flare duration [1, 2, 5]
	continuum	Å	10^{-6} vis. hemis.	min
Dark hydrogen flocculus	0·07			
Normal sun surface	0·16			
Bright hydrogen flocculus	0·4			
Flare, importance 1	0·8	2·6	100 to 250	20
2	1·2	4·1	250 to 600	35
3	1·6	7	600 to 1 200	70
3+	2	10	> 1 200	

Physical condition of flares (derived from optical data and perhaps bearing very little relation to the source of high energy particles and synchrotron radio emission) [1, 7, 8, 9]

log (electron density) $\qquad = 13·0$ [in cm^{-3}]

log (2nd state H atoms per unit column)

$\qquad\qquad = 15$ [in cm^{-2}]

Temperature $\qquad\qquad = 12\,000\,°K$

Scale height [14] $\qquad = 20\,000$ km

Physical condition of prominences [1, 9, 10, 11, 12, 13]

log (electron density) $\qquad = 10·5$ [in cm^{-3}]

log (H atom density) $\qquad = 11$ [in cm^{-3}]

Kinetic temperature [16] $\qquad = 8\,000\,°K$

Prominence normal dimensions [1]

Height $\qquad\qquad\qquad = 30\,000$ km

Length $\qquad\qquad\qquad = 200\,000$ km

Thickness $\qquad\qquad\quad = 5\,000$ km

Volume $\qquad\qquad\qquad = 10^{28}\,cm^3$

Distribution in prominence height [15]

90% are less than 40 000 km

Scale height in number beyond height of 40 000 km [15]

$\qquad\qquad = 20\,000$ km

Number of dark filaments on sun
    at sp. max. $\simeq$ 20
    at sp. min. $\simeq$ 4

Mean life of quiescent prominences   = 2·3 rotations of sun

Rate of increase of prominence length in early stages
                          = 100 000 km/rotation

Time for material of a quiescent prominence to move into sun
                          $\simeq$ 5 days

[1] *A.Q.* **1**, § 80.
[2] FLARE WORKING GROUP, *I.A.V. Trans.*, **9**, 146, 1955.
[3] M. A. ELLISON, *Pub. R.O. Edinburgh*, **1**, 75, 1952.
[4] H. W. DODSON, HEDEMAN, and McMATH, *Ap. J. Supp.*, **2**, 241, 1956.
[5] M. WALDMEIER and H. BACHMANN, *Z. Ap.*, **47**, 81, 1959.
[6] T. S. RAZMADZE, *Abatsumani*, B 22, 115, 1958.
[7] Z. SUEMOTO and E. HIEI, *P.A.S. Jap.*, **11**, 185, 1959.
[8] Z. ŠVESTKA, *B.A. Czech.*, **7**, 130, 1956; *Cz. Ac. Sci. Ast. I.*, No. 32, 1957.
[9] J. T. JEFFERIES, *M.N.*, **116**, 629, 1956; **117**, 493, 1957.
[10] V. N. ZUYKOV, *Iz. Pulkovo*, **20**, No. 159, 65, 1958.
[11] G. S. IVANOV-KHOLODNYI, *A. Zh.*, **36**, 589, 1959; *Sov. A.*, **3**, 578.
[12] R. G. ATHAY and F. Q. ORRALL, *Ap. J.*, **126**, 167, 1957.
[13] A. B. SEVERNY, *A. Zh.*, **31**, 131, 1954.
[14] J. W. WARWICK, *Ap. J.*, **121**, 376, 1955.
[15] R. ANANTHAKRISHNAN, *Ap. J.*, **133**, 969, 1961.
[16] J. T. JEFFERIES and F. Q. ORRALL, *Ap. J.*, **135**, 109, 1962.

§ 92. Solar Radio Emission (Solar Noise)

The following five components of radio emission (*a*) to (*e*) may be recognized on single frequency recordings, and the spectra of rapidly changing phenomena may be classified into the types I, II, III, IV, and V:

   (*a*) quiet thermal emission,

   (*b*) slowly varying (steady sunspot) emission, associated with sunspots,

   (*c*) noise storms (enhanced radiation) composed mainly of type I bursts, associated with sunspots,

   (*d*) outbursts, complexes containing type II, III, IV, V bursts or emission, associated with flares,

   (*e*) isolated (non-polarized) bursts, type III, V, and U bursts, associated with sunspots or flares.

Solar emission may be expressed quantitatively by f_ν the flux density usually in watts m^{-2} $(c/s)^{-1}$ at the earth, or by T_a the apparent temperature, i.e. the black body temperature of the visible disk to give the flux density.

$f_\nu = 2·089 \times 10^{-44} T_a \nu^2$ [f_ν in w m^{-2} $(c/s)^{-1}$, T_a in °K, ν = frequency in c/s]

I_ν = radiation intensity = $2·599 \times 10^{-47} T_b \nu^2$ w $m^{-2}('$ arc$)^{-2}$ $(c/s)^{-1}$

T_b = brightness temperature.

T_c = brightness temperature at centre of quiet sun disk.

Quantities that vary with the sunspot cycle are (as far as possible) reduced to the conditions of either sunspot maximum (sp. max. at $R = 100$, $A_c = 1\,650$) or sunspot minimum (sp. min. at $R = 0$, $A = 0$), R = sunspot number, A_c = corrected sunspot area (in millionths of the hemisphere), A_p = projected sunspot area (in millionths of disk).

Quiet sun radiation (other components eliminated)

Band	λ	ν	$\log T_a$ Sp. max. [3, 4, 7, 8]	$\log T_a$ Sp. min.	$\log T_c$ Sp. max. [3, 6]	$\log T_c$ Sp. min.	T_c/T_a Sp. max. [2, 3, *]	T_c/T_a Sp. min.	f_ν Sp. max.	f_ν Sp. min.
	cm	Mc/s	°K		°K				10^{-22} w m^{-2} (c/s)$^{-1}$	
m	600	50	5·97	5·84	5·77	5·73	0·63	0·78	0·49	0·36
	300	100	6·04	5·93	5·83	5·81	0·62	0·75	2·3	1·8
	150	200	6·05	5·92	5·85	5·79	0·62	0·73	9·4	6·9
dm	60	500	5·75	5·54	5·56	5·40	0·65	0·72	29	18
	30	1 000	5·32	5·11	5·15	4·98	0·68	0·73	44	27
	15	2 000	4·92	4·77	4·79	4·67	0·73	0·79	69	49
cm	6	5 000	4·48	4·34	4·38	4·26	0·79	0·81	155	115
	3	10 000	4·20	4·09	4·15	4·02	0·85	0·85	340	260
	1·5	20 000	3·99	3·94	3·95	3·90	0·91	0·91	820	730
	0·6	50 000	3·81	3·81	3·80	3·80	0·97	0·97	3 400	3 400

* For determining T_c/T_a in the m band it was assumed that the ellipticity of the radio emission changed similarly to that of the visible corona.

Flux associated with solar activity

Band	λ	ν	Slowly varying emission for $R = 100$ $A_c = 1\,650 \times 10^{-6}$ hemi. $A_p = 2\,200 \times 10^{-6}$ disk [1, 4, 6, 9, 10]	Typical T_b	Typical noise storm [1, 8]	Typical outburst [1, 8]
			10^{-22} w m^{-2} (c/s)$^{-1}$	10^6 °K	10^{-22} w m^{-2} (c/s)$^{-1}$	
m	600	50	0·0		70	500
	300	100	0·0		100	500
	150	200	0·2	0·8	70	400
dm	60	500	7	4·6	5	300
	30	1 000	20	3·2	0	200
	15	2 000	48	1·9		100
cm	6	5 000	52	0·35		50
	3	10 000	45	0·09		20
	1·5	20 000				
	0·6	50 000				

Typical active area [6, 9]
    Sunspot area $= 700 \times 10^{-6}$ hemisphere
    Plage area $= 6\,000 \times 10^{-6}$ hemisphere
    Plage area at centre of disk $= 12\,000 \times 10^{-6}$ disk

Plage diameter $= 3'\cdot5$

Flux $= 0\cdot4 \times$ flux for $R = 100$.

The tabulated typical brightness T_b is based on this data with radio area $=$ plage area. The observed trend is for the radio diameter to increase with λ [5] and this can reduce T_b to less than $1\cdot5 \times 10^6\ °K$ over the whole λ range.

Observed height of emission above photosphere [5]

$= 25\ 000$ km

and tending to increase with λ.

The mean intensity of the 'typical' noise storm would be exceeded on about 10 days per year at sp. max. The mean intensity of all storm noise at sp. max. is about $0\cdot16 \times$ typical noise storm.

The intensity of the 'typical' outburst would be exceeded by about 100 outbursts per year at sp. max. The life of a typical outburst is about 10 minutes. The mean flux of outburst reduction for a sp. max. year is $0\cdot01 \times$ typical outburst flux.

Type I bursts [1, 11]

Whole-$\frac{1}{4}$-band width $= 4$ Mc/s

Life $= 0\cdot5$ sec.

Complete circular polarization.

R polarization from S magnetic pole sunspots [R polarization is used in *radio-convention*: vector rotates *clockwise* in a *fixed plane* viewed *in the direction of* propagation, i.e. with the source behind you; R polarization is oriented in space like a *left-hand screw*].

Type II bursts [1, 13]

Whole-$\frac{1}{4}$-band width $= 10$ Mc/s

Life $\simeq 1$ min

Frequency drift $d\nu/dt = -0\cdot3(\nu/100)^2$ (Mc/s) s^{-1} [ν in Mc/s]

Type III bursts [1, 2]

Whole-$\frac{1}{4}$-band width $= 10$ Mc/s

Life (at one frequency) $\simeq 2$ sec

Frequency drift $d\nu/dt = -\nu/4\cdot5$ s^{-1}

Turning point for U bursts $\nu = 100$ Mc/s

Type IV emission [12]

Band width > 100 Mc/s

Life $\simeq 1$ hour

Circularly polarized

Type V emission

Similar to IV but shorter period and lower frequency.

[1] *A.Q.* 1, § 81.
[2] C. DE JAGER, *Handb. der Phys.*, **52**, 283, 1959.
[3] C. W. ALLEN, *Radio Astronomy*, I.A.U. Symp. **4**, 253, 1957.
[4] C. W. ALLEN, *M.N.*, **117**, 174, 1957.
[5] G. NEWKIRK, *Ap. J.*, **133**, 983, 1961.
[6] G. SWARUP, *Stanford Lab.*, No. 13, 1961.
[7] W. N. CHRISTIANSEN, WARBURTON, and DAVIES, *Aust. J. Phys.*, **10**, 491, 1957.
[8] *Quarterly Bulletin of Solar Activity.*
[9] K. KAWABATA, *Pub. A.S. Jap.*, **12**, 513, 1960.
[10] T. KAKINUMA, *A.J.*, **66**, 287, 1961.
[11] Ø. ELGARØY and Ø. HAUGE, *Ap. Norveg.*, **6**, 85, 1958.
[12] J. P. WILD, SHERIDAN, and TRENT, *Radio Astronomy*, I.A.U. Symp., **9**, p. 176, 1959.
[13] A. MAXWELL and A. R. THOMPSON, *Ap. J.*, **135**, 138, 1962.

CHAPTER 10

NORMAL STARS

§ 93. Stellar Quantities and Inter-relations

$\mathscr{M}$ = mass ($\odot$ = sun, i.e. $\mathscr{M}_\odot$ = sun's mass)

$\mathscr{R}$ = radius

$\mathscr{L}$ = luminosity = total outflow of radiation

L = outflow of luminous radiation

$\bar{\rho}$ = mean density = $\mathscr{M}/(\tfrac{4}{3}\pi\mathscr{R}^3)$

Sp = spectral classification, which may be combined with a luminosity class

m = apparent magnitude = $-2\cdot5$ log brightness. Subscripts:—p or pg = photographic, v or $_v$ = visual, b = blue, u = ultra-violet, r = red, ir = infra-red, bol = bolometric (total radiation)

$U, B, V = m_U, m_B, m_V$ = apparent magnitudes in the ultra-violet, blue, and visual systems

M = absolute magnitude = apparent magnitude standardized to 10 pc without absorption

$m_v(10)$ = apparent visual magnitude of the 10th brightest object of the type concerned

$B - V$ = colour index; $(B - V)_0$ = intrinsic colour index. Various other colour indices (e.g. $U - B$) can be formed

B.C. = bolometric correction = $m_v - m_{bol}$ (always positive)

A = space absorption in magnitudes (usually visual)

m_0 = corrected magnitude = $m - A$

E = colour excess = $B - V - (B - V)_0$

$m - M$ = distance modulus = 5 log (dist. in pc) $- 5 + A$

$m_0 - M$ = corrected distance modulus = 5 log (dist. in pc) $- 5$

$\mathscr{F}$ = total radiant surface flux per stellar surface. $\mathscr{F}_\lambda$, $\mathscr{F}_v$ are similar, smoothed through absorption lines

$\mathscr{F}'$ = is similar to $\mathscr{F}$ but refers to the continuum. $\mathscr{F}' - \mathscr{F}$ = radiation absorbed in spectrum lines

f = radiant surface flux from a star outside the earth's atmosphere. Also f_λ, f'_λ, etc. as for $\mathscr{F}$

T = stellar surface temperature. T_e = effective temperature (from $\mathscr{F} = \sigma T_e^4$), T_b = brightness temperature, T_c = colour temperature (visible continuum)

ϕ, G = gradient of a stellar spectrum continuum; ϕ = absolute gradient = $5\lambda - d (\ln \mathscr{F}'_\lambda)/d(1/\lambda)$ [with λ in μ]; G = relative gradient (= $\phi +$ a constant)

g = surface gravity

D = Balmer discontinuity = log $(\mathscr{F}'3700^+/\mathscr{F}'3700^-)$ where 3700 Å is taken as the discontinuity wavelength

B_λ, V_λ, K_λ = sensitivity relative to the maximum of standard blue, visual, and normal eye observations (§ 96)

d = distance, usually in pc (also used for differential)

π = parallax, in " = $1/d$ with d in pc

μ = annual proper motion (in ")

v_r = sight-line velocity away from the sun (in km/s)

v_t = transverse velocity, in km/s = $4\cdot741\ \mu/\pi$

α, δ, l^{II}, b^{II} = equatorial and new galactic coordinates

Numerical relations

$\log (\mathscr{R}/\mathscr{R}_\odot) = (5\ 680°/T_\mathrm{b}) - 0\cdot20\ M_\mathrm{v} - 0\cdot02 + 0\cdot5 \log [1 - \exp(-c_2/\lambda_\mathrm{v}T)]$
where T_b is brightness temperature at visual wavelength $\lambda_\mathrm{v} = 5500$ Å, and the last term is usually negligible. $5\ 680° = c_2 \log e/2\lambda_\mathrm{v} = 3\ 124°/\lambda_\mathrm{v}$ [in μ].

$\log (\mathscr{R}/\mathscr{R}_\odot) = (7\ 200°/T_\mathrm{b}) - 0\cdot20\ M_\mathrm{B} - 0\cdot19 + 0\cdot5 \log [1 - \exp(-c_2/\lambda_\mathrm{B}T)]$
where T_b is now the brightness temperature at $\lambda_\mathrm{B} = 4350$ Å.

$$M = m + 5 + 5 \log \pi - A = m + 5 - 5 \log d - A$$

$$M_\mathrm{bol} = 4\cdot72 - 2\cdot5 \log (\mathscr{L}/\mathscr{L}_\odot)$$
$$= 42\cdot35 - 10 \log T_\mathrm{e} - 5 \log (\mathscr{R}/\mathscr{R}_\odot)$$
$$= 96\cdot56 - 10 \log T_\mathrm{e} - 5 \log \mathscr{R}$$

$$\log \mathscr{L} = -3\cdot147 + 2 \log \mathscr{R} + 4 \log T_\mathrm{e}$$

$$B - V \simeq (7\ 300°/T_\mathrm{c}) - 0\cdot52$$

$$\text{B.C.} \simeq -42\cdot5 + 10 \log T + 29\ 000/T \quad (\text{§ 99})$$

$$(m_\mathrm{bol} = 0) \text{ star} \equiv 2\cdot52 \times 10^{-5} \text{ erg cm}^{-2}\text{ s}^{-1}$$
$$\text{outside earth atmosphere}$$

$$(M_\mathrm{bol} = 0) \text{ star} \equiv 3\cdot02 \times 10^{28} \text{ watt of emitted radiation}$$

$$(m_\mathrm{v} = 0) \text{ star} \equiv 2\cdot65 \times 10^{-10} \text{ phot} = 2\cdot65 \times 10^{-6} \text{ lux}$$
$$\text{outside earth atmosphere}$$

$$(M_\mathrm{v} = 0) \text{ star} \equiv 2\cdot52 \times 10^{29} \text{ candela}$$

$$1(m_\mathrm{v} = 0) \text{ star deg}^{-2} \equiv 0\cdot87 \times 10^{-6} \text{ stilb} = 2\cdot74 \times 10^{-6} \text{ lambert}$$
$$\text{outside earth atmosphere}$$

$$m_\mathrm{v} \text{ of 1 lux} = -13\cdot94.$$

The reason why this differs from the value ($m_0^{(3)} = -13\cdot78$) of Martynov [3], whose data has been used, is that we have compared the eye sensitivity curve (K_λ) with the V_λ system (§ 96) on the basis of the solar spectral distribution, whereas Martynov used a $T = 2\ 042$ °K black body for this purpose.

$$m_\mathrm{v} = -2\cdot5 \log \left(\int V_\lambda f_\lambda\, d\lambda \right) - 14\cdot08$$

$$m_\mathrm{B} = -2\cdot5 \log \left(\int B_\lambda f_\lambda\, d\lambda \right) - 12\cdot92$$

where $\int f_\lambda\, d\lambda$ is in erg cm^{-2} s^{-1}; V_λ and B_λ in § 96.

$$\log f_\lambda(V) = -0.4\, m_\mathrm{v} - 8.42 \quad [1, 2]$$

where $f_\lambda(V)$ is flux in erg cm^{-2} Å^{-1} s^{-1} outside atmosphere near 5500 Å. This relation is almost unchanged from B to M stars.

$$\log f_\lambda(B) = -0.4\, m_\mathrm{B} - 8.21 \quad [1, 2]$$

where $f_\lambda(B)$ is flux in erg cm^{-2} Å^{-1} s^{-1} outside atm. near 4350 Å.

$$\log \mathscr{F}(V) = -0.4\, M_\mathrm{v} + 8.87 - 2 \log (\mathscr{R}/\mathscr{R}_\odot)$$
$$\log \mathscr{F}(B) = -0.4\, M_\mathrm{B} + 9.08 - 2 \log (\mathscr{R}/\mathscr{R}_\odot)$$

where $\mathscr{F}(V)(B)$ is flux in erg cm^{-2} Å^{-1} s^{-1} at star surface near 5500 Å (V) and 4350 Å (B)

$$A_\mathrm{v} = 3.0\, E_{\mathrm{B-v}}$$

$$\log (\mathscr{L}/\mathscr{L}_\odot) \simeq 3.0 \log (\mathscr{M}/\mathscr{M}_\odot) \quad [\text{see } \S\,100]$$

$$T_\mathrm{R} \simeq 0.93\, T_\mathrm{e}$$

$$T_0 \simeq 0.78\, T_\mathrm{e} \quad (\text{less for early types } [3, 4])$$

where T_R and T_0 are the temperatures of the reversing layer and the extreme surface.

[1] *A.Q.* **1**, § 92.
[2] R. V. WILLSTROP, *M.N.*, **121**, 17, 1960; also thesis 1959.
[3] D. YA. MARTYNOV, *A.Zh.*, **36**, 648, 1959; *Sov. A.*, **3**, 633.
[4] J.-C. PECKER, Liège Symp. on *Spectra in Far Ultra-violet*, p. 487, 1961.

§ 94. Spectral Classification

The features of normal stellar line spectra permit a spectral classification, *Sp*, in the scheme:

Class	Class characteristics
O	Hot stars with He II absorption
B	He I absorption; H developing later
A	Very strong H, decreasing later; Ca II increasing
F	Ca II stronger; H weaker; metals developing
G	Ca II strong; Fe and other metals strong; H weaker
K	Strong metallic lines; CH and CN bands developing
M	Very red; TiO bands developing strongly

Further subdivision of classes (e.g. B0, B1, B2, etc.) is based on detailed systems [2, 3] with interagreement of about ± 1 subdivision. Not all subdivisions are used in the standard systems.

In addition each class may be subdivided on the basis of luminosity as follows:

Yerkes luminosity class, etc.		Examples	
I	supergiants, including Ia, Ib, and c stars	B0 I	cB0
II	bright giants	B5 II	
III	giants	G0 III	gG0
IV	subgiants	G5 IV	
V	main sequence, dwarfs	G0 V	dG0
(VI)	subdwarfs		sdK5
	white dwarfs		wA4

In later tabulations the classification, *Sp*, has adopted the Yerkes system [3] as far as possible. However for smoothing purposes each class is taken to have 10 equally spaced subdivisions. This particularly affects our K5 ($\simeq$ Yerkes K3 or K4).

Additional classes

Sp		Class characteristics
R	[4, 6]	Strong CN bands and C_2 bands increasing
N	[4, 6]	C_2 bands, CN bands decreasing
S	[5]	ZrO bands

Other characteristics sometimes included in the *Sp* notation

$$e = \text{emission lines, e.g. Be (§§ 106, 109)}$$
$$f = \text{certain O type emission line stars}$$
$$p = \text{peculiar spectrum}$$
$$\text{WC, WN} = \text{Wolf-Rayet stars}$$
$$n = \text{nebulous lines}$$
$$s = \text{sharp lines}$$
$$k = \text{interstellar lines present}$$
$$m = \text{metallic line star.}$$

[1] *A.Q.* **1**, § 93.
[2] 'Henry Draper Catalogue,' *Harv. Ann.*, **91–99**, 1918–24.
[3] W. W. MORGAN, KEENAN, and KELLMAN, *Atlas of Stellar Spectra*, Chicago, 1943.
[4] C. D. SHANE, *Lick Ob. Bull.*, **13**, 123, 1928.
[5] P. C. KEENAN, *Ap. J.*, **120**, 484, 1954.
[6] P. C. KEENAN and W. W. MORGAN, *Ap. J.*, **94**, 501, 1941.

§ 95. Stellar Classification and Absolute Visual Magnitude

The sequences are not always well separated from one another. In later tables stars are usually segregated only into dwarfs, giants, and supergiants. There may be more than one sequence of white dwarfs (§ 111).

A plot of the data in this section is usually called the Hertzsprung-Russell (H.R.) Diagram.

$$M_\mathrm{v}$$

Sp	Supergiants		Bright giants	Giants	Sub-giants	Main sequence dwarfs	Sub-dwarfs	White dwarfs	Zero age main seq.
	Ia	Ib	II	III	IV	V			
	[1, 2, 3, 6, 8]			[1, 2, 3, 4, 8]		[1, 2, 3, 5]	[1, 4, 5, 7]		[2]
O5						$- 6$			
B0	$-6 \cdot 7$	$-6 \cdot 1$	$-5 \cdot 4$	-5	-5	$- 3 \cdot 7$		10	$-0 \cdot 2$
B5		$-5 \cdot 8$	$-4 \cdot 7$	$-2 \cdot 6$	$-1 \cdot 9$	$- 0 \cdot 9$		11	
A0	$-6 \cdot 8$	$-5 \cdot 3$	-3	$-0 \cdot 6$	$-0 \cdot 2$	$+ 0 \cdot 7$		$11 \cdot 4$	$+1 \cdot 5$
A5		$-4 \cdot 9$	-2	$+0 \cdot 9$	$+1 \cdot 4$	$+ 2 \cdot 0$		$12 \cdot 1$	$+2 \cdot 5$
F0	$-6 \cdot 8$	$-4 \cdot 7$	-2	$+1 \cdot 5$	$+2 \cdot 2$	$+ 2 \cdot 8$		$12 \cdot 8$	$+3 \cdot 2$
F5		$-4 \cdot 5$	-2	$+1 \cdot 7$	$+2 \cdot 9$	$+ 3 \cdot 8$	5	$13 \cdot 5$	$+4 \cdot 0$
G0		$-4 \cdot 4$	-2	$+1 \cdot 8$	$+3 \cdot 2$	$+ 4 \cdot 6$	$5 \cdot 9$	$14 \cdot 1$	$+4 \cdot 8$
G5		$-4 \cdot 4$	$-2 \cdot 0$	$+1 \cdot 5$	$+3 \cdot 3$	$+ 5 \cdot 2$	$6 \cdot 6$	$14 \cdot 6$	$+5 \cdot 3$
K0		$-4 \cdot 4$	$-2 \cdot 1$	$+0 \cdot 8$	$+3 \cdot 3$	$+ 6 \cdot 0$	$7 \cdot 5$	15	$+6 \cdot 1$
K5		$-4 \cdot 4$	$-2 \cdot 3$	$0 \cdot 0$		$+ 7 \cdot 4$	$9 \cdot 0$	15	$+7 \cdot 5$
M0		$-4 \cdot 4$	$-2 \cdot 4$	$-0 \cdot 3$		$+ 8 \cdot 9$	$10 \cdot 6$	15	$+9 \cdot 0$
M2			$-2 \cdot 4$	$-0 \cdot 4$		$+ 9 \cdot 9$	$12 \cdot 0$		
M5				$-0 \cdot 6$		$+12 \cdot 0$	$13 \cdot 7$		
M8						$+16$	16		
R0[9]				$+0 \cdot 4$					
R5				$-1 \cdot 0$					

[1] A.Q. **1**, § 94.
[2] H. C. Arp, *Handb. der Phys.*, **51**, 75, 1958.
[3] Parenago, Baum, Greenstein, Wilson, and Kopylov, I.A.U. Symp. No. 10 on *Hertz-sprung-Russell Diagram*, pp. 11, 23, 33, 39, 41, 1959.
[4] G. A. Starikova, *A. Zh.*, **37**, 476, 1960; *Sov. A.*, **4**, 451.
[5] W. Gleise, *Z. Ap.*, **39**, 1, 1956.
[6] R. M. Petrie and B. N. Moyls, *Dom. Ap. Ob.*, **10**, 287, 1956.
[7] P. P. Parenago, *A. Zh.*, **35**, 169, 1958; *Sov. A.*, **2**, 151.
[8] H. L. Johnson and B. Iriarte, *Lowell Ob. Bull.*, Nos. 90, 91, 1958.
[9] G. L. Vandervort, *A.J.*, **63**, 477, 1958.

§ 96. Star Colour Systems

Star colours are determined by relating the intensity of their radiations in two or more regions of the spectrum. The regions may be indicated by their effective wavelength (λ_U for ultra-violet, λ_B for blue, λ_V for visual, etc.). It is the difference in the reciprocal wavelength (e.g. $1/\lambda_\mathrm{B} - 1/\lambda_\mathrm{V}$) that defines the base-length of the colour system; this may be denoted $\Delta(1/\lambda)$. The zeros of the various colour systems are defined by standard stars. *Colour indices* are related to $\mathscr{F}_\lambda$ the actual smoothed flux of radiation near the effective wavelength, while *gradients* are related to $\mathscr{F}'_\lambda$ the flux of the continuum. The colour temperature T_c is related to $\mathscr{F}'_\lambda$. An unfortunate complication is introduced by the fact that the effective wavelengths of a colour index system change with the colour itself.

The U, B, V system

This system [2, 3] has replaced the international photographic and photovisual systems. The alternative notation for the stellar magnitudes is

$$U = m_U, \quad B = m_B, \quad V = m_V$$

The colour indices normally used are $B - V$ and $U - B$

$$B - V = 2 \cdot 5 \log (\mathscr{F}_{\lambda V}/\mathscr{F}_{\lambda B}) + 0 \cdot 71$$

Effective wavelengths

T_c	$B-V$	Sp	λ_U	λ_B	λ_V	$\Delta(1/\lambda)$	
						$B-V$	$U-B$
°K			Å	Å	Å	μ^{-1}	μ^{-1}
25 000	− 0·2	B4	3550	4330	5470	0·48	0·50
10 000	+ 0·2	A7	3650	4400	5480	0·46	0·46
4 000	+ 1·3	K7	3800	4500	5510	0·42	0·41

Response curves for the U, B, V sensitivities and also for the normal and dark-adapted eye. The data does not include the aluminium-reflectivity variation with λ which however is small. It also does not include atmospheric absorption which may be large [1, 3].

λ	U_λ	B_λ	V_λ	Eye	
				K_λ Normal	Dark
Å					
3000	0·14	0·00	0·00	0·00	0·00
3200	0·62	0·00	0·00	0·00	0·00
3400	0·92	0·00	0·00	0·00	0·00
3600	1·00	0·00	0·00	0·00	0·00
3800	0·70	0·14	0·00	0·00	0·00
4000	0·06	0·94	0·00	0·00	0·01
4200	0·00	0·99	0·00	0·00	0·06
4400	0·00	0·90	0·00	0·02	0·17
4600	0·00	0·73	0·00	0·05	0·36
4800	0·00	0·54	0·00	0·13	0·61
5000	0·00	0·36	0·36	0·31	0·88
5200	0·00	0·21	0·93	0·69	0·98
5400	0·00	0·07	0·98	0·94	0·70
5600	0·00	0·00	0·80	1·00	0·36
5800	0·00	0·00	0·59	0·88	0·15
6000	0·00	0·00	0·40	0·65	0·05
6200	0·00	0·00	0·24	0·39	0·02
6400	0·00	0·00	0·10	0·18	0·00
6600	0·00	0·00	0·03	0·06	0·00

Equivalent width of spectrum ranges referred to the maximum response

$$U_\lambda \quad 690 \text{ Å} \qquad K_\lambda \text{ (normal eye)} \quad 1070 \text{ Å}$$
$$B_\lambda \quad 960 \text{ Å} \qquad K_\lambda \text{ (dark adapted)} \quad 880 \text{ Å}$$
$$V_\lambda \quad 900 \text{ Å}$$

Relative response to equal energy in all wavelength ranges

$$U : B : V = 1 \cdot 04 : 1 \cdot 40 : 1 \cdot 00$$

For $T = \infty$ [15]
$$B - V = -0 \cdot 46$$
$$U - B = -1 \cdot 33$$

Gradients

Gradient between wavelength λ_1 and λ_2

$$\phi = -\ln (\lambda_1^5 \mathscr{F}_1' / \lambda_2^5 \mathscr{F}_2') \Big/ \left(\frac{1}{\lambda_1} - \frac{1}{\lambda_2} \right) \quad [\lambda \text{ in } \mu]$$

Black body gradient

$$\phi(T) = 5\lambda - \frac{d}{d(1/\lambda)} (\ln \mathscr{F}_\lambda') = (c_2/T)/[1 - \exp(-c_2/\lambda T)]$$

where T = black body temperature, c_2 = radiation constant. $\phi(T)$ is dependent on T and (for hot stars) on mean wavelength λ.

$$\phi(T)$$

T	$\dfrac{c_2}{T}$	λ in μ		T	$\dfrac{c_2}{T}$	λ in μ	
		0·4	0·5			0·4	0·5
°K		μ		°K		μ	
∞	0·00	0·40	0·50	6 500	2·21	2·22	2·23
50 000	0·29	0·56	0·66	6 000	2·40	2·40	2·42
30 000	0·48	0·68	0·77	5 500	2·61	2·61	2·62
20 000	0·72	0·86	0·94	5 000	2·88	2·88	2·88
15 000	0·96	1·06	1·12	4 500	3·20	3·20	3·20
12 000	1·20	1·26	1·32	4 000	3·60	3·60	3·60
11 000	1·31	1·36	1·42	3 500	4·11	4·11	4·11
10 000	1·44	1·48	1·52	3 000	4·80	4·80	4·80
9 000	1·60	1·63	1·66	2 500	5·75	5·75	5·75
8 000	1·80	1·82	1·85	2 000	7·20	7·20	7·20
7 000	2·05	2·06	2·08	1 500	9·59	9·59	9·59

Relative gradient G used in the visible spectrum 4100–6500 Å (most values published in the visible are on the Greenwich system G_G [4])

$$\phi = G_G + 1 \cdot 11$$

For unreddened A0 stars $G_G = 0$; $\phi = 1 \cdot 11$; $T_c = 15\,400$ °K.

Violet gradient ϕ_1 (3700–4900 Å) [5]

For unreddened A0 stars

$$\phi_1 = 1 \cdot 02, \quad T_c = 16\,000 \text{ °K}$$

Ultra-violet gradients ϕ_2 (3150–3700 Å) [5]

For unreddened A0 stars

$$\phi_2 = 1 \cdot 39, \quad T_c = 10\,500 \text{ °K}$$

Effective wavelengths for some other photometric systems

System	T_c	λ						$\Delta(1/\lambda)$	
	°K	Å						$1/\mu$	
International pg, pv [1]	25 000			4170	5420			0·55	
	10 000			4250	5430			0·51	
	4 000			4400	5460			0·44	
Photoelectric C_1 [6]	10 000			4250	4750			0·25	
Photoelectric C_2 [7]	10 000			4300	4650			0·17	
Six colour [12]	10 000	U 3550	Vi 4200	B 4900	G 5700	R 7200	I 10300	Vi−I 1·40	Vi−R 0·98
Infra-red [8]	10 000			6750	8300			0·27	
Photo-red [9]	10 000			4250	6200			0·75	
U, G, R [10]	10 000		U 3660	G 4630	R 6380			U−G 0·57	G−R 0·60

Inter-relations between colour systems

The various comparisons between $B - V$ and the international colour $C = m_{pg} - m_{pv}$ do not justify a relation any more elaborate than the following [3, 14]:

$$B - V = C + 0·11 = P - V + 0·11$$

Other colour relations

$$
\begin{aligned}
B - V &= 0·59\,G_G - 0·07 = 0·58\,\phi - 0·72 \quad [4] \\
&= 1·9\,C_1 + 0·1 \quad [6] \\
&= 3·0\,C_2 + 0·1 \quad [7] \\
&= 0·75\,(\text{photo-red colour}) + 0·1 \quad [9] \\
&= 1·10\,C_p \quad [11] \\
&= 0·37\,(\text{Vi} - \text{I}) + 0·69 \quad \text{six colour} \quad [12] \\
&= 0·78\,(\text{Vi} - \text{G}) + 0·67 \quad \text{six colour} \quad [12] \\
&= 0·63\,(\text{P} - \text{R}) + 0·1 \quad [8] \\
&= 0·62\,(c_2/T) - 1·06 \quad [13] \\
&= 1·0\,(\text{G} - \text{R}) - 0·21 \quad [10]
\end{aligned}
$$

$$
\begin{aligned}
C &= B - V - 0·11 \\
\phi &= G_G + 1·11 \\
G_G &= 0·67\,(\text{Vi} - \text{I}) + 1·30 \quad \text{non-reddened} \\
&= 0·67\,(\text{Vi} - \text{I}) + 1·39 \quad \text{reddened}
\end{aligned}
$$

$$
\begin{aligned}
B &= m_{pg} + 0·11 \\
V &= m_{pv} + 0·00
\end{aligned}
$$

[1] *A.Q.* **1**, § 95.
[2] H. L. JOHNSON and W. W. MORGAN, *Ap. J.*, **114**, 522, 1951; **117**, 313, 1953.
[3] H. L. JOHNSON, *Ann. d'Ap.*, **18**, 292, 1955.
[4] W. M. H. GREAVES, DAVIDSON, and MARTIN, *M.N.*, **94**, 488, 1934.

[5] D. Barbier and D. Chalonge, *Ann. d'Ap.*, **4**, 30, 1941.
[6] J. Stebbins and C. M. Huffer, *Pub. Washburn Ob.*, **15**, 217, 1934.
[7] J. Stebbins and A. E. Whitford, *Ap. J.*, **84**, 132, 1936.
[8] G. E. Kron and J. L. Smith, *Ap. J.*, **113**, 324, 1951.
[9] J. J. Nassau and V. Burger, *Ap. J.*, **103**, 25, 1946.
[10] W. Becker and J. Stock, *Z. Ap.*, **45**, 269, 1958.
[11] O. J. Eggen, *Ap. J.*, **111**, 65, 81, 414, 1950.
[12] J. Stebbins and A. E. Whitford, *Ap. J.*, **102**, 318, 1945.
[13] E. Hertzsprung, *B.A.N.*, **9**, 101, 1940.
[14] H. L. Johnson, *Ap. J.*, **116**, 272, 1952.
[15] H. Arp, *Ap. J.*, **133**, 874, 1961.

§ 97. North Polar Sequence

The North Polar Sequence (N.P.S.) no longer defines the magnitude and colour standards of stellar photometry. Instead the U, B, V system is used and certain lists of well measured stars [2, 3] virtually define the standards.

Shortened list of N.P.S. stars [1, 3, 4]

N.P.S.	Sp	V	$B-V$	$U-B$	N.P.S.	Sp	V	$B-V$	$U-B$
1	A0	4·37	+0·02	+0·02	1r	M	5·07	+1·65	+1·97
2	A0	5·27	−0·03	−0·11	2r	M	6·39	+1·59	+1·79
3	F0	5·59	+0·23	+0·13	3r	K2	7·51	+1·45	+1·59
4	A3	5·80	+0·23	+0·07	4r	K0	8·23	+1·08	+1·00
5	A2	6·49	+0·10	+0·07	5r	K0	8·65	+1·58	
6	A0	7·11	+0·18	+0·08	6r	G5	9·27	+1·32	
7	B8	7·52	−0·01	−0·07	7r	G2?	9·86	+1·19	
8	F0	8·09	+0·39	−0·04	8r		10·42	+1·09	+0·86
9	A	8·81	+0·31	+0·11	12r		12·52	+1·34	
10	A5	9·06	+0·27	+0·04	2s	F0	6·29	+0·33	−0·01
13	A	10·29	+0·34	+0·25	3s	F2	6·35	+0·41	−0·08
16	A?	11·21	+0·48	+0·07	4s	G	9·83	+0·60	
19		12·22	+0·56	+0·13	6s		10·68	+0·82	

[1] *A.Q.* **1**, § 96.
[2] H. L. Johnson and W. W. Morgan, *Ap. J.*, **117**, 313, 1953.
[3] H. L. Johnson, *Ann. d'Ap.*, **18**, 292, 1955.
[4] G. E. Kron and N. U. Mayall, *A.J.*, **65**, 581, 1960.

§ 98. Absolute Magnitude and Colour Index

$$M_v$$

$B - V$	Supergiants		Bright giants II	Giants III	Sub-giants IV	Main sequence		Sub-dwarfs	White dwarfs
	ɪa	ɪb [1, 2]			[1, 2, 3, 4, 6, 11]	Mean v	Zero age		
−0·5				−6·6		− 6·5			
−0·4				−6·4		− 5·8			
−0·3	−6·7	−6·4	−5·7	−5·2		− 3·7	−3·3		
−0·2	−6·7	−6·2	−4·9	−3·2		− 1·6	−1·0		+10·4
−0·1	−6·8	−5·9	−4·0	−1·7		− 0·2	+0·5		
0·0	−6·8	−5·5	−3·3	−0·5		+ 0·7	+1·5		+11·4
0·1	−6·8	−5·2	−2·7	+0·3	+1·0	+ 1·5	+2·1		
0·2	−6·8	−5·0	−2·3	+0·9	+1·6	+ 2·1	+2·6		+12·4
0·3				+1·5	+2·3	+ 2·7	+3·1		
0·4	−6·9	−4·7	−2·0	+1·7	+2·7	+ 3·3	+3·6	+4·0	+13·4
0·5				+1·8	+2·9	+ 4·0	+4·2	+5·0	
0·6	−6·9	−4·6	−2·0	+1·8	+3·1	+ 4·6	+4·8	+5·7	+14·2
0·7				+1·7	+3·3	+ 5·2	+5·4	+6·4	
0·8	−7·0	−4·5	−2·0	+1·5	+3·3	+ 5·8	+5·9	+6·9	+15·0
0·9				+1·3	+3·2	+ 6·2	+6·3	+7·4	
1·0	−7·0	−4·5	−2·0	+1·0	+3·1	+ 6·7	+6·8	+7·9	+15·8
1·1				+0·7	+3	+ 7·0	+7·2		
1·2		−4·5	−2·1	+0·4	+3	+ 7·5	+7·6		
1·3				+0·1		+ 8·0	+8·1		
1·4		−4·4	−2·2	0·0		+ 8·6	+8·6		
1·5				−0·1		+ 9·6			
1·6		−4·4	−2·4	−0·2		+12·0			
1·7				−0·3		+16			
1·8		−4·4	−2·4	−0·4					
1·9				−0·5					

$$B - V$$

M_v	Neighbouring stars		Globular clusters	
	Main seq.	Giants (no super-g's) [7, 8, 9, 10]	Blue branch	Red branch [7, 8, 9, 10, 11]
−3	−0·27		+1·8	+1·8
−2	−0·23		+1·3	+1·3
−1	−0·16		+1·0	+1·0
0	−0·07	+1·45	+0·5	+0·84
1	+0·05	+1·08	−0·1	+0·80
2	+0·18	+0·95	−0·2	+0·73
3	+0·32	+0·7		+0·6
4	+0·50			+0·5
5	+0·67			+0·67
6	+0·84			+0·84

[1] *A.Q.* **1**, § 97.
[2] H. L. JOHNSON (and B. IRIARTE), *Lowell Ob. Bull.*, No. 91, 1958; *Ap. J.*, **126**, 121, 1957.
[3] A. SANDAGE, *Ap. J.*, **125**, 435, 1957.
[4] H. C. ARP, *Handb. der Phys.*, **51**, 75, 1958.
[5] G. A. STARIKOVA, *A. Zh.*, **37**, 476, 1960; *Sov. A.*, **4**, 451.
[6] G. S. MUMFORD, *A.J.*, **61**, 213, 1956.
[7] P. P. PARENAGO, W. A. BAUM, J. L. GREENSTEIN, O. C. WILSON; in I.A.U. Symp. on *The H.-R. Diagram*, 11, 23, 33, 39, 1959.
[8] J. B. OKE, *Ap. J.*, **130**, 487, 1959.
[9] O. C. WILSON, *Ap. J.*, **130**, 496, 1959.
[10] V. B. NIKONOV et al., *Iz. Crimea*, **17**, 42, 1957.
[11] O. J. EGGEN, *P.A.S.P.*, **67**, 315, 1955.

§ 99. Stellar Radiation, Temperature and Colour

Bolometric correction, B.C., and effective temperature, T_e [1, 2, 3, 14, 15]

$\log T_e$	B.C.
5·0	7
4·8	5·4
4·6	3·9
4·4	2·7
4·2	1·5

$\log T_e$	B.C.
4·1	0·92
4·0	0·45
3·9	0·11
3·8	0·00
3·7	0·15

$\log T_e$	B.C.
3·6	0·72
3·5	1·6
3·4	3·0
3·3	4·5
3·2	6·7

Stellar colours, temperatures, and bolometric corrections

Notation is from § 93. T_c refers to visible region. M_v is included for easy reference to § 95.

Sp	M_v	$B-V$ [1, 4, 5, 6, 7, 8]	$U-B$	T_e [1, 2, 9, 10, 12]	T_c	B.C. [1, 2, 3, 4]	M_{bol}
				°K	°K		
Main sequence, v							
O5	− 6	−0·45	−1·2	35 000	70 000	4·6	− 10·6
B0	− 3·7	−0·31	−1·07	21 000	38 000	3·0	− 6·7
B5	− 0·9	−0·17	−0·56	13 500	23 000	1·6	− 2·5
A0	+ 0·7	0·00	0·00	9 700	15 400	0·68	0·0
A5	+ 2·0	+0·16	+0·09	8 100	11 100	0·30	+ 1·7
F0	+ 2·8	+0·30	+0·02	7 200	9 000	0·10	+ 2·7
F5	+ 3·8	+0·45	−0·01	6 500	7 600	0·00	+ 3·8
G0	+ 4·6	+0·57	+0·04	6 000	6 700	0·03	+ 4·6
G5	+ 5·2	+0·70	+0·20	5 400	6 000	0·10	+ 5·1
K0	+ 6·0	+0·84	+0·46	4 700	5 400	0·20	+ 5·8
K5	+ 7·4	+1·11	+1·06	4 000	4 500	0·58	+ 6·8
M0	+ 8·9	+1·39	+1·24	3 300	3 800	1·20	+ 7·6
M5	+12·0	+1·61	+1·19	2 600	3 000	2·1	+ 9·8
Giants, III							
G0	+ 1·8	+0·65	+0·30	5 400	6 000	0·1	+ 1·7
G5	+ 1·5	+0·84	+0·52	4 700	5 000	0·3	+ 1·2
K0	+ 0·8	+1·06	+0·90	4 100	4 400	0·6	+ 0·2
K5	0·0	+1·40	+1·6	3 500	3 700	1·0	− 1·0
M0	− 0·3	+1·65	+1·9	2 900	3 400	1·7	− 2·0
M5	− 0·5	+1·85			3 000	3·0	− 3·4
Supergiants, I							
B0	− 6·4	−0·21	−1·20			3	− 9·4
A0	− 6·0	0·00	−0·30			0·7	− 6·7
F0	− 5·6	+0·30	+0·26	6 400		0·2	− 5·8
G0	− 4·4	+0·76	+0·62	5 400	6 200	0·3	− 4·7
G5	− 4·4	+1·06	+0·86	4 700	5 300	0·6	− 5·0
K0	− 4·4	+1·42	+1·35	4 000	4 600	1·0	− 5·4
K5	− 4·4	+1·71	+1·73	3 400		1·6	− 6·0
M0	− 4·4	+1·94	+1·75	2 800		2·5	− 6·9
M5		+2·15				4·0	

Factor Q depending on Sp only (eliminating interstellar reddening) [11]

$$Q = (U-B) - \frac{E_{U-B}}{E_{B-V}}(B-V)$$

Sp	O5	B0	B5	A0
Q	-0.93	-0.89	-0.44	0.00

Stellar radiation flux [1, 13]

Sp	$\log \mathscr{F}_v$		$\log \left(\dfrac{\mathscr{F}'_v}{\mathscr{F}_v}\right)$	Line absorption			$D =$ Balmer discontinuity	
	Main sequence	Giants		λ			Main sequence	c stars
				$0.4\,\mu$	$0.5\,\mu$	$0.6\,\mu$		
	in erg cm^{-2} s^{-1} Å^{-1}			% of continuum			dex	
O5			0.00				0.02	0.00
B0	8.6		0.00	3	1	0	0.04	0.02
B5	8.12		0.00	5	2	0	0.22	0.13
A0	7.79		0.00	8	3	0	0.45	0.33
A5	7.53		0.01	12	5	0	0.40	0.42
F0	7.33		0.02	18	8	1	0.23	0.35
F5	7.16	7.16	0.03	24	10	2	0.12	0.22
G0	7.00	6.75	0.04	32	12	3	0.04	0.09
G5	6.84	6.50	0.05	43	16	5	0.00	0.03
K0	6.64	6.28	0.07	54	22	8		0.00
K5	6.33	5.9	0.10	70?	33	11		
M0	6.0	5.5	0.13	80?	40	15		

[1] *A.Q.* **1**, § 98.
[2] D. M. Popper, *Ap. J.*, **129**, 647, 1959.
[3] D. N. Limber, *Ap. J.*, **131**, 168, 1960.
[4] H. C. Arp, *Handb. der Phys.*, **51**, 75, 1958.
[5] P. P. Parenago, in I.A.U. Symp. No. 10 on *The H.-R. Diagram*, p. 11, 1959.
[6] A. Feinstein, *Z. Ap.*, **47**, 218, 1959; **49**, 12, 1960.
[7] I. M. Kopylov, *Iz. Crimea*, **18**, 41, 1958.
[8] H. L. Johnson, *Lowell Ob., Bull.*, **90**, 1958.
[9] R. C. Bless, *Ap. J.*, **132**, 532, 1960.
[10] R. P. Kraft, *Ap. J.*, **133**, 57, 1961.
[11] H. L. Johnson and W. W. Morgan, *Ap. J.*, **117**, 313, 1953.
[12] O. A. Mel'nikov, *A. Zh.*, **35**, 218, 1958; *Sov. A.*, **2**, 195.
[13] R. L. Wildey, Burbidge, and Sandage, *Ap. J.*, **135**, 94, 1962.
[14] A. Sandage, *Ap. J.*, **135**, 349, 1962.
[15] J. K. McDonald and A. Underhill, *Ap. J.*, **115**, 577, 1952.

§ 100. Stellar Mass, Luminosity, Radius, and Density

Notation from § 93.

The mass-luminosity law may be represented conveniently by the approximation

$$\log (\mathscr{L}/\mathscr{L}_\odot) = 3.3 \log (\mathscr{M}/\mathscr{M}_\odot)$$

Mass, radius, luminosity, and mean density with spectral class
s-g = supergiant,   g = giant,   d = dwarf
A single column between g and d represents the main sequence

Sp	$\log(\mathscr{M}/\mathscr{M}_\odot)$			$\log(\mathscr{R}/\mathscr{R}_\odot)$			$\log(\mathscr{L}/\mathscr{L}_\odot)$			$\log\bar{\rho}$		
	s–g	g [1, 2, 3, 4, 5, 6]	d	s–g	g [1, 2, 7]	d	s–g	g	d	s–g	g	d
										in g cm^{-3}		
O5	+2·2	+1·60				+1·25		+5·5				−2·0
B0	1·7	1·23		+1·3	+1·2	0·88	+5·5	4·1		−2·1		−1·3
B5	1·4	0·85		1·5	1·0	0·60	4·9	2·8		−2·9		−0·8
A0	1·2	0·55		1·6	0·8	0·42	4·4	1·9		−3·5		−0·6
A5	1·1	0·34		1·7		0·25	4·1	1·3		−3·8		−0·3
F0	1·1	0·25		1·8		0·13	3·9	0·8		−4·2		0·0
F5	1·0	0·15		1·9	0·6	0·08	3·8	0·4		−4·5		+0·1
G0	1·0	+0·4	+0·03	2·0	0·8	+0·02	3·8	+1·5	+0·1	−4·9	−1·8	+0·1
G5	1·1	0·5	−0·03	2·1	1·0	−0·03	3·8	1·7	−0·1	−5·2	−2·4	+0·2
K0	1·1	0·6	−0·09	2·3	1·2	−0·07	4·0	2·0	−0·4	−5·7	−2·9	+0·3
K5	1·2	0·7	−0·16	2·6	1·4	−0·13	4·3	2·3	−0·8	−6·4	−3·4	+0·4
M0	1·2	0·8	−0·32	2·7		−0·20	4·5	2·6	−1·2	−6·7	−4	+0·5
M2	1·3		−0·40	2·9		−0·3	4·7	2·8	−1·5	−7·2		+0·7
M5			−0·65			−0·5		3·0	−2·1			+1·1
M8			−1·1			−0·9			−3·3			+1·7

Luminosity and radius with mass
White dwarfs and massive Trumpler stars [8] are omitted

$\log\dfrac{\mathscr{M}}{\mathscr{M}_\odot}$	M_{bol} [1, 6, 9, 10, 11, 12, 17]	$\log\dfrac{\mathscr{L}}{\mathscr{L}_\odot}$	M_v [1, 2, 13, 14, 15, 16]	M_B	$\log\dfrac{\mathscr{R}}{\mathscr{R}_\odot}$ Main seq.
−1·0	+11·3	−2·7	+14·8	+16·6	−0·9
−0·8	+10·3	−2·4	+13·7	+15·4	−0·7
−0·6	+ 9·4	−1·9	+12·4	+14·0	−0·5
−0·4	+ 8·1	−1·3	+10·6	+12·1	−0·3
−0·2	+ 6·6	−0·7	+ 7·8	+ 9·0	−0·15
0·0	+ 4·7	0·0	+ 4·8	+ 5·6	0·00
+0·2	+ 2·7	+0·8	+ 2·8	+ 2·9	+0·10
+0·4	+ 0·8	+1·6	+ 1·2	+ 1·1	+0·30
+0·6	− 0·9	+2·2	− 0·1	+ 0·2	+0·45
+0·8	− 2·4	+2·8	− 1·2	− 1·1	+0·56
+1·0	− 3·9	+3·4	− 2·5	− 2·5	+0·7
+1·2	− 5·4	+4·0	− 3·7	− 3·7	+0·9
+1·4	− 6·8	+4·6	− 4·8	− 4·8	+1·0
+1·6	− 8·1	+5·1	− 5·9	− 6·0	+1·2
+1·8	− 9·5	+5·7	− 7·0	− 7·1	+1·5

[1] *A.Q.* **1**, § 99.
[2] O. FRANZ, *Mitt. U.-S. Wien*, **8**, 1, 1956.
[3] J. HOPMANN, *Mitt. U.-S. Wien*, **8**, p. 252, 1956.
[4] A. BEER, *Vistas in Astronomy*, **2**, 1387, 1956.
[5] O. J. EGGEN, *A.J.*, **61**, 361, 1956.
[6] K. KAMINISI, *P.A.S. Jap.*, **12**, 398, 1960.

[7] Su-Shu Huang and O. Struve, *A.J.*, **61**, 300, 1956.
[8] R. J. Trumpler, *P.A.S.P.*, **47**, 249, 1935.
[9] K. F. d'Occhieppo, *Mitt. U.-S. Wien*, **6**, 59, 1952.
[10] E. Lamla, *A.N.*, **285**, 33, 1959.
[11] P. van de Kamp, *Handb. der Phys.*, **50**, p. 222, 1958.
[12] K. Aa. Strand, *J.R.A.S. Canada*, **51**, 46, 1957.
[13] M. Schmidt, *Ap. J.*, **129**, 243, 1959.
[14] E. E. Salpeter, *Ap. J.*, **121**, 161, 1955.
[15] D. N. Limber, *Ap. J.*, **131**, 168, 1960.
[16] L. Plaut, *Groningen*, No. 55, 1953.
[17] A. Sandage, *Ap. J.*, **135**, 349, 1962.

§ 101. Stellar Rotation

High rotational velocities occur only in early type stars O, B, A, and F; and *not* in G to M stars, supergiants, cepheids, or long-period-variables. A noticeable difference can be detected between giants, III, and main-sequence stars, V. If the inclination i of the axis to the line of sight is unknown spectroscopic observations give only $v_e \sin i$, where v_e is the equatorial velocity. Mean random $\sin i$ is $\pi/4$.

Mean rotational velocities

Sp	$v_e \sin i$		$\bar{v}_e$	
	III	V	III	V
	km/s	km/s	km/s	km/s
Oe, Be		275		350
O5		150		190
B0	75	160	95	200
B5	95	165	120	210
A0	110	150	140	190
A5	125	125	170	160
F0	100	75	130	95
F5	45	20	60	25
G0	15	< 10	20	< 12
K, M	< 10	< 10	< 12	< 12

The *distribution of velocities* with v_e [2, 4] has a maximum near $\bar{v}_e$. Among the Oe, Be stars there are no stars of low v_e, but for other types there are about half as many low v_e stars (per Δv_e) as at $\bar{v}_e$.

[1] *A.Q.* **1**, § 100.
[2] A. Slettebak (and R. F. Howard), *Ap. J.*, **119**, 146, 1954; **121**, 102, 653, 1955.
[3] G. H. Herbig and J. F. Spalding, *Ap. J.*, **121**, 118, 1955.
[4] Su-Shu Huang, *Ap. J.*, **118**, 285, 1953.
[5] J. B. Oke and J. L. Greenstein, *Ap. J.*, **120**, 384, 1954.
[6] P. J. Treanor, *M.N.*, **121**, 503, 1960.

§ 102. Stellar Interiors

Notation: ρ = density, T = temperature, $\mathscr{R}$ = stellar radius, P = pressure, $\mathscr{M}$ = stellar mass, r = central distance, $\mathscr{M}_r$ = mass within central distance r, etc., $\mathscr{L}$ = luminosity, subscript $_c$ = central value.

$\quad X$ = fraction of H by mass $\simeq 0 \cdot 63$

$\quad Y$ = fraction of He by mass $\simeq 0 \cdot 36$

$\quad Z = 1 - X - Y$ = fraction of heavy elements $\simeq 0 \cdot 014$

$\quad \mu$ = mean molecular weight

$\qquad = 4/(6X + Y + 2) \simeq 4/(5X + 3) \simeq 0 \cdot 65$

Stellar models: (Solar model given in § 76.)

Standard model [1, 2]

$\rho_c = 54 \cdot 2\, \bar{\rho}$

$\quad = 76 \cdot 4\, (\mathscr{M}/\mathscr{M}_\odot)(\mathscr{R}/\mathscr{R}_\odot)^{-3}$ g cm^{-3}

$T_c = 19 \cdot 7 \times 10^6$ °K

$\quad \times \mu(\mathscr{M}/\mathscr{M}_\odot)(\mathscr{R}/\mathscr{R}_\odot)^{-1}$

$r/\mathscr{R}$	ρ/ρ_c	T/T_c	P/P_c	$\mathscr{M}_r/\mathscr{M}$
0·0	1·000	1·000	1·000	0·000
0·05	0·941	0·982	0·925	0·007
0·1	0·793	0·928	0·734	0·047
0·2	0·429	0·752	0·322	0·262
0·3	0·179	0·568	0·102	0·548
0·4	0·069	0·403	0·028	0·765
0·5	0·022 7	0·284	0·006 4	0·898
0·6	0·007 2	0·194	0·001 4	0·963
0·7	0·001 9	0·125	$0 \cdot 0^3\, 24$	0·989
0·8	$0 \cdot 0^3\, 39$	0·071	$0 \cdot 0^4\, 28$	0·999
0·9	$0 \cdot 0^4\, 38$	0·032	$0 \cdot 0^5\, 12$	1·000
0·95	$0 \cdot 0^5\, 6$	0·015 7	$0 \cdot 0^7\, 9$	1·000
0·98	$0 \cdot 0^5\, 16$	0·006 5	$0 \cdot 0^7\, 10$	1·000
1·00	0·0	0·0	0·0	1·000

Point convective model [1, 3]

$\rho_c = 37 \cdot 0\, \bar{\rho}$

$\quad = 52 \cdot 2\, (\mathscr{M}/\mathscr{M}_\odot)(\mathscr{R}/\mathscr{R}_\odot)^{-3}$ g cm^{-3}

$T_c = 20 \cdot 8 \times 10^6$ °K

$\quad \times \mu(\mathscr{M}/\mathscr{M}_\odot)(\mathscr{R}/\mathscr{R}_\odot)^{-1}$

$r/\mathscr{R}$	ρ/ρ_c	T/T_c	P/P_c	$\mathscr{M}_r/\mathscr{M}$
0·0	1·000	1·000	1·000	0·000
0·05	0·970	0·980	0·950	0·006
0·1	0·890	0·919	0·817	0·035
0·2	0·606	0·719	0·435	0·220
0·3	0·290	0·523	0·152	0·512
0·4	0·110	0·369	0·041	0·762
0·5	0·036	0·257	0·009	0·902
0·6	0·010 3	0·173	0·001 8	0·966
0·7	0·002 5	0·120	$0 \cdot 0^3\, 30$	0·991
0·8	$0 \cdot 0^3\, 44$	0·066	$0 \cdot 0^4\, 29$	0·999
0·9	$0 \cdot 0^4\, 31$	0·029	$0 \cdot 0^6\, 9$	1·000
0·95	$0 \cdot 0^5\, 25$	0·013 8	$0 \cdot 0^7\, 35$	1·000
0·98	$0 \cdot 0^6\, 15$	0·005 5	$0 \cdot 0^9\, 8$	1·000
1·00	0·0	0·0	0·0	1·000

Initial main seq., $\mathscr{M} = 10\,\mathscr{M}_\odot$ [7]

$r/\mathscr{R}$	$\log \rho$	$\log T$	$\mathscr{L}_r/\mathscr{L}$	$\mathscr{M}_r/\mathscr{M}$
	in g cm^{-3}	in °K		
0·00	+0·89	7·44	0·00	0·00
0·01	+0·89	7·44	0·00	0·00
0·1	+0·85	7·41	0·51	0·02
0·2	+0·72	7·33	0·98	0·17
0·3	+0·50	7·20	1·00	0·43
0·4	+0·14	7·05	1·00	0·69
0·5	−0·31	6·89	1·00	0·87
0·6	−0·82	6·72	1·00	0·95
0·7	−1·42	6·53	1·00	0·99
0·8	−2·17	6·30	1·00	1·00
0·9	−3·29	5·95	1·00	1·00
0·98	−5·66	5·20	1·00	1·00

Red giant, $\mathscr{M} = 1 \cdot 3\,\mathscr{M}_\odot$ [7]

$r/\mathscr{R}$	$\log \rho$	$\log T$	$\mathscr{L}_r/\mathscr{L}$	$\mathscr{M}_r/\mathscr{M}$
	in g cm^{-3}	in °K		
0·00	+5·54	7·60	0·00	0·00
0·000 1	+5·52	7·60	0·00	0·00
0·000 5	+5·10	7·60	0·00	0·13
0·001	+3·21	7·60	0·00	0·26
0·01	−0·73	6·78	1·00	0·27
0·1	−2·54	6·07	1·00	0·29
0·2	−2·88	5·84	1·00	0·36
0·3	−3·11	5·69	1·00	0·46
0·5	−3·52	5·42	1·00	0·70
0·7	−4·00	5·11	1·00	0·91
0·8	−4·34	4·87	1·00	0·97
0·9	−4·87	4·52	1·00	1·00

Central temperature and densities of stars [1, 7]

Sp	Main sequence						Red giants	White dwarfs
	B0	A0	F0	G0	K0	M0		
T_c in 10^6 °K	30	22	18	16	13	9	40	
$\log \rho_c$ in g cm^{-3}	0·8	1·5	2·0	2·1	2·0	1·9	5·5	7·2

Opacity of stellar material: see § 39.

The mass rate of energy generation in the proton-proton chain (pp) [4, 5, 6]

$$\epsilon_{pp} = \rho X^2 f_H E_{pp} \text{ erg g}^{-1} \text{ s}^{-1}$$

where ρ = density in g cm^{-3}, f_H = hydrogen electron shielding factor $\simeq 1$, and E_{pp} is tabulated. The factor $X^2 f_H \simeq 0·36$ for population I.

The mass rate of energy generation in the carbon-nitrogen cycle (CN) [4, 5, 6,]

$$\epsilon_{CN} = \rho X (100\, \alpha_N) f_N E_N \text{ erg g}^{-1} \text{ s}^{-1}$$

where α_N = nitrogen fraction by mass $\simeq 0·01$ (and hence $100\, \alpha_N$ is inserted to make E_{pp} and E_{CN} comparable), f_N = nitrogen electron shielding factor $\simeq \exp (7·25 \times 10^6 \text{ °K}/T) \simeq 1·5$ [5].

The factor $\quad X (100\, \alpha_N) f_N \simeq 0·36$ for population I
$$\simeq 0·02 \text{ for population II}$$

There is a possibility that a resonance ^{14}N process exists, in which case the energy production would be increased by about 2 dex [4]. E_N is tabulated.

T	$\log E_{pp}$	$\log E_N$		T	$\log E_{pp}$	$\log E_N$
10^6 °K	C.G.S.	C.G.S.		10^6 °K	C.G.S.	C.G.S.
1	−8			16	−0·2	− 1·1
2	−5·3			18	−0·1	− 0·1
3	−4·0			20	+0·1	+ 0·7
4	−3·2			25	+0·4	+ 2·3
5	−2·6	−13·3		30	+0·7	+ 3·6
6	−2·2	−11·0		35	+0·9	+ 4·6
7	−1·9	− 9·2		40	+1·0	+ 5·5
8	−1·6	− 7·8		45	+1·2	+ 6·2
10	−1·1	− 5·5		50	+1·3	+ 6·8
12	−0·8	− 3·7		70	+1·7	+ 9·4
14	−0·5	− 2·3		100	+2·3	+12·1

Energy conversion per cycle leading to 1 He atom [5]

Without neutrino loss	= $4·28 \times 10^{-5}$ erg	= 26·8 Mev
For pp cycle	= $4·19 \times 10^{-5}$ erg	= 26·2 Mev
For CN cycle	= $4·00 \times 10^{-5}$ erg	= 25·0 Mev

Corresponding energies per gram of H

$$= 6.40,\ 6.27,\ \text{and}\ 5.99 \times 10^{18}\ \text{erg/g}.$$

Time scale of a star [1] $= 1.0 \times 10^{11}\ (\mathcal{M}/\mathcal{M}_\odot)/(\mathcal{L}/\mathcal{L}_\odot)$ years

[1] *A.Q.* **1** § 101.
[2] A. S. EDDINGTON, *Internal Constitution of Stars*, Cambridge, 1930.
[3] T. G. COWLING, *M.N.*, **96**, 42, 1936.
[4] E. M. and G. R. BURBIDGE, FOWLER and HOYLE, *Rev. Mod. Phys.*, **29**, 547, 1957.
[5] M. H. WRUBEL, *Handb. der Phys.*, **51**, 1, 1958.
[6] W. A. FOWLER, Liège Symp. on *Star Models and Stellar Evolution*, 207, 1959.
[7] M. SCHWARZSCHILD, *Structure and Evolution of Stars*, Princeton, 1958.

§ 103. Stellar Reversing Layers

N = atoms per cm^3 in reversing layer

NH = effective number of atoms per cm^2 above photosphere

H = exponential scale height in stellar atmosphere

g = stellar surface gravity

T_R = reversing layer temperature $\simeq 0.93\ T_e$

P = gas pressure in reversing layer

P_e = electron pressure in reversing layer

P_r = radiation pressure in reversing layer

$\bar{\kappa}$ = mass absorption coefficient for visible radiation

m-s = main sequence, g = giants, s-g = supergiants.

Numbers of atoms, gravity, and temperature

Sp	$\log N$		$\log NH$		$\log H$		$\log g$			$\log T_R$	
	m-s [1]	g	m-s [1, 7]	g	m-s [1]	g	m-s [1, 2, 6]	g	s-g	m-s [1]	g
	in cm^{-3}		in cm^{-2}		in cm		in cm s^{-2}			in °K	
O5	15·0		23·3		8·3		4·1			4·6	
B0	15·0		23·0		8·0		4·1	3·8	3·2	4·32	
B5	15·1		22·8		7·7		4·1	3·7	2·8	4·12	
A0	15·2		22·9		7·7		4·2	3·6	2·4	3·98	
A5	15·4		23·2		7·8		4·2	3·5	1·9	3·88	
F0	15·9		23·7		7·8		4·3	3·4	1·7	3·83	
F5	16·4	16	24·1	24·3	7·7		4·4	3·4	1·5	3·78	
G0	16·8	16·2	24·2	24·8	7·4	8·6	4·4	3·1	1·2	3·75	3·69
G5	16·9	16·5	24·3	25·3	7·4	8·8	4·5	2·8	1·0	3·70	3·64
K0	17·0	16·4	24·4	25·7	7·4	9·3	4·5	2·5	0·6	3·64	3·58
K5	17·2	16·3	24·4	25·9	7·2	9·6	4·6	2·1	0·2	3·58	3·51
M0	17·3	16·2	24·4	26·1	7·1	9·9	4·8	1·8	0·0	3·50	3·45
M5	17·4		24·4	26·3	7·0		5·0			3·40	

Pressures and absorption coefficient

Sp	$\log P$		$\log P_e$			$\log P_r$		$\log \bar{\kappa}$	
	m-s [1, 3, 4, 7]	g	m-s [1, 3, 4, 5, 6, 7]	g	s-g	m-s [1]	g	m-s [1, 7]	g
	in dyn cm^{-2}		in dyn cm^{-2}			in dyn cm^{-2}		in exp cm^{-2} g^{-1}	
O5	3·6		+3·3			+4·1		−0·1	
B0	3·4		+3·0	+2·4	+2·0	+2·9		+0·3	
B5	3·2		+2·7	+1·9	+1·3	+2·0		+0·8	
A0	3·4		+2·4	+1·7	+1·0	+1·4		+0·9	
A5	3·6		+2·3	+1·6	+0·5	+1·0		+0·4	
F0	4·0		+2·1	+1·4	+0·1	+0·8		−0·1	
F5	4·4	3·8	+1·6	+1·0	−0·4	+0·5		−0·4	
G0	4·7	3·9	+1·3	+0·5	−1·0	+0·4	+0·1	−0·6	−1·1
G5	4·8	3·9	+0·8	−0·1	−1·7	+0·2	−0·1	−0·7	−1·4
K0	4·9	3·7	+0·5	−0·6	−2·5	+0·1	−0·2	−0·9	−1·7
K5	5·1	3·5	+0·2	−1·2	−3·4	−0·2	−0·5	−0·9	−1·9
M0	5·1	3·2	−0·1	−1·7	−4	−0·5	−0·6	−0·9	−2·2
M5	5·2	2·8	−0·5	−2·3		−0·9		−0·9	−2·5

[1] *A.Q.* **1**, § 102.
[2] J. HOPMANN, *Mitt. U.-S. Wien*, **8**, p. 245, 1956.
[3] L. H. ALLER, *A.J.*, **65**, 399, 1960.
[4] A. UNSÖLD, *Phys. der Sternatmosphären*, 2nd. ed., p. 426–9, 1955.
[5] W. K. BONSACK, *Ap. J.*, **130**, 843, 1959.
[6] I. M. KOPYLOV, *Iz. Crimea*, **26**, 232, 1961.
[7] L. H. ALLER, in *Stellar Atmospheres*, ed. Greenstein, p. 244, Chicago, 1961.

CHAPTER 11

STARS WITH SPECIAL CHARACTERISTICS

§ 104. Variable Stars

ALL types of variables are collected in the Catalogue of Variable Stars [2]. The numbers of the various types listed in 1958 are [3]:

Pulsating variables

C	classical cepheids	610
I	irregular variables	1 370
M	Mira Ceti type stars	3 657
SR	semi-regular variables	1 675
RR	RR Lyrae variables	2 426
RV	RV Tauri stars	92
βC	β Cephei stars	11
δSc	δ Scuti stars	5
αCV	α^2CVn stars	9

9 855

Explosive variables

N	novae	146
Ne	nova-like variables	35
SN	super novae	7
RCB	R Cr B stars	39
RW	RW Aurigae stars	590
UG	U Gem stars	112
UV	UV Ceti stars	15
Z	Z Cam stars	15

959

E	eclipsing variables of all types	2 763
	unique variables	10
	unstudied variables	982
	constant stars (suspected variables)	142

Total number catalogued (3 counted twice) = 14 708

The *great sequence of variable stars* includes the main pulsating variables and to some extent the explosive variables. They follow the approximate magnitude variation law [1]

$$\Delta m_v \simeq 0\cdot5 + 1\cdot7 \log P$$

where P = period in days, and $\Delta m_v = m_{min} - m_{max}$.

[1] *A.Q.* 1, §§ 103–107.
[2] B. V. KUKARKIN et al., *General Catalogue of Variable Stars*, Moscow, 1958; First supplement, 1960.
[3] *Trans. I.A.U.*, **10**, p. 405, 1960.

§ 105. Cepheid Variables

Cepheid types

I.A.U. Desig.	Name	Population	Period	$m_v(10)$
Cδ	Classical cepheids (δ Cep)	Extreme I	days 2 to 40	5·2
RR	Cluster variables (RR Lyr)	Extreme II	0·4 to 1	10
	Dwarf cepheids [26]	I	0·06 to 0·3	10
δSc	δ Scuti stars [25]		0·08 to 0·19	8
CW	W Vir type	II	1 to 50	
βC	β CMa, β Cep type [3]	I	0·15 to 0·25	5·3

Mean light curve of Cepheids reduced to mean amplitude [1]

$$\Delta m = m_{min} - m_{max} \equiv 1{\cdot}0; \quad \overline{m} = \tfrac{1}{2}(m_{min} + m_{max}). \quad \text{Phase } 0{\cdot}0 = \max$$

Phase	0·0	0·1	0·2	0·3	0·4	0·5	0·6	0·7	0·8	0·9	1·0
$m - \overline{m}$	−0·50	−0·28	−0·06	+0·09	+0·25	+0·39	+0·48	+0·50	+0·40	+0·06	−0·50

There is a tendency for slower decline, sharper rise, and therefore later minimum for the shorter periods.

Cepheid characteristics as a function of period, P

log P	$\overline{M}_v$	$\overline{M}_B$	Sp max	Sp min	$\Delta M_v = \Delta m_v$	$\overline{B-V}$	$\Delta(B-V)$	$\log \frac{\mathcal{M}}{\mathcal{M}_\odot}$	$\log \frac{\mathcal{R}}{\mathcal{R}_\odot}$	$\log \frac{\mathcal{L}}{\mathcal{L}_\odot}$
	[1, 4, 5, 6, 7, 9]		[1, 24]			[10, 11, 12]			[1, 18]	
in days										
Classical cepheids										
0·4	−2·6	−2·2	F5	F8	0·4	+0·42	0·13	0·8	1·4	3·0
0·6	−3·0	−2·5	F5	G1	0·6	+0·52	0·22	0·9	1·6	3·2
0·8	−3·5	−2·9	F6	G3	0·8	+0·60	0·32	0·9	1·8	3·5
1·0	−3·9	−3·2	F6	G3	0·8	+0·68	0·43	1·0	2·0	3·6
1·2	−4·4	−3·6	F7	G8	1·0	+0·76	0·55	1·1	2·1	3·8
1·4	−4·8	−4·0	F7	K1	1·3	+0·81	0·64	1·2	2·3	4·0
1·6	−5·3	−4·4	F8	K1	1·4	+0·88	0·67	1·3	2·5	4·2
Cluster variables [13, 14, 15, 27]										
−0·6	+0·6	+0·7	A4	A9				0·3	0·6	1·9
−0·4	+0·6	+0·7	A5	F1	1·3	+0·15	0·35	0·3	0·7	1·9
−0·2	+0·5	+0·7	A5	F2	0·9	+0·20	0·22	0·4	0·9	1·8
0·0	+0·5	+0·7	A7	F3	0·6	+0·25	0·1	0·4	1·0	1·8
Dwarf cepheids [24, 26, 27]										
−1·2	+4			A2	0·5	+0·11	0·14			
−1·0	+3			A4	0·5	+0·15	0·14			
−0·8	+2			A7	0·5	+0·18	0·14			
δ Scuti stars [25]										
−0·9	+1·8			F2	0·2	+0·32				
W Virginis stars [8, 9]										
0·4	−1·3	−0·9	F2	F5	0·6	+0·4	0·1	0·6	1·4	2·4
0·6	−1·8	−1·3	F3	F8	0·6	+0·5	0·2	0·7	1·6	2·6
0·8	−2·2	−1·6	F4	G0	0·7	+0·6	0·3	0·7	1·7	2·8
1·0	−2·7	−2·0	F5	G1	0·7	+0·7	0·4	0·8	1·9	3·0
1·2	−3·1	−2·3	F6	G3	0·8	+0·8	0·5	0·9	2·0	3·2
1·4	−3·5	−2·7	F7	G4	0·9	+0·8	0·6	1·0	2·2	3·4
1·6	−4·0	−3·1	F7	G5	1·0	+0·9	0·7	1·0	2·3	3·6
β CMa, β Cep stars [3, 16, 17, 23]										
−0·8	−3·0	−3	B2 IV		0·1	−0·2		1·5		3·8
−0·6	−4·5	−4	B1 III		0·1	−0·2		1·7		4·2

Velocity amplitudes:

Classical cepheids $\Delta v = \Delta m_\mathrm{v} \times 54$ km/s   [19]

$= \Delta m_\mathrm{B} \times 35$ km/s   [1, 24]

Cluster variables $\Delta v = \Delta m_\mathrm{B} \times 64$ km/s   [20]

Period-density relation for pulsating stars [21, 22, 24].

$Q = P(\bar{\rho}/\bar{\rho}_\odot)^{1/2}$ $= 0{\cdot}041$ day

$P = 0{\cdot}049\,\bar{\rho}^{-1/2}$ [P in d, $\bar{\rho}$ in g cm^{-3}]

Observed Q [24]

Cepheids	$Q = 0{\cdot}041$ day
Cluster variables	$Q = 0{\cdot}145$,,
W Vir stars	$Q = 0{\cdot}160$,,
βCMa, βCep stars	$Q = 0{\cdot}027$,,

Theoretical Q [24, 25]

	$\rho_\mathrm{c}/\bar{\rho}$	Q
Homogeneous model	1	$0{\cdot}116$ day
Polytrope $n = 1{\cdot}5$ (convective)	6	$0{\cdot}075$,,
Standard model	54	$0{\cdot}039$,,
Original Epstein model	2×10^6	$0{\cdot}031$,,
Modified Epstein model (large external convection)	$1{\cdot}2 \times 10^6$	$0{\cdot}056$,,

[1] *A.Q.* **1**, § 103.
[2] O. STRUVE, Second Berkeley Symp. on *Math. Stats. and Prob.*, p. 403, 1951.
[3] O. STRUVE, *Ann. d'Ap.*, **15**, 157, 1952.
[4] H. SHAPLEY, *Proc. Nat. Ac. Sci.*, **26**, 541, 1940; *Harv. Repr.*, No. 207.
[5] S. M. KUNG, *Mitt. St. Budapest*, No. 47, 1960.
[6] A. BLAAUW and H. R. MORGAN, *B.A.N.*, **12**, 95, 1954.
[7] F. JANÁK, *B.A. Czech.*, **10**, 72, 1959.
[8] H. C. ARP, *A.J.*, **60**, 1, 1955.
[9] M. PETIT, *Ann. d'Ap.*, **23**, 681, 710, 1960.
[10] D. W. N. STIBBS, *M.N.*, **115**, 323, 363, 1955.
[11] P. TH. OOSTERHOFF, *B.A.N.*, **15**, 199, 1960.
[12] R. P. KRAFT, *Ap. J.*, **132**, 404, 1960.
[13] M. ROBERTS and A. SANDAGE, *A.J.*, **60**, 185, 1955.
[14] A. STAWIKOWSKI et al., *Bull. A. O. Torun*, No. 16, 1958.
[15] G. W. PRESTON and H. SPINRAD, *P.A.S.P.*, **71**, 497, 1959.
[16] A. VAN HOOF, *Mitt. St. Budapest*, No. 42, p. 85, 1957.
[17] R. M. PETRIE, *J.R.A.S. Canada*, **48**, 185, 1954.
[18] K. F. d'OCCHIEPPO, *Mitt. U.-S. Wien*, **8**, 265, 1956.
[19] O. J. EGGEN, GASCOIGNE, and BURR, *M.N.*, **117**, 406, 430, 1957.
[20] L. WOLTJER, *B.A.N.*, **13**, 58, 1956.
[21] R. P. KRAFT, *P.A.S.P.*, **65**, 146, 1953.
[22] G. THIESSEN, *Z. Ap.*, **39**, 65, 1956.
[23] M. TAKEUTI, *Sendai A.R.*, No. 66, 1958.
[24] P. LEDOUX and TH. WALRAVEN, *Handb. der Phys.*, **51**, 353, 1958.
[25] D. H. McNAMARA and G. AUGASON, *Ap. J.*, **135**, 64, 1962.
[26] O. STRUVE, LYNDS, and PILLANS, *Elementary Astronomy*, p. 338, N.Y. and Oxford, 1959.
[27] E. GEYER, *Z. Ap.*, **52**, 229, 1961.

§ 106. Long-period Variables (Mira Stars)

Long-period variables (L.P.V.'s) or Mira Stars (M) are late type giant stars, usually with bright line spectra. They belong to Older Population I.

Period P mainly > 200 d

Variation $\Delta M_\mathrm{v} = M_{\min} - M_{\max} > 2{\cdot}5$

If $\Delta M_\mathrm{v} < 2{\cdot}5$ the variables are designated $M?$, or are regarded as semi-regular [7].

Magnitudes	$m_v(10) = 5 \cdot 4$
Galactic latitude	$\bar{b} = 20°$
Pulsation	$Q\ (\S\ 105) = 0 \cdot 096$ d

Distribution of L.P.V.'s with spectral classification [1]

Sp	K	M	S	R	N
% with bright lines	0·5	73	4	0·2	2·3
% without bright lines	0·7	13	0·6	0·4	5

Physical condition of L.P.V.'s with spectral classification [1, 2, 3, 4]

Sp at max	$\log P$	T_e max	T_e min	$\log \frac{\mathscr{M}}{\mathscr{M}_\odot}$	$\log \frac{\mathscr{R}}{\mathscr{R}_\odot}$	$\log \frac{\mathscr{L}}{\mathscr{L}_\odot}$	$\bar{M}_v$	$\bar{M}_{bol}$	ΔM_v
	in deg	°K	°K	*					
K5e	2·0	3 700		1·02	1·9	3·3	−2·5	−3·4	
M0e	2·1	3 400	3 200	1·09	2·1	3·5	−2·5	−3·8	2
M5e	2·4	2 800	2 200	1·11	2·3	3·6	−0·6	−4·0	4
M8e	2·7	2 300	1 700	1·23	2·7	3·9	+0·3	−5·0	6
R8e	2·4	2 800	2 200	1·01	2·1	3·2	−1·7	−3·2	5
N0e	2·5	2 400	1 900	1·05	2·3	3·4	−1·2	−3·6	4
N5e	2·7	2 100	1 800	1·15	2·7	3·7	0·0	−4·4	3
S, Se	2·5	2 500	1 900				−1		6

* Much smaller values suggested in [6].

Condition of L.P.V.'s with period [1, 2, 3]

Period	*Sp*	$\bar{M}_v$	ΔM_v	Relative occurrence	Space velocity
days				%	km/s
< 100		−2		4	
100 to 200	M2e	−2·6	3·2	18	115
200 to 300	M4e	−1·8	4·5	40	100
300 to 400	M5e	−0·4	4·8	28	56
400 to 500	M6e	+0·5	4·9	9	40
500 to 600	M7e	+1	5·1	1	
> 600				0·5	

[1] *A.Q.* 1, § 104.
[2] P. LEDOUX and TH. WALRAVEN, *Handb. der Phys.*, **51**, p. 402, 1958.
[3] C. P.- and S. GAPOSCHKIN, *Harv. Repr.* II, No. 2, 1943.
[4] C. PAYNE-GAPOSCHKIN, *Variable Stars and Galactic Structure*, London, 1954.
[5] C. P.- and S. GAPOSCHKIN, *Variable Stars*, Harv. Mon., No. 5, 1938.
[6] J. D. FERNIE and A. A. BROOKER, *Ap. J.*, **133**, 1088, 1961.
[7] B. V. KUKARKIN et al., *General Catalogue of Variable Stars*, Moscow, 1958.

§ 107. Irregular and Semi-regular Variables

The conditions of irregular and semi-regular variables are in some respects intermediate between those of cepheids and long-period variables. There are many types but a strict classification is not always possible.

Types of irregular and semi-regular variables [1]

Desig.	Type and features	Pop.	Mean period	Sp	M_v	ΔM_v	$m_v(10)$	Mean gal. lat.
			days					
RV	RV Tau, UU Her, Irreg. min. alternating depth	II	75	G to K	−2	1·3	7·4	23
SR a,b,c,d	Long period semi-reg. including μ Cep, δ Ori	I to II	100	G to M N	−1	1·6	5·4	22
I	Irregular			K to M N	−0·5	1·3	5·4	22
RW	T Tau, RW Aur. Ass. with neb. em. lines	I Extreme		dFe dGe	+5	3	11	14
RCB	RCrB Sudden decr. of brightness	I		G, K R	−5?	4	10·5	14
UG	SS Cyg, U Gem ⎰ Sudden periodic incr. of		60	B, A	8±3	3·6	13	25
Z	Z Cam, CN Ori ⎱ brightness		20	F	10±3	3·2	13·5	22
	SX Cen. Superimp. long and short periods		⎰ 30 ⎱ 800	F to M		⎰1·2 ⎱2·0	13·5	15
UV	Flare stars, UV Cet			dM3 to 6e	15	2	13	

Physical conditions of semi-regular types [1, 2, 4]

Sp at max	$\log P$	T_e at max	$\log \dfrac{\mathscr{M}}{\mathscr{M}_\odot}$	$\log \dfrac{\mathscr{R}}{\mathscr{R}_\odot}$	$\log \dfrac{\mathscr{L}}{\mathscr{L}_\odot}$	$\bar{M}_v$
	in days	°K				
M0	1·6	3 400	0·7	1·6	2·2	+0·3
M5	2·1	2 700	1·0	2·2	3·2	+0·3
M8	2·6	2 000	1·7	3·6	5·3	+0·3
cM0	2·5	3 400	1·5	2·8	4·7	−5·2
N0	2·0	2 800	1·0	2·2	3·2	−0·8
N4	2·6	2 400	1·2	2·6	3·7	−0·1

Relative spectral occurrence

Sp % occurrence	F 2	G 4	K 14	M 58	R 2	N 18	S 2

[1] *A.Q.* 1, § 105.
[2] C. P.- and S. GAPOSCHKIN, *Harv. Repr.* II, No. 2, 1943.
[3] C. P.- and S. GAPOSCHKIN, *Variable Stars*, Harv. Mon., No. 5, 1938.
[4] C. PAYNE-GAPOSCHKIN, *Variable Stars and Galactic Structure*, London, 1954.
[5] B. V. KUKARKIN et al., *General Catalogue of Variable Stars*, Moscow, 1958.

§ 108. Novae and Supernovae

Galactic novae detected per year, including recurrent novae [1]

$$= 2 \cdot 2 \text{ novae y}^{-1}$$

Total novae per year per galaxy [2]

$$\simeq 40 \text{ novae y}^{-1} \text{ gal}^{-1}$$

$$\simeq 4 \times 10^{-10} \text{ novae (pop. II stars)}^{-1} \text{ y}^{-1}$$

Galactic latitude [1, 2]

	$\bar{b}$ = mean	$\bar{b}$ = median
Novae	9°	6°
Recurrent novae	16°	11°

Spectral class of post novae   O, WC, (WC + WN)

Colour of novae near maximum [5]

$$B - V \simeq +0 \cdot 2$$

Types of novae [1, 8]

t_3 = time for brightness to decline 3 magnitudes from the maximum

I.A.U. Desig.	Type	Pop.	Occurrence	Freq.	M_{pg} pre-nova	M_{pg} max.	M_{pg} post-nova	log Energy output	t_3
				gal^{-1}y^{-1}				in erg	day
SN I	Supernova, Type I	II	E to Sc gal.	0·003		−16	+3?	49·5	30*
SN II	Supernova, Type II	I	Sp, Sc spiral	0·01		−14	+3?	47·5	100
N	Nova	II		30	+5	− 7·5	+4	44·5	40
Nd	Recurrent nova							43	

* After 30 days Type I supernovae decline at 1 mag per 70 days.

Nova characteristics and speed of decline [4]

t_3	in days	10	30	100	300
Principal ejection vel., v_1	in km/s	1 600	900	500	300
Diffusion, enhanced vel., v_2	in km/s	2 600	1 700	1 100	700
Velocity for supernovae	in km/s		6 000		
M_{pg} (max)		− 8·6	− 7·6	−6·5	−5·3
m_{pg} (pre and post min) − m_{pg} (max)		12	10·5	9	8

Selected list of galactic novae [1, 3]

> = fainter than;   e = emission line

Nova	Year	l^{II}	b^{II}	m pre-nova	m max	m post-nova	$m-M$	Post-nova Sp	t_3	Type
		°	°						day	
Tau (Crab)	1054	184	− 5		−6			e neb		SN I
Cas (Tycho)	1572	120	+ 2		−4·1		8	e neb		SN I
Oph (Kepler)	1604	4	+ 6		−2·2					SN I
η Car	1843	287	− 1		−0·8		7·9	7	pec	3 000	N
V841 Oph 2	1848	7	+17	>10	3	12·7	10	O con	300	N
Q Cyg	1876	90	− 8		3·0	14·9	11·3	O e	11	N
T Aur	1891	177	− 1	>13	4·0	14·8	10·2	O e	120	N
V1059 Sgr	1898	22	− 9		3	16·5	11		19	N
GK Per 2	1901	151	−10	13·5	0·2	13·3	8·5	O e	12	N
DM Gem 1	1903	185	+12	>14	5·0	16·5	13·1	O con	14	N
DI Lac	1910	103	− 5	13·7	4·6	14·3	11·6	O con	37	N
DN Gem 2	1912	183	+15	15	3·5	14·6	11·5	O e	34	N
V603 Aql 3	1918	33	0	10·6	−1·1	10·6	7·3	O e	7	N
HR Lyr	1919	60	+12	16·0	6·5	15·0	13·3	O con	70	N
V476 Cyg 3	1920	87	+13	>15	2·0	16·1	10·6	O e	14	N
RR Pic	1925	271	−25	12·7	1·2	9	7·6		150	N
DQ Her	1934	72	+26	14·3	1·4	13·8	7·6		105	N
CP Lac	1936	102	− 1	15·3	2·1	14·9	10·2		9	N
V630 Sgr	1936	357	− 7	14	4·5		13		8	N
BT Mon	1939	214	− 2	16	6	17·6	11		36	N
CP Pup	1942	253	− 1	17	0·2		10·6	O e	8	SN ?
V500 Aql	1943	47	−10	>17	6·3		13		29	N

List of recurrent novae [1, 2, 3]

Nova	Appearances	l^{II}	b^{II}	Period	m max	m min	$m-M$	t_3
				y				day
U Sco	1863, 1906, 1936	358	+21	37	8·9	17·6	16	6
T CrB	1866, 1946	42	+48	79	1·9	10·6	9·8	6
T Pyx	1890, 1902, 1920, 1944	256	+ 9	18	7·1	13·8	14·0	113
RS Oph	1898, 1933, 1958	20	+10	35	4·3	11·6	12·7	10
WZ Sge	1913, 1946	58	− 8	32	7·3	15·8	14·4	33
V1017 Sgr	1901 ?, 1919	3	− 9	17	7·2	14·2	14	130

Maximum nova brightness in relation to speed of decline [6, 7]

$$M_v \text{ (max)} = -11·3 + 2·3 \log t_3 \quad [t_3 \text{ in days}]$$

[1] *A.Q.* **1**, § 107.
[2] C. PAYNE-GAPOSCHKIN, *Variable Stars and Galactic Structure*, p. 56, London, 1954.
[3] C. PAYNE-GAPOSCHKIN, *Galactic Novae*, North-Holland, 1957.
[4] D. B. McLAUGHLIN, *Ap. J.*, **91**, 369, 1940; *P.A.S.P.*, **57**, 69, 1945.
[5] H. C. ARP, *A.J.*, **61**, 15, 1956.
[6] W. BUSCOMBE and G. DE VAUCOULEURS, *Obs.*, **75**, 170, 1955.
[7] T. SCHMIDT, *Z. Ap.*, **41**, 182, 1957.
[8] G. R. and E. M. BURBIDGE, *Handb. der Phys.*, **51**, p. 248, 1958.

§ 109. Wolf-Rayet and Early Emission Stars

Types of early emission stars [1, 2, 3]

Star	Pop.	Sp	M_v	$m_v(10)$	T	$\mathcal{R}$
					°K	$\mathcal{R}_\odot$
Planetary nuclei (§ 121)	II	O	0	11	90 000	0·4
Wolf-Rayet stars	I					
nitrogen sequence		WN	−4·0	8·0	80 000	2
carbon sequence		WC	−4·2	8·5		
Of stars		Of	−5·7	7·4		
P Cygni stars		Be	−4	6·5	27 000	8
α Cygni stars		Ae	−7	6·5	12 000	60
Be stars		Be		3·5	20 000	
Shell stars		B, A		6		

Proportion of early stars showing emission lines [1, 2]

Sp	O	B0	B2	B5	B8	A0	A2
% of stars with emission	13	14	17	6	1	0·1	0·05

Principal lines in Wolf-Rayet spectra [1]

WN stars contain He and N; WC stars contain He, O, and C

Ion	I.P.	λ
	ev	Å
He I	24·6	5876, 4471, 4026, 3889
He II	54·4	4686, 3203, 5412, 4859, 4542
C II	24·3	4267
C III	47·9	4650, 5696, 4069
C IV	64·5	5805, 3934
N III	47·4	4638, 4525, 4100, 3360

Ion	I.P.	λ
	ev	Å
N IV	77·4	3480, 4058
N V	97·9	4609
O III	54·9	3962, 3760, 3708, 3265
O IV	77·4	3730, 3411
O V	113·9	5590, 5114
O VI	138·1	3812, 3835

[1] *A.Q.* **1**, §§ 106, 110.
[2] R. H. GARSTANG, *Occ. Notes R.A.S.*, **3**, No. 21, 234, 1959.
[3] L. H. ALLER, *Gaseous Nebulae*, Chapman and Hall, 1956.

§ 110. Peculiar A Stars

The peculiar A stars comprise:

Ap or αCV	Stars having anomalously intense and variable lines of Mn, Si, Cr, Sr, etc. Spectrum variables and magnetic stars.
Am	Stars having a general well developed metallic line spectrum by comparison with H and Ca^+.

Spectral classification

Ap	Sp = B9p to F0p (sharp lined)
Am	Sp = A1 to A6 (from Ca^+)
	= A5 to F6 (from metals)

Magnitudes and colours in approximate agreement with Sp from metals.

M_v about 0·7 above main sequence in $M_v \cdot \cdot B - V$ diagram [4].

Relation between colour and absolute magnitude [5, 6]

$B - V$	0	+0·1	+0·2	+0·3
M_v	+0·4	+1·1	+1·8	+2·5
Type	peculiar		metallic	

Magnetic field in magnetic stars

order of	1 000 gauss	[2]
extreme	34 000 gauss	[3].

[1] No reference in *A.Q.* **1**.
[2] H. W. Babcock, *Ap. J. Supp.*, **3**, 141, 1958.
[3] H. W. Babcock, *Ap. J.*, **132**, 521, 1960.
[4] H. A. Abt, *Ap. J. Supp.*, **6**, No. 52, 37, 1961.
[5] O. J. Eggen, *Observatory*, **79**, 197, 1959.
[6] M. and C. Jaschek, *Z. Ap.*, **45**, 35, 1958.

§ 111. Sub-luminous Stars

Types of stars fainter than the main sequence

Star	Pop.	Sp	Brightness below main sequence
White dwarfs, dense degenerate stars. Possibly of two types [2]	I	B to G	10 mag
Subdwarfs, high velocity stars (relative to sun). May be identified from colour luminosity array, but not clearly defined [7]	II	F to M	1·4 mag
Faint blue stars, pre- and post-novae. Probably include normal pop. II stars of $M_v \simeq 0$, and nuclei of planetary nebulae	II	O, B	5 mag

Mean white dwarf conditions

Characteristic	All white dwarfs	Type [2]	
		I	II
Molecular weight	1·7	1·2	2·2
$\log (M/M_\odot)$	−0·1	+0·2	−0·3
$\log (R/R_\odot)$	−1·8	−1·6	−2·0
$\log \bar\rho$ in g cm^{-3}	5·8	5·5	5·9
H content		70%	0%
Sp	wA6	wA3	wA8
M_v	12	10·8	12·8

White dwarf conditions with Sp

Characteristic	Sp				
	wB0	wA0	wF0	wG0	wK0
M_v [6]	10·0	11·4	12·8	14·1	15·1
M_v Type I [2]	10·0	10·6	11·1		
Type II [2]	11·5	12·3	13·3	14·3	15·1
$B-V$	−0·27	0·00	+ 0·28	+ 0·55	+ 0·82
Mass	No clear change				
Radius	No clear change				
M_{bol} [5]	7·5	10·4	12·3	13·4	14·2

Selected white dwarfs [1, 3, 4, 5]

Star	1900 α	δ	μ	π	Sp [1, 3, 4, 5]	m_v [1, 6]	M_v	$B-V$ [1, 6]	$\log (M/M_\odot)$	$\log (R/R_\odot)$ [1, 2, 4, 5]	$\log (\bar\rho/\bar\rho_\odot)$
	h m	° ′	″	0″·001							
v. Maanen	0 44	+ 4 55	3·00	238	wF8	12·35	14·24	+0·61	+0·1	−1·95	6·0
L870−2	1 33	− 5 31	0·67	65	wA5	12·82	11·89	+0·32		−1·9	
h Per 1166	2 10	+56 39	0·17	16	wA	13·64	9·6	−0·10			
40 Eri B = 0² Eri	4 11	− 7 49	4·07	202	wA2	9·50	11·02	+0·03	−0·37	−1·82	5·1
Sirius B	6 41	−16 35	1·32	376	wA5	8·4	11·3	+0·4	−0·01	−1·7	5·1
He 3 = Ci$_{20}$398	6 41	+37 39	0·95	61	wA	12·03	10·95	−0·10	+0·2	−1·88	5·8
Procyon B	7 34	+ 5 29	1·25	291	wF8	10·8	13·1	+0·5	−0·29	−1·9	5·4
L745−46	7 36	−17 10	1·28	162	wA8	13·02	14·07	+0·28		−2·1	
−32° 5613	8 38	−32 37	1·68	105	wA0	11·6	11·8	+0·2	−0·5	−2·0	5·5
R627	11 19	+21 54	1·01	81	wA5	14·24	13·79	+0·25	−0·2	−2·3	6·7
L145−141	11 40	−64 18	2·68	204	wA	12·0	13·55	+0·1			
−7° 3632 A	13 25	− 8 03	1·18	61	wA2	12·33	11·25	+0·06		−1·9	
W489	13 32	+ 4 13	3·91	131	wK	14·68	15·25	+0·96		−1·6	
Grw+70° 5824	13 36	+70 48	0·40	28	wA	12·79	10·02	−0·09		−1·75	
Grw+70° 8247	19 01	+70 30	0·52	69	wA	13·15	12·33	+0·05		−1·9	
LDS 678°A	19 15	− 7 51	0·20	30	wA	12·30	9·7	+0·10		−1·5	
W1346	20 30	+24 44	0·65	72	wA2	11·51	10·79	−0·07	+0·4	−1·81	5·8
L1512−34	23 39	+31 54	0·22	49	wA4	12·88	11·33	+0·20		−1·76	
L362−81	23 57	−43 41	0·90	124	wA	12·7	13·2	+0·3			

[1] *A.Q.* 1, § 108.
[2] P. P. PARENAGO, *A. Zh.*, **33**, 340, 1956.
[3] E. PAVLOVSKAYA, *A. Zh.*, **33**, 660, 1956.
[4] E. SCHATZMAN, *White Dwarfs*, North-Holland, 1958.
[5] J. L. GREENSTEIN, *Handb. der Phys.*, **50**, 161, 1958.
[6] D. L. HARRIS, *Ap. J.*, **124**, 665, 1956.
[7] A. D. CODE, *Ap. J.*, **130**, 473, 1959.

§ 112. Double Stars

Of the 7 nearest star systems including the sun, 5 are at least double (binary), 1 has a planetary system, and 1 may be simple. Faint companions for most stars cannot be detected but may be present. Double and multiple star statistics may be severely influenced by such unseen companions.

In the following estimate of the number of double stars a triple star counts 2, a quadruple 3, etc., and invisible companions neglected [1]

Sp for star system	A, F, G, K	M	white dwarfs
% of double stars	50	20	0

The proportion of visible stars that are double within an orbital radius range of 1 dex (extending from twice the star's radius to about 1 000 A.U.) [2, 5, § 114]

$$\simeq 8\%$$

Distribution of double stars with total mass $\mathscr{M}$ [1]

$\mathscr{M}/\mathscr{M}_\odot$	$> 1 \cdot 0$	$1 \cdot 0$ to $0 \cdot 5$	$0 \cdot 5$ to $0 \cdot 25$	$0 \cdot 25$ to $0 \cdot 1$	$< 0 \cdot 1$
% single stars	32	72	85	92	100
% double stars	52	24	15	8	0
% triple stars	13	4	0	0	0
% quadruple stars	3	0	0	0	0

Eccentricity of binary star orbits and orbital period P [1, 3, 4]

$\log P$ in days	0	1	2	3	4	5	6	7
Mean eccentricity	0·03	0·18	0·29	0·37	0·46	0·58	0·70	0·83
	eclipsing, spectroscopic					visual		

Visual doubles

Theoretical telescopic resolution of double stars (Dawes' rule)

$$= 4'' \cdot 6/D_{in} \text{ where D is O.G. diam. in inches}$$

$$= 11'' \cdot 6/D_{cm} \text{ where D is O.G. diam. in cm}$$

Limiting resolution under best terrestrial seeing conditions

$$= 0'' \cdot 1$$

Separation ρ beyond which it is unlikely that star pairs are physical doubles

$$\log \rho = 2 \cdot 8 - 0 \cdot 2 \, m_v \quad [\rho \text{ in } '' \text{ arc}]$$

This limit is often used in compiling double star catalogues.

Number of known visual doubles [6, 7, 8]

$$\simeq 40\ 000$$

Proportion of observed visual double pairs ($m_v < 9$) in each spectral class [1]

Sp % visual doubles	O	B	A	F	G	K	M
		2	8	6	9	4	2

Distribution of visual double separations
($m_v < 9$ and $\rho < 2 \cdot 5 - 0 \cdot 2 \, m_v$) [1, 2]

Range of ρ in $''$ arc	0 to 0·5	0·5 to 1	1 to 2	2 to 4	> 4
% of visual doubles	21	15	19	22	23

Proportion of visual doubles with measurable orbital motions [1]

$$= 12\%$$

About 300 satisfactory orbital analyses have been made although more are listed in the catalogues [9, 10].

Mean and modal elements of visual doubles with determinable
orbital motions (therefore favouring small a) [1]

	Mean	Mode
a, semi-major axis of true orbit	$0''{\cdot}87$	$0''{\cdot}42$
a/π (π = parallax)	26 AU	18 AU
m_v	6·1	6·3
M_v	3·6	3·6
Period	76 y	32 y
Eccentricity	0·54	0·46

Elements for visual binaries [8]

Star	a	P	π	m_v		Sp		M_{bol}		$\mathcal{M}$	
				1	2	1	2	1	2	1	2
	$''$	y	$''$							$\mathcal{M}_{\odot}$	
η Cas	11·99	480	0·170	3·44	7·18	G0 v	K5	4·54	7·51	0·94	0·58
o^2 Eri B, C	6·89	247·9	0·201	9·62	11·10	B9	M5e	10·26	9·5	0·45	0·21
ξ Boo	4·88	150·0	0·148	4·66	6·70	G8 v	K5	5·41	6·70	0·85	0·75
70 Oph	4·55	87·8	0·199	5·09	8·49	K0 v	K4	5·56	6·85	0·90	0·65
α Cen A, B	17·66	80·1	0·760	0·09	1·38	G4	K1	4·40	5·65	1·08	0·88
Sirius	7·62	49·9	0·379	− 1·47	8·64	A1 v	wA5	0·80	11·22	2·28	0·98
Krü 60	2·41	44·6	0·253	9·80	11·46	dM4	dM6	9·11	9·97	0·27	0·16
Procyon	4·55	40·6	0·287	0·34	10·64	F5 iv–v	wF8	2·59	12·62	1·76	0·65
ζ Her	1·35	34·4	0·104	2·91	5·54	G0 iv	dK0	2·94	5·52	1·07	0·78
85 Peg	0·83	26·3	0·080	5·81	8·85	G2 v		5·26	7·18	0·82	0·80
Ross 614 A, B	0·98	16·5	0·251	11·3	14·8	dM6+		9·9	11·9	0·14	0·08
Fu 46	0·71	13·1	0·155	10·01	10·39	M4	M4	8·26	8·64	0·31	0·25

Ephemerides of visual doubles: [16].

Spectroscopic doubles

Proportion of all stars ($m_v < 5$) whose radial velocity variation shows clear duplicity [1]

$$= 9\%$$

Proportion of all stars showing variable radial velocity [1]

$$= 19\%$$

Most of these variations will be due to double star systems.

Number of spectroscopic binaries for which orbital and physical elements are available in the catalogues [11, 12] $\simeq 600$

Median periods and eccentricities [1]

Sp	O	B	A	F	G	K	M
Median period (in days)							
Main sequence	4	4	5	6	10	10	1?
Giants				20	50	500	3 000
Eccentricity,							
period < 10 d	0·07	0·09	0·07	0·04	0·03	0·03	0·00?
10 to 100 d	0·07	0·17	0·31	0·25	0·17	0·10	
> 100 d	0·3?	0·39	0·38	0·43	0·35	0·30	0·38?
Proportion of stars with duplicity in rad. vel., %		24	13	7	6	4	6

Constant for determining mass of spectroscopic doubles

$$(\mathcal{M}_1 + \mathcal{M}_2) \sin^3 i = 1 \cdot 036 \times 10^{-7} (1 - e^2)^{3/2} (K_1 + K_2)^3 P$$

where total mass $\mathcal{M}_1 + \mathcal{M}_2$ is in $\mathcal{M}_\odot$, radial velocity semi-amplitudes K_1, K_2 are in km/s, period P in days, e = eccentricity, and i = orbital inclination.

Distribution of mass ratio of spectroscopic doubles [1]

$\log (\mathcal{M}_1/\mathcal{M}_2)$ % of total	0·0 to 0·1	0·1 to 0·2	0·2 to 0·3	0·3 to 0·4	0·4 to 0·5
	64	21	10	4	1

Eclipsing variables

Proportion of clear spectroscopic binaries that are eclipsing variables [1]

$$= 9\%$$

Number of eclipsing variables with well derived elements available in the catalogues

[13, 14, 15] $\simeq 90$

Eclipsing variable types [1]

P = period, ϵ = stellar ellipticity

Type	Rel. occurrence	Mean amplitude	ϵ	Median P	Sp	$\bar{M}_v$
	%	mag		day		
EA Non-elliptical, Algol type	60	1·4	1·0	3	A	1·0
EB Elliptical, β Lyr type, P > 12 h	20	⎫	0·93	1·5	B–A	
EW Elliptical, W UMa type, P < 12 h	10	⎬ 0·9	0·79	0·4	F–G	4·0
Giant eclipsing variables	1	⎭		1 000		
Ell Ellipsoidal (non eclipse), b Per	1		0·95		B–F	
All (including un-classified)	100	1·2		2·6		

Rotation period and spectral type [1]

The table gives the general range and omits a few exceptional cases.
The minimum period is governed by contact of the two components.

Type	Sp						
	O	B	A	F	G	K	M
				days			
Algol type		2–20	0·8–30	0·7–30	0·6–10	0·5–5	
β Lyr type	7	1–7	0·5–2	0·5–2	0·6–10		
W UMa type			0·6–1·3	0·4–0·7	0·3–0·6	0·26–0·5	
Minimum period	3	1·0	0·4	0·27	0·20	0·13	0·10

[1] *A.Q.* 1, § 109.
[2] J. JACKSON, *M.N.*, **115**, 204, 1955.
[3] J. PENSADO, *Madrid, Astr. and Geoph. Pub.*, No. 28, 1955.
[4] J. HOPMANN, *Mitt. U.-S. Wien.*, **8**, 221, 1956.
[5] G. P. KUIPER, *P.A.S.P.*, **47**, 121, 1935.
[6] R. G. AITKEN, *N.G. Catalogue of Double Stars*, Carnegie, 1932.
[7] R. T. A. INNES, DAWSON, and VAN DEN BOS, *Southern Double Star Catalogue*, Union Observatory, 1927.
[8] P. VAN DE KAMP, *Handb. der Phys.*, **50**, 187, 1958.
[9] P. BAIZE, *J.O.*, **33**, 1, 1950.
[10] W. S. FINSEN, *Union Obs. Circ.*, **4**, No. 100, 465, 1938.
[11] J. H. MOORE and F. J. NEUBAUER, *Lick Ob. Bull.*, **20**, No. 521, 1928.
[12] R. BOUIGUE, *Ann. Ob. Toulouse*, **21**, 31, 1952; **22**, 49, 1954; **23**, 45, 1955; **24**, 67, 1956.
[13] Z. KOPAL and M. B. SHAPLEY, *Jodrell Bank Ann.*, **1**, 141, 1956.
[14] L. PLAUT, *Pub. Kapteyn Astr. Lab. Groningen*, No. 55, 1953.
[15] S. GAPOSCHKIN, *Handb. der Phys.*, **50**, 225, 1958.
[16] P. MULLER, *J. Obs.*, **36**, 61, 1953; **37**, 153, 1954.

Elements of eclipsing binaries [13]

Star		P	Separation	Sp		M		R		M_{bol}		m_v	M_v	Dist
Variable	HD			1	2	1	2	1	2	1	2			
		day	$\mathscr{R}_\odot$			$\mathscr{M}_\odot$		$\mathscr{R}_\odot$						pc
Detached systems														
σ Aql	185 507	1·95	15·1	B8	B9	6·8	5·4	4·2	3·3	−1·9	−0·9	5·1	−0·6	137
WW Aur	46 052	2·52	11·8	A7	F0	1·92	1·90	1·92	1·90	1·7	2·0	5·7	1·2	77
AR Aur	34 364	4·13	18·5	B9	A0	2·55	2·30	1·82	1·82	0·3	0·6	5·5	0·5	100
β Aur	40 183	3·96	17·5	A0	A0	2·33	2·25	2·48	2·27	−0·1	0·2	2·1	0·0	27
YZ Cas	4 161	4·47	19·4	A3	F5	3·3	1·6	2·75	1·49	0·4	3·1	5·6	0·7	90
AR Cas	221 253	6·07	34·8	B3	A0·5	11·9	3·0	7·1	2·3	−4·8	0·2	4·7	−3·0	350
AH Cep	216 014	1·77	18·7	B0	B0·5	16·5	14·2	6·06	5·50	−5·6	−5·2	6·6	−1·9	500
α Cr B	139 006	17·36	41·9	A0	G6	2·5	0·89	2·9	0·87	−0·1	5·4	2·3	0·7	22
AR Lac	210 334	1·98	9·13	G5	gK0	1·32	1·31	1·54	2·86	3·8	3·4	6·5	3·1	48
U Oph	156 247	1·68	12·8	B5	B6	5·30	4·65	3·4	3·1	−2·4	−1·9	5·9	−1·6	310
VV Ori	36 695	1·49	16·0	B1	B5	18	6·1	6·2	3·0	−5·3	−2·1	5·1	−3·4	500
AG Per	25 833	2·03	14·1	B5	B7	5·1	4·5	3·0	2·7	−2·3	−1·7	6·6	−0·8	300
ξ Phe	6 882	1·67	10·0	B7	A0·5	3·0	2·1	2·8	1·6	−1·2	1·0	4·1	−0·2	70
RS Sgr	167 647	2·42	10·1	B5	A5	1·4	0·94	3·2	2·6	−2·2	0·7	6·1	−0·9	250
Semi-detached systems														
R CMa	57 167	1·14	3·84	F0	gG9	0·49	0·11	1·06	0·97	3·3	5·5	5·9	3·3	33
RZ Cas	17 138	1·20	6·35	A0	gG1	1·80	0·63	1·53	1·80	0·9	3·4	6·3	1·5	90
U Cep	5 679	2·49	12·6	B8	gG8	2·9	1·4	2·4	3·9	−0·6	2·3	6·8	0·5	180
u Her	156 633	2·05	15·0	B3	B7·5	7·9	2·8	4·5	4·3	−3·8	−2·1	4·7	−2·4	260
δ Lib	132 742	2·33	11·6	A0	gG2	2·6	1·1	3·5	3·5	−0·8	−2·2	4·8	−0·2	100
β Per	19 356	2·87	15·7	B8	gK0	5·2	1·01	3·57	3·76	−1·0	2·7	2·2	0·0	27
V Pup	65 818	1·45	16·2	B1	B3·5	16·6	9·8	6·0	5·3	−5·1	−3·9	4·5	−3·5	400
U Sge	181 182	3·38	19·5	B9	gG2	6·7	2·0	4·1	5·4	−1·4	1·2	6·4	−0·6	250
V356 Sgr	173 787	8·90	46	B3	A2	12	4·7	5·0	13	−3·9	−3·2	6·8	−3·2	1 000
V505 Sgr	187 949	1·18	7·2	A1	gF8	2·33	1·21	2·27	2·26	2·7	0·3	6·5	0·7	145
μ¹ Sco	151 890	1·45	15·3	B9	gK1	14·0	9·2	4·8	5·3	−4·2	−3·3	3·1	−3·3	190
λ Tau	25 204	3·95	16·1	B3	A3	2·3	0·92	3·4	4·8	−3·2	−0·9	3·8	−1·8	132
TX UMa	93 033	3·06	13·7	B8	gG3	2·8	0·85	2·16	3·79	−0·4	2·1	6·9	0·6	180
RS Vul	180 939	4·48	20·9	B5	gF9	4·6	1·4	3·9	5·3	−2·6	0·9	6·9	−1·4	450

CHAPTER 12

STAR POPULATIONS AND THE
SOLAR NEIGHBOURHOOD

§ 113. The Nearest Stars

THE list gives 100 nearest stars or star components, but does not give a separate entry for invisible companions. The star designations are taken, as usual, from various catalogues. Stars are identified by α, δ. Most of the information is available in the 1950·0 Catalogues of Stars nearer than 20 parsecs [2].

V and $B - V$ = visual magnitude and colour, M_v = absolute magnitude, μ = proper motion, θ = direction of proper motion (from N towards E), π = parallax, v_r = radial velocity (+ = moving away from sun), $\mathcal{M}$ = mass, $\mathcal{R}$ = radius. In the Sp column, w = white dwarf, sd = subdwarf. Since nearly all the near stars are on the main sequence the luminosity classification is not given.

The notes give the fairly recent separation of doubles or some orbital elements when known. P = period, a = semi-major axis of secondary relative to primary. Flare, indicates that the star has exhibited sudden variations of brightness (flare star). db and tr = double and triple star with invisible components. sp = spectroscopic.

	V	$B-V$	$V-R$	$R-I$	$U-I$	M_v
LHS 288 = L143-23(-)	13.92	1.82	1.59	2.04	3.61	15.6
LHS 1070 = MBT 45(M6e)	15.42	—	1.70	2.16	3.86	16.0

	π	M_v
	0."221±.008	15.59±.08
	0.133±.009	16.04±.14

Janne & Bessell   PASP, 98, 658 (1986)

The nearest stars

Star		1900 α (h m)	1900 δ (° ')	V [1, 2, 3, 4, 6, 7, 8]	B − V	M_v	Sp [1, 2]	μ ("/y) [1, 2]	θ (°) [1, 2]	π (0"·001) [1, 2, 9]	v_r (km/s) [1, 2, 10]	ℳ☉ [1, 12, 13]	ℛ☉ [1, 12, 13]	Notes
Grm 34 = +43° 44	A	0 13	+43 27	8·08	1·55	10·30	M2	2·89	82	278	+ 14			A = sp db
(= CC19)	B	"	"	11·05	1·78	13·27	M5				+ 21			AB = 38"
β Hyi		0 20	−77 49	2·79	0·61	3·71	G2	2·25	82	153	+ 23			
η Cas	A	0 43	+57 17	3·44	0·57	4·73	G0	1·22	115	181	+ 9	0·85	0·84	a = 12"·0
"	B	"	"	7·25		8·54	M0				+ 13	0·52	0·07	P = 490 y
v. Maanen = Wolf 28		0 44	+ 4 55	12·34	0·55	14·19	wF5	2·949	155·4	235	+260 ?			
L726−8 [13]	A	1 34	−18 28	12·41	1·9	15·28	M6e	3·36	80	375	+ 29	0·044		a = 5", P = 200y
(= UV Cet)	B			12·95		15·87						0·035		B = Flare st.
τ Cet		1 39	−16 28	3·50	0·72	5·70	sdG8	1·934	296·5	275	− 16			
82 Eri = o Eri		3 16	−43 27	4·23	0·71	5·19	G5	3·14	76	156	+ 87			
ε Eri		3 28	− 9 48	3·74	0·87	6·14	K2	0·990	271·7	303	+ 15	0·11		
o² Eri = 40 Eri	A	4 11	− 7 49	4·44	0·81	5·96	K1	4·08	213	201	+ 42	0·44		A db? 0"·01, 3 y
"	B	"	"	9·64		11·16	wA			"	− 42		0·018	BC a = 6"·9
"	C	"	"	11·05		12·57	M5e				+ 45	0·21	0·43	P = 248 y
Kapteyn = −45° 1841		5 08	−44 59	8·9	1·48	10·9	sdM0	8·73	131	251	+242			Nearest subdwarf
HD 36395 = −3° 1123		5 26	+ 3 42	7·97		9·03	M1	2·24	160	163	+ 11			
Ross 47		5 36	+12 29	11·58		12·65	sdM4	2·54	127	164	+103			
−21° 1377		6 06	−21 49	8·18	1·51	9·33	M1	0·72	188	170	+ 2			
Ross 614	A	6 24	+ 2 44	11·25		13·23	M5	1·00	131	249	+ 24	0·14		a = 1"·0
(= CC390)	B	"	"	14·8		16·8						0·08		P = 16·5 y
Sirius = αCMa	A	6 41	−16 35	−1·46	0·01	1·41	A1	1·32	204	375	− 8	2·31	1·8	a = 7"·6
"	B	"	"	8·67		11·54	wA5					0·98	0·022	P = 49·9 y
Wolf 294		6 48	+33 24	10·15		11·29	M4	0·86	240	169	+ 36			
Ross 986		7 03	+38 43	11·68		12·86	M5e	1·12	208	172	+ 39			
Luyten = +5° 1668		7 22	+ 5 32	9·92		12·02	M4	3·75	171	266	+ 26			db ?
Procyon = αCMi	A	7 34	+ 5 29	0·35	0·40	2·64	F5	1·25	214	287	− 3	1·75	1·7	a = 4"·5
"	B	"	"	10·8		13·1	wF					0·64	0·01	P = 40·6 y
L745−46	A	7 36	−17 10	13·06		14·14	wF	1·26	117	164				
"	B	"	"	17·6		18·7	M							21"
L97−12		7 53	−67 30	14·9		16·1	wF-G	2·04	135	170				

The nearest stars

Star		1900 α (h m)	δ (° ')	V [1, 2, 3, 4, 6, 7, 8]	B−V	M$_v$	Sp [1, 2]	μ ("/y) [1, 2]	θ (°) [1, 2]	π (0".001) [1, 2, 9]	v$_r$ (km/s) [1, 2, 10]	ℳ☉ [1, 12, 13]	ℛ☉	Notes
Ross 619	A	8 06	+ 9 11	12.88		13.78	M5	5.40	167	151	− 35			
LFT571 = L674−15	B	8 08	− 21 15	13.8		14.9	M	0.73	175	166				
+53° 1320		9 08	+ 53 07	7.68	1.44	8.74	K8	1.68	248	163	+ 10			} 19"
+53° 1321				7.77		8.82	M0			162	+ 9			} P = 1 000 y
Grm 1 618 = +50° 1725		10 05	+ 49 57	6.60	1.37	8.33	M0	1.464	249.8	222	+ 27			
AD Leo = +20° 2465		10 14	+ 20 22	9.41	1.55	11.04	M4	0.429	258	212	+ 10			Flare st. invis. comp.
Wolf 359		10 52	+ 7 36	13.66		16.80	M6e	4.71	235	425	+ 13			Invis. comp. ℳ = 0.03
Lal 21185 = +36° 2147		10 58	+ 36 38	7.47	1.51	10.42	M2	4.78	187	398	+ 87	0.35		
+44° 2051	A	11 01	+ 44 02	8.76	1.54	9.94	M2	4.53	295	172	+ 64			} 28"
(= WX UMa)	B	"	"	14.8		16.0	M6	"	"	"				} B = flare star
I(UC37) = CC658		11 40	− 64 17	12.5		14.0	wA	2.68	97	203	− 119			
AC 79° 3888		11 41	+ 79 14	10.92		12.41	sdM4	0.87	57	198	− 13			} 15"
Ross 128		11 43	+ 1 23	11.13		13.50	M5	1.38	153	298				
L68−28	A	12 23	− 70 56	15.7		16.6	K−M	1.17	339	152				} 0".5
L68−29	B	"	"	17.7		18.6	K−M	"	"	"				
Wolf 424	A	12 28	+ 9 34	12.63		14.44	M6	1.87	276	230	− 5			
+15° 2620	B	13 41	+ 15 26	12.7	1.44	14.5	M7	2.30	129	201	+ 15	0.1		
Proxima Cen		14 23	− 62 15	10.7		15.1	M5e	3.85	282	763				Flare st. nearest st.
−11° 3759		14 29	− 12 06	11.38		12.37	M4	0.69	334	158				
α Cen	A	14 33	− 60 25	0.00	0.69	4.38	G2	3.69	281	752	− 22	1.09	1.23	} a = 17".7
	B	"	"	1.38		5.76	K4	"	"	"		0.88	0.87	} P = 80.1 y
−20° 4125	A	14 52	− 20 58	5.82	1.12	7.00	K5	1.99	149	172	+ 20			} 20"
−20° 4123	B	"	"	8.10		9.28	M2	"	"	"	+ 25			
−40° 9712		15 26	− 40 54	10.1		11.1	M4	1.55	229	166				
−12° 4523 = CC995	A	16 25	− 12 25	10.07	1.60	12.01	M4	1.18	182	244	− 13	0.38		} AB 0".20, 1.7 y
−8° 4352	B	16 50	+ 8 09	9.72	1.59	10.63	M3e	1.19	222	152	+ 19	0.34		
(= Wolf 629)	C	"	"	9.8		10.7	M4	"	"	"				} BC 72"
+45° 2505 [5]	A	17 09	+ 45 50	11.76		12.78	sdM4	1.58	172	160	+ 25	0.31		} 0".7
				9.95		10.97	M3			160	− 18			} P = 13.1
36 Oph (= Fu46)	B	17 09	− 26 27	10.31	0.85	11.33	M4	1.24	203	177	− 1	0.25		} AB 5"
(= −26° 12026)	A	17 10	− 26 24	5.07		6.31	K1	"	"	172	0			
(= −26° 12036)	B			5.11	1.14	6.35	K1	"	"	172	0			} BC 732"
−46° 11540	C	17 21	− 46 47	6.34	1.5	7.52	K5	1.04	147	213				
				9.4		11.0	M4							

The nearest stars

Star		α (1900)	δ (1900)	V [1,2,3,4,6,7,8]	B−V [1,2,3,4,6,7,8]	Mv	Sp [1,2]	μ [1,2]	θ [1,2]	π [1,2,9]	vr [1,2,10]	M [1,12,13]	R [1,12,13]	Notes
		h m	° '					"/y	° "	0".001	km/s	M☉	R☉	
−44° 11909		17 30	−44 14	11·1		12·7	M5	1·16	217	209				
+68° 946		17 37	+68 26	9·13	1·52	10·67	M4	1·331	194·1	203	− 17			
I (UC48)		17 38	+57 14	12·9	1·75	14·0	M	1·72	219	167	−108			? db. 0".06, 1·1 y
Barnard = +4° 3561		17 53	+ 4 25	9·53	0·87	13·21	M5	10·27	356	545	− 7			
70 Oph (= +2° 3482)	A	18 01	+ 2 31	4·22		5·64	K0	1·13	167	192	+ 10	0·89		4".5 db; 87·8 y
	B	"	"	5·94	1·54	7·36	K5				+ 1	0·68		db
+59° 1915 (= Σ2398)	A	18 42	+59 29	8·90	1·58	11·16	M4	2·28	324	283	+ 14			⎱ 17"
	B	"	"	9·69		11·95	M5				+ 4			⎰
Ross 154		18 44	−23 54	10·6	1·49	13·3	M5	0·72	103	350				Flare star
+4° 4048		19 12	+ 5 02	9·13		10·29	M3	1·46	203	171	+ 34			⎱ 74"
L 347−14	A	19 13	−45 42	18·0		19·2	M5	2·93	168	169				⎰
	B	"	"	13·7		14·8	M7							
σ Dra		19 33	+69 29	4·69	0·80	5·92	K0	1·84	162	176	+ 27			
Altair = αAql		19 46	+ 8 36	0·75	0·25	2·23	A7	0·66	54	198	− 26			
δ Pav		19 59	−66 26	3·56	0·75	4·71	G7	1·64	134	170	− 22			
−36° 13940 (= HR7703)	A	20 05	−36 21	5·33	0·85	6·51	K4	1·63	164	172	−130			⎱ 7"
	B	"	"	11·5		12·7	M5							⎰
−45° 13677		20 07	−45 28	8·0	1·44	9·0	M0	0·78	100	159	− 30			
61 Cyg	A	21 02	+38 15	5·20	1·21	7·53	K5	5·20	52	292	− 64	0·59		a = 24".6, 720 y; ? invis. trip.
	B	"	"	6·03	1·4	8·36	K7				− 63	0·50		
−39° 14192		21 11	−39 15	6·69	1·42	8·73	M0	3·47	251	256	+ 20			
−49° 13515		21 27	−49 26	8·9		10·6	M3	0·81	185	219	+ 18			
ε Ind		21 56	−57 12	4·73	1·05	7·01	K5	4·69	123	286	− 40			
Krüger 60 = DO Cep (= +56° 2783)	A	22 24	+57 12	9·83	1·63	11·82	M3	0·86	246	250	− 24	0·27	0·51	a = 2".4, 45 y; B = Flare st.
	B	"	"	11·37		13·36	M4e				− 28	0·16		
L789-6		22 33	−15 52	12·58		14·93	M6e	3·260	45·2	296	− 60			
−21° 6267		22 33	−21 08	9·3		11·0	M2	0·46	99	219	− 8			
+43° 4305	A	22 42	+43 49	11·0	1·39	12·7	Me	0·83	238	198	− 1			⎱ 23"
	B	"	"	10·05		11·53	M5e							⎰
−15° 6290 = Ross 780		22 48	−14 47	10·16	1·60	11·73	M5	1·11	123	206	+ 9			
−36° 15693		22 59	−36 26	7·39	1·50	9·57	M2	6·90	79	273	+ 10			
+56° 2966		23 08	+56 37	5·58	1·01	6·49	K3	2·09	82	152	+ 18			
Ross 248		23 37	+43 39	12·25	1·8	14·75	M6e	1·82	176	316	− 81			Flare star
+1° 4774		23 44	+ 1 52	8·99	1·49	10·05	M2	1·38	134	163	− 64			
−37° 15492		23 59	−37 51	8·59	1·48	10·29	M3	6·08	113	219	+ 24			

[1] *A.Q.* **1**, § 111.
[2] W. GLIESE, *Astr. Rech.-Inst. Heidelberg*, Mitt. A., No. 8, 1957.
[3] H. C. ARP, *Handb. der Phys.*, **51**, 75, 1958.
[4] V. B. NIKONOV et al., *Iz. Crimea Ap. Ob.*, **17**, 42, 1957.
[5] S. L. LIPPINCOTT, *A.J.*, **64**, 419, 1959.
[6] M. BEYER, *A.N.*, **282**, 211, 1955.
[7] O. J. EGGEN, *A.J.*, **60**, 401, 1955; **62**, 45, 1957.
[8] H. L. JOHNSON and C. F. KNUCKLES, *Ap. J.*, **126**, 113, 1957.
[9] L. F. JENKINS, *Gen. Cat. Trig. Parallaxes*, 1952.
[10] R. E. WILSON, *Gen. Cat. Radial Vel.*, Carnegie Inst., 1953.
[11] W. J. LUYTEN, *Cat. of 1849 Stars with p.m.* $> 0''\cdot5$, Minnesota, 1955.
[12] S. L. LIPPINCOTT and P. V. D. KAMP, *Sproul Repr.*, No. 115, 1960.
[13] P. V. D. KAMP, *A.J.*, **64**, 236, 1959; *Handb. der Phys.*, **50**, 187, 1958.

§ 114. The Brightest Stars

The list contains 100 visually brightest stars. For multiple stars the data refer to the combined system, and the multiplicity is given in the notes where db = double, tr = triple, qu = quadruple, sp = spectroscopic, vis = visual, var = variable, ecl = eclipsing. Approximate separations of visual doubles and periods of spectroscopic doubles and variables are also given in the notes.

The star magnitudes V and colours $B - V$ are given on the B, V system, and the spectral classifications Sp are on the MKK system [11] (sometimes smoothed by averaging). μ = proper motion per year, and θ = direction of μ (from N through E). The distance d is from the parallax π when $\pi > 0''\cdot030/\text{y}$, and from the luminosity spectral class when $\pi < 0''\cdot015/\text{y}$. Some averaging has been introduced. In the radial velocity column v_r, v = variable, + = distance increasing, i.e. red shift.

The absolute magnitudes M_v are derived from the V and d columns. In a few cases an interstellar absorption correction has been introduced from measured colour excess [10].

For star name pronunciations see [12].

The brightest stars

Star		1900 α (h m)	1900 δ (° ')	V [3, 4, 5, 6, 13]	B−V [4, 5, 6, 13]	M_v	Sp [1, 2]	μ [1, 2] (0″·001/y)	θ [1] (°)	d [1, 3, 7] (pc)	v_r [1, 3, 8] (km/s)	Notes [1, 3, 7]
Alpheratz	α And	0 03	+28 32	2·07	−0·07	−0·5	B9p III	211	139	31	−12 v	sp. var, 96·7 d, Mn star
Caph	β Cas	0 04	+58 36	2·26	+0·34	+1·5	F2 IV	557	109	14	−11·7	
Ankaa	α Phe	0 21	−42 51	2·37	+1·07	+0·2	K0 III	444	154	27	+75 v	sp. and vis. db, 3849 d
Schedar	α Cas	0 35	+55 59	2·20	+1·16	−1·3	K0 II−III	59	121	50	−3·7	irreg. var.
Diphda	β Cet	0 39	−18 32	2·04	+1·01	+0·8	K0 III	234	80	18	+13·1	
Cih	γ Cas	0 51	+60 11	2·15	−0·2	−0·9	B0e IV	28	94	40	−7 v	vis. db 2″, irreg. var.
Mirach	β And	1 04	+35 05	2·07	+1·62	+0·2	M0 III	213	122	24	+0·3	
Polaris	α UMi	1 23	+88 46	2·02	+0·6	−4·5	F8 Ib	45	95	200	−17 v	sp. db, 30 y, var. 4·0 d
Achernar	α Eri	1 34	−57 45	0·49	−0·17	−2·2	B5 IV	96	108	35	+19	
Almach	γ And	1 58	+41 51	2·16	+1·3	−2·3	K3 II−III	70	138	80	−11·7	tr. vis. and sp. db, 10″, 55 y
Hamal	α Ari	2 02	+22 59	2·00	+1·17	+0·3	K2 III	241	127	22	−14·2	
Mira	o Cet	2 14	−3 26	2·0	+1·5	−1·0	M6e III	234	181	40	+63	var. 332 d, vis. db (close)
Menkar	α Cet	2 57	+3 42	2·53	+1·16	−1·0	M2 III	75	187	50	−25·9	
Algol	β Per	3 02	+40 34	2·10	−0·05	−0·5	B8 V	8	125	31	+5 v	ecl., sp. tr., 2·87 d, 1·87 y
Mirfak	α Per	3 17	+49 30	1·80	+0·48	−4·1	F5 Ib	36	132	150	−2·4	
Aldebaran	α Tau	4 30	+16 19	0·80	+1·55	−0·8	K5 III	203	160	21	+54·2	vis. db, 31″
Capella [9]	α Aur	5 09	+45 54	0·09	+0·81	−0·6	G8, G0	436	168	14	+30 v	sp. db, 104 d
Rigel	β Ori	5 10	−8 19	0·11	−0·05	−7·0	B8 Ia	2	135	270	+22 v	qu., vis. db 9″, sp. db 22 d
Bellatrix	γ Ori	5 20	+6 16	1·63	−0·22	−4·1	B2 III	17	200	140	+18·2	
El Nath	β Tau	5 20	+28 32	1·65	−0·13	−2·9	B7 III	179	169	80	+8·0	
Mintaka	δ Ori	5 27	−0 22	2·19	−0·21	−6·0	O9·5 II	3	146	450	+17 v	
Arneb	α Lep	5 28	−17 54	2·58	+0·22	−4·8	F0 Ib	6	30	300	+24·7	ecl., tr., vis. db 53″, sp. db 5·7 d
Alnilam	ε Ori	5 31	−1 16	1·70	−0·18	−6·8	B0 Ia	1	180	500	+26·1	
Alnitak	ζ Ori	5 36	−2 00	1·79	−0·21	−6·2	O9·5 Ib	7	131	400	+18·1	tr., vis. db 2″·5, sp. db 19 d
Saiph	κ Ori	5 43	−9 42	2·06	−0·16	−7·1	B0·5 Ia	6	149	700	+20·8	
Betelgeuse	α Ori	5 50	+7 23	0·4	+1·85	−5·9	M2 I	30	74	180	+21 v	semi-reg. var. 5·8 y, db 40″
Menkalinan	β Aur	5 52	+44 56	1·89	+0·04	−0·2	A2 V	49	264	26	−18 v	ecl. sp. db 3·96 d
Mirzam	β CMa	6 18	−17 54	1·96	−0·23	−4·5	B1 II−III	4	270	200	+34 v	sp. var. 0·25 and 42 d
Canopus	α Car	6 22	−52 38	−0·72	+0·16		F0 I−II	24	56		+20·4	
Alhena	γ Gem	6 32	+16 29	1·93	−0·00	−0·5	A0 IV	66	136	30	−12 v	sp. db 2175 d

The brightest stars

Star	1900 α (h m)	δ	V [3, 4, 5, 6, 13]	B−V [5, 6, 13]	M_v	Sp [1, 2]	μ [1, 2] (0″·001/y)	θ [1] (°)	d [1, 3, 7] (pc)	v_r [1, 3, 8] (km/s)	Notes [1, 3, 7]
Sirius	6 41	−16 35	−1·44	−0·01	+1·41	A1 v	1 324	204	2·7	− 8 v	vis. db 49·9 y, 9″
Adhara ε CMa	6 55	−28 50	1·48	−0·17	−5·0	B2 II	4	135	200	+27·4	vis. db 8″
Wezen δ CMa	7 04	−26 14	1·85	+0·63	−7·0	F8 Ia	5	292	600	+34·3	
Aludra η CMa	7 20	−29 06	2·42	−0·07	−7·1	B5 Ia	8	294	800	+40·2	vis. tr., each sp. db
Castor α Gem	7 28	+32 06	1·56	+0·05	+0·8	A1, A5	202	237	14	+ 3 v	
Procyon α CMi	7 34	+ 5 29	0·36	+0·41	+2·7	F5 IV–V	1 247	214	3·5	− 3·2	vis. db 4″ 41 y
Pollux β Gem	7 39	+28 16	1·15	+1·01	+1·0	K0 III	624	264	10·7	+ 3·4	nearest giant
Naos ζ Pup	8 00	−39 43	2·23	−0·27	−7·3	O5	33	282	800	−24	vis. db 41″
γ Vel	8 06	−47 03	1·85	−0·25	−4·2	WC7	8	290	160	+35	db, composite sp.
Avior ε Car	8 20	−59 11	1·94	+1·2	−3·1	K0, B	30	296	100	+11·5	
Suhail δ Vel	8 42	−54 21	1·93	+0·04	+0·1	A0 v	89	170	23	+ 2·2	vis. tr. 3″, 69″
λ Vel	9 04	−43 02	2·23	+1·7	−4·3	K5 Ib	25	281	200	+18·4	
Miaplacidus β Car	9 12	−69 18	1·68	−0·01	−0·4	A0 III	186	301	26	− 5	
Scutulum ι Car	9 14	−58 51	2·24	+0·18	−4·2	F0 Ib	21	266	180	+13·3	sp. db 117 d
κ Vel	9 19	−54 35	2·45	−0·16	−3·0	B2 IV	12	275	120	+22 v	
Alphard α Hya	9 23	− 8 14	2·05	+1·43	−0·7	K4 III	35	333	35	− 4·3	
Regulus α Leo	10 03	+12 27	1·34	−0·11	−0·8	B7 v	248	269	26	+ 3·2	vis. tr. 177″, 3″
Algeiba γ Leo	10 14	+20 21	2·02	+1·2	−0·5	K0p III	349	119	32	−36·7	vis. db 400 y, high vel.
Merak β UMa	10 56	+56 55	2·36	−0·02	+0·6	A1 v	88	71	23	−12·0	
Dubhe α UMa	10 58	+62 17	1·81	+1·06	−0·6	G9 III	138	240	30	− 8·9	close vis. db
Zosma δ Leo	11 09	+21 04	2·55	+0·12	+0·8	A4 v	204	135	23	−21	
Denebola β Leo	11 44	+15 08	2·13	+0·08	+1·6	A3 v	509	256	13	− 1	
Phecda γ UMa	11 49	+54 15	2·43	0·00	−0·1	A0 v	94	88	32	−12	
Gienah γ Crv	12 11	−16 59	2·58	−0·09	−2·4	B8 III	161	275	100	− 4·2	
Acrux α Cru	12 21	−62 33	0·83	−0·26	−3·7	B1, B3	44	228	80	− 6 v	vis. db 5″, each sp. db
Gacrux γ Cru	12 26	−56 33	1·68	+1·58	−2·5	M3 II	272	176	70	+21·3	optical pair
Muhlifain γ Cen	12 36	−48 25	2·16	−0·01	−1·7	A0 IV	198	266	60	− 7·5	vis. db 85 y
Mimosa β Cru	12 42	−59 09	1·29	−0·25	−4·3	B0 III	51	240	130	+20·0	
Alioth ε UMa	12 50	+56 30	1·78	−0·02	−0·2	A0p	115	95	25	−10	sp. db 4·15 y, Cr-Eu star
Mizar ζ UMa	13 20	+55 27	2·12	+0·03	0·0	A2 v	129	103	26	− 9 v	tr., vis db 14″, sp. db 20 d
Spica α Vir	13 20	−10 38	0·97	−0·23	−3·1	B1 v	53	229	65	+ 1 v	
ε Cen	13 34	−52 57	2·34	−0·23	−3·6	B1 IV	35	229	150	+ 5·6	ecl. sp. db 4·0 d
Alcaid η UMa	13 44	+49 49	1·86	−0·19	−2·3	B3 v	120	260	70	−10·6	
Hadar β Cen	13 57	−59 53	0·63	−0·24	−5·0	B1 II	36	220	130	−1·3	vis. db 1″·2

Star		α 1900 (h m)	δ 1900 (° ′)	V [3, 4, 5, 6, 13]	B−V [3, 4, 5, 6, 13]	M_v	Sp [1, 2]	μ [1, 2] (0″·001/y)	θ [1] (°)	d [1, 3, 7] (pc)	v_r [1, 3, 8] (km/s)	Notes [1, 3, 7]
Arcturus	α Boo	14 11	+19 42	−0·05	+1·24	−0·2	K1 III	2 285	209	11	− 5·2	db, composite sp.
Rigil Kent	η Cen	14 29	−41 43	2·39	−0·21	−3·0	B2 V	48	224	120	− 0·2	vis. tr. 80·1 y, 2°·2
	α Cen	14 33	−60 25	−0·27	+0·71	+4·2	G2, K1	3 678	281	1·3	−22 v	
	α Lup	14 35	−46 58	2·5	−0·22	−2·5	B1 V	33	220	100	− 7·3	
Izar	ε Boo	14 41	+27 30	2·39	+0·93	−0·6	K1, A	49	280	40	−16·5	vis. db 3″, composite sp.
Kochab	β UMi	14 51	+74 34	2·04	+1·49	−0·6	K4 III	31	280	33	+16·9	
Alphecca	α CrB	15 30	+27 03	2·22	−0·02	+0·5	A0 III	156	130	22	+ 2 v	ecl. sp. db 17-36 d
Dzuba	δ Sco	15 54	−22 20	2·32	−0·14	−4·0	B0 V	35	200	180	−15	
Acrab	β Sco	16 00	−19 32	2·52	−0·09	−4·0	B0·5 V	27	200	200	− 7 v	vis. tr., 14″, 1″
Antares	α Sco	16 23	−26 13	0·94	+1·83	−4·7	M1, B	30	192	130	− 3·2	vis. db 3″
	ζ Oph	16 32	−10 22	2·56	0·00	−3·4	O9·5 V	22	35	160	−19	
Atria	α TrA	16 38	−68 51	1·93	+1·43	−0·4	K2 III	43	148	29	− 3·6	
	ε Sco	16 44	−34 07	2·29	+1·15	+0·6	K2 III-IV	664	248	22	− 2·5	
Sabik	η Oph	17 05	−15 36	2·44	+0·05	+0·8	A2·5 V	96	23	21	− 1·0	close db
Shaula	λ Sco	17 27	−37 02	1·60	−0·23	−3·2	B1 V	33	180	90	0	sp. db 5-6 d
	θ Sco	17 30	−42 56	1·86	+0·38	−4·0	F0 rb	12	110	150	+ 1·4	
Ras-Alhague	α Oph	17 30	+12 38	2·07	+0·15	+0·9	A5 III	262	154	17	+13	
	κ Sco	17 36	−38 59	2·39	−0·21	−3·3	B2 IV	30	203	140	−10	
Eltanin	γ Dra	17 54	+51 30	2·21	+1·54	−0·8	K5 III	23	197	40	−27·7	
Kaus Australis	ε Sgr	18 18	−34 26	1·81	−0·02	−1·7	B9 IV	137	198	50	−11	
Vega	α Lyr	18 34	+38 41	0·03	0·00	+0·5	A0 V	346	36	8·1	−13·7	vis. db 21 y
Nunki	σ Sgr	18 49	−26 25	2·09	−0·20	−2·4	B2 V	62	173	80	−11	
	ζ Sgr	18 56	−30 01	2·57	+0·09	−0·4	A2 V	20	270	40	+22	
Altair	α Aql	19 46	+8 36	0·77	+0·22	+2·3	A7 IV-V	658	54	4·9	−26·2	sp. db 11-8 d
Peacock	α Pav	20 17	−57 03	1·94	−0·20	−2·9	B3 IV	87	177	90	+ 2 v	
Sadir	γ Cyg	20 19	+39 56	2·22	+0·66	−4·8	F8 rb	1		250	− 7·5	
Deneb	α Cyg	20 38	+44 55	1·25	+0·08	−7·2	A2 Ia	3		500	− 4·6	
Gienah	ε Cyg	20 42	+33 36	2·46	+1·03	+0·6	K0 III	483	47	24	−10 v	
Alderamin	α Cep	21 16	+62 10	2·43	+0·23	+1·5	A7 IV-V	159	72	15	− 9	
Enif	ε Peg	21 39	+9 25	2·38	+1·56	−4·6	K2 rb	26	92	250	+ 4·9	
Al Na'ir	α Gru	22 02	−47 27	1·75	−0·14	−0·2	B5 v	197	141	25?	+11·8	
	β Gru	22 37	−47 24	2·16	+1·62	−2·6	M3 III	133	99	90	+ 1·6	
Fomalhaut	α PsA	22 52	−30 09	1·16	+0·09	+1·9	A3 v	367	117	7·0	+ 6·5	
Scheat	β Peg	22 59	+27 32	2·50	+1·7	−1·4	M2 II-III	234	55	60	+ 8·7	vis. db 82″
Markab	α Peg	23 00	+14 40	2·49	−0·04	0·0	B9·5 III	73	125	32	− 3·5	

[1] *A.Q.* **1**, § 112.
[2] F. SCHLESINGER and L. F. JENKINS, *Cat. of Bright Stars*, Yale, 1940.
[3] D. A. MacRAE, *Obs. Handb.*, 1960, R.A.S. Canada.
[4] H. L. JOHNSON (MORGAN and HARRIS), *Ap. J.*, **117**, 313, 1953; **120**, 196, 1954.
[5] O. J. EGGEN, *A.J.*, **60**, 65, 1955; **62**, 45, 1957.
[6] A. R. HOGG, *Mt. Stromlo Mimeograms*, 1958.
[7] *Handb. B.A.A.*, 1960, p. 59.
[8] R. E. WILSON, *Gen. Cat. of Stellar Rad. Velocities*, Carnegie, 1953.
[9] K. O. WRIGHT, *Ap. J.*, **119**, 471, 1954.
[10] G. E. KRON, *P.A.S.P.*, **70**, 561, 1958.
[11] W. W. MORGAN, KEENAN, and KELLMAN, *Atlas of Stellar Spectra*, Chicago, 1943.
[12] E. G. ORAVEC, *Sky and Tel.*, **17**, 219, 1958.
[13] G. S. MUMFORD, *A.J.*, **61**, 213, 1956.

§ 115. Population Types

Characteristics of populations I and II

	Population I	Population II
Objects	Diffuse nebulae Open clusters Resolvable irregular galaxies Spiral arms Interstellar hydrogen and grains	Planetary nebulae Globular clusters Irresolvable irregular galaxies Nuclei of spirals Elliptical galaxies
Stars	Main sequence Classical cepheid variables Supergiants T Tau stars G to M giants, $M_v \simeq 0$ Neighbouring stars	Globular cluster sequences Cluster cepheids (RR Lyr, W Vir) Sub-luminous O and B stars RV Tau variables Subdwarfs High velocity stars Novae?
Occurrence	New stellar systems	Old stellar systems

Trumpler's subdivision of populations found in open clusters [1, 3].

Type 1o	Only main sequence. Containing O stars
1b	,, ,, ,, Classes A and B predominate
1a	,, ,, ,, Classes A to G predominate
2b	Main sequence and few giants. Early classes predominate
2a	,, ,, ,, ,, ,, Classes A to K
2f	Giants and dwarfs, F to K
3	More luminous stars are giants G to M.

Fraction of high-velocity stars in solar neighbourhood [4]

Main sequence			White dwarfs	Giants
B, A	F	G, K, M		
<1%	3%	20%	50%	5%

Five type subdivision of population [2]

	Extreme population I	Older population I	Disk population	Intermediate population II	Halo population II
Objects	Gas Galactic clusters (Tumpler's 1) Young spiral arms		Planetary nebulae Galactic nucleus		Globular clusters of high v_z
Stars	Supergiants	A stars		High velocity stars $v_z > 30$ km/s	Subdwarfs
	Cepheids		RR Lyr $P < 0.4$ d	L.P.V.'s, $P < 250$ d Sp, K to M4e	RR Lyr $P > 0.4$ d
	T Tau stars	Me dwarfs Strong-line stars	Novae Weak-line stars		
Conditions					
$\bar{z}$ in pc	120	160	400	700	2 000
$\bar{v}_z$ in km/s	8	10	16	25	75
Axial ratio	100	?	25 ?	5	2
Distribution	v patchy, arms	Patchy, arms	Smooth ?	Smooth	Smooth
Central core	Little	Little	Strong ?	Strong	Strong
h.e./H	0.04	0.03	0.02	0.01	0.001
Age in 10^9 y	< 0.1	0.1 to 1.5	1.5 to 5	5 to 6	6
Mass in 10^9 $\mathcal{M}_\odot$	2	5	47		16

P = period, z = distance from, and v_z = velocity perpendicular to galactic plane, h.e./H = ratio by mass of elements heavier than He to that of H.

[1] *A.Q.* **1**, § 113.
[2] J. H. OORT (et al.), *Stellar Populations*, ed. O'Connell, pp. 414, 533, Vatican Ob., 1958.
[3] R. J. TRUMPLER, *P.A.S.P.*, **37**, 307, 1925.
[4] G. P. KUIPER, *A.J.*, **53**, 194, 1948.

§ 116. Star Numbers

N_m = number of stars per square degree brighter than magnitude m

A_m = number of stars per square degree within the brightness range $m + \frac{1}{2}$ to $m - \frac{1}{2}$.

The variations of N_m and A_m with galactic latitude are given for the photographic (pg) magnitudes only. The corresponding data for visual magnitudes may be derived approximately by applying the ratio vis/pg from the 'Mean' columns.

Variation of N_m with galactic latitude, b [1]

log N_m

m	Galactic latitude											Mean 0° to 90°	Mean 0° to 90°
	0°	±5°	±10°	±20°	±30°	±40°	±50°	±60°	±70°	±80°	±90°		
	photographic magnitudes												visual
0·0													$\bar{5}$·7
1·0													$\bar{4}$·4
2·0		$\bar{3}$·18			$\bar{4}$·8				$\bar{4}$·7			$\bar{4}$·96	$\bar{4}$·99
3·0		$\bar{3}$·68			$\bar{3}$·27				$\bar{3}$·0			$\bar{3}$·40	$\bar{3}$·55
4·0	$\bar{2}$·25	$\bar{2}$·17	$\bar{2}$·12	$\bar{3}$·99	$\bar{3}$·85	$\bar{3}$·75	$\bar{3}$·70	$\bar{3}$·66	$\bar{3}$·64	$\bar{3}$·62	$\bar{3}$·60	$\bar{3}$·89	$\bar{2}$·11
5·0	$\bar{2}$·72	$\bar{2}$·64	$\bar{2}$·57	$\bar{2}$·44	$\bar{2}$·32	$\bar{2}$·24	$\bar{2}$·20	$\bar{2}$·17	$\bar{2}$·14	$\bar{2}$·12	$\bar{2}$·11	$\bar{2}$·37	$\bar{2}$·60
6·0	$\bar{1}$·18	$\bar{1}$·10	$\bar{1}$·03	$\bar{2}$·90	$\bar{2}$·78	$\bar{2}$·71	$\bar{2}$·66	$\bar{2}$·63	$\bar{2}$·62	$\bar{2}$·60	$\bar{2}$·58	$\bar{2}$·86	$\bar{1}$·07
7·0	$\bar{1}$·61	$\bar{1}$·54	$\bar{1}$·47	$\bar{1}$·34	$\bar{1}$·23	$\bar{1}$·16	$\bar{1}$·11	$\bar{1}$·08	$\bar{1}$·06	$\bar{1}$·04	$\bar{1}$·03	$\bar{1}$·31	$\bar{1}$·54
8·0	0·05	$\bar{1}$·99	$\bar{1}$·91	$\bar{1}$·78	$\bar{1}$·68	$\bar{1}$·60	$\bar{1}$·55	$\bar{1}$·52	$\bar{1}$·49	$\bar{1}$·47	$\bar{1}$·46	$\bar{1}$·75	0·00
9·0	0·52	0·43	0·35	0·22	0·12	0·04	$\bar{1}$·99	$\bar{1}$·94	$\bar{1}$·91	$\bar{1}$·89	$\bar{1}$·88	0·19	0·45
10·0	0·97	0·88	0·80	0·66	0·54	0·46	0·40	0·35	0·31	0·29	0·27	0·62	0·92
11·0	1·43	1·33	1·23	1·08	0·96	0·87	0·80	0·75	0·70	0·64	0·66	1·05	1·34
12·0	1·88	1·77	1·65	1·50	1·37	1·26	1·19	1·12	1·08	1·04	1·03	1·46	1·77
13·0	2·30	2·19	2·07	1·90	1·76	1·64	1·54	1·47	1·42	1·40	1·39	1·87	2·17
14·0	2·72	2·61	2·48	2·28	2·12	1·98	1·88	1·79	1·75	1·71	1·71	2·26	2·56
15·0	3·12	3·00	2·88	2·65	2·46	2·31	2·20	2·10	2·03	2·00	1·97	2·62	2·95
16·0	3·40	3·41	3·24	3·00	2·77	2·61	2·48	2·38	2·28	2·25	2·24	2·98	3·30
17·0	3·83	3·78	3·60	3·33	3·07	2·89	2·75	2·64	2·55	2·52	2·48	3·33	3·64
18·0	4·20	4·10	3·93	3·63	3·35	3·14	2·99	2·87	2·78	2·75	2·72	3·64	3·96
19·0	4·5	4·4	4·3	3·9	3·6	3·4	3·2	3·1	3·0	2·9	2·9	3·90	4·20
20·0	4·7	4·7	4·6	4·2	3·8	3·6	3·4	3·3	3·2	3·1	3·1	4·17	4·45
21·0	5·0	4·9	4·8	4·5	4·0	3·7	3·6	3·4	3·3	3·3	3·2	4·4	

Distribution in absolute magnitude ranges $M \pm \frac{1}{2}$ for stars counted to a given apparent magnitude ($m \simeq 6$) [1]. The table gives percentage distribution

		M											
		−6	−5	−4	−3	−2	−1	0	1	2	3	4	5
Photographic. All stars		1	1	3	7	10	14	18	21	15	6	3	1
Visual.	Class O	3	15	31	37	12	2	0	0	0	0	0	0
	B	3	8	14	22	23	22	7	1	0	0	0	0
	A	4	13	14	8	2	2	16	25	13	2	0	0
	F	1	8	11	7	9	5	2	16	18	18	5	0
	G	1	5	9	11	8	1	11	29	7	9	6	2
	K	0	1	4	11	10	13	30	18	5	2	1	2
	M	3	8	7	3	9	24	29	13	3	1	0	0

$$10 + \log A_m \text{ and } star\ light\ [1]$$

m	Photographic magnitudes						Visual magnitudes	
	$10 + \log A_m$			Star light			Mean $10 + \log A_m$	Mean star light
	$b = 0°$	$b = 90°$	Mean	$b = 0°$	$b = 90°$	Mean		
				10th mag stars deg⁻²				10th m_v deg⁻²

m	$b = 0°$	$b = 90°$	Mean	$b = 0°$	$b = 90°$	Mean	Mean $10+\log A_m$	Mean star light
0			5·7	0·7	0·3	0·5	5·9	0·8
1			6·3	1·3	0·6	0·8	6·5	1·3
2			6·9	2	0·8	1·3	7·14	2·2
3			7·43	3	1·0	1·7	7·68	3·0
4	8·2	7·68	7·92	4·0	1·2	2·1	8·25	4·5
5	8·72	8·18	8·40	5·2	1·5	2·5	8·70	5·0
6	9·19	8·64	8·90	6·1	1·7	3·2	9·15	5·6
7	9·63	9·08	9·33	6·7	1·9	3·4	9·60	6·3
8	10·10	9·50	9·75	7·9	2·0	3·5	10·03	6·8
9	10·58	9·92	10·19	9·6	2·1	3·9	10·47	7·4
10	11·04	10·28	10·62	11·0	1·9	4·1	10·94	8·7
11	11·50	10·63	11·05	12·6	1·7	4·6	11·34	8·7
12	11·94	10·98	11·46	13·8	1·5	4·6	11·77	9·3
13	12·35	11·29	11·86	14·1	1·2	4·6	12·15	8·9
14	12·76	11·57	12·24	14·4	0·9	4·4	12·53	8·5
15	13·15	11·80	12·59	14·1	0·6	3·9	12·91	8·1
16	13·46	12·06	12·94	11·5	0·5	3·5	13·24	6·9
17	13·84	12·28	13·26	11·0	0·3	2·9	13·54	5·5
18	14·2	12·50	13·53	10·0	0·2	2·1	13·84	4·4
19	14·5	12·7	13·71	7·9	0·1	1·3	14·02	2·6
20	14·7	12·8	14·00	5·0	0·1	1·0	14·25	1·8
21	14·9	12·9	14·2	3·1		0·6	14·5	1·2
> 21·5				5·0		0·8		1·5
Total				180	22	61		119

Integrated star light as a function of galactic latitude b [1, 3]

b	Star light			b	Star light	
	pg	V			pg	V
	10th mag deg⁻²				10th mag deg⁻²	
0	184	397		40	30	56
5	126	262		50	24	44
10	91	187		60	21	38
15	71	146		70	18	34
20	55	110		80	18	33
30	38	74		90	17	33

Star light from whole sky [1, 3]

$$= 230 \text{ zero pg mag stars} = \ 580 \text{ 1}^{st} \text{ mag (pg)}$$
$$= 460 \text{ zero } V \text{ mag stars} = \ 1160 \text{ 1}^{st} \text{ mag (v)}$$

Relative number of stars of each class

(up to V = 8·5 in H.D. Catalogue) [1]

Sp % of stars	B 10	A 22	F 19	G 14	K 32	M 3

Mean secular parallax $= 4\cdot2 \times$ annual parallax

Mean secular parallax as a function of apparent magnitude [1, 2, 4]

V	b		
	0°	30°	90°
	" per annum		
4	0·092	0·098	0·113
5	0·064	0·068	0·082
6	0·045	0·048	0·061
7	0·032	0·035	0·047
8	0·023	0·025	0·036
9	0·016	0·020	0·028
10	0·012	0·015	0·023

V	b		
	0°	30°	90°
	" per annum		
11	0·009	0·013	0·019
12	0·007	0·011	0·016
13	0·005	0·009	0·013
14	0·004	0·007	0·011
15	0·003	0·006	0·009
16	0·002	0·004	0·007

Correction factor by which mean secular parallax should

be multiplied for classified stars [2]

Sp Correction factor, $V \simeq 6$ $V \simeq 12$	A 0·7 0·7	F 1·5 1·0	G 1·5 1·2	K 1·1 0·8

[1] *A.Q.* 1, § 114.
[2] W. D. Heintz, *A.N.*, **282**, 221, 1955.
[3] F. E. Roach and L. R. Negill, *Ap. J.*, **133**, 228, 1961.
[4] E. R. Hill, *B.A.N.*, **15**, 1, 1960.

§ 117. Star Densities in the Solar Neighbourhood

Density limit of all matter in the solar neighbourhood (the Oort limit derived from z velocities) [2, 3] $= 0\cdot14 \, \mathscr{M}_\odot \, \mathrm{pc}^{-3} = 9\cdot5 \times 10^{-24} \, \mathrm{g \, cm}^{-3}$

Density due to stars in the solar neighbourhood [4, 5]

$$= 0\cdot057 \, \mathscr{M}_\odot \, \mathrm{pc}^{-3} = 3\cdot9 \times 10^{-24} \, \mathrm{g \, cm}^{-3}$$

Densities due to various objects [3]

Object	Density
	$10^{-3} \mathcal{M}_\odot$ pc^{-3}
O, B stars	0·9
A	1
F	3
dG	4
dK	9
dM	29

Object	Density
	$10^{-3} \mathcal{M}_\odot$ pc^{-3}
gG	0·8
gK	0·1
gM	0·01
dark companions	5
white dwarfs	8
subdwarfs	1·5

Object	Density
	$10^{-3} \mathcal{M}_\odot$ pc^{-3}
long-per. vars.	0·001
RR Lyr. vars.	0·000 01
Cep. vars.	0·001
Planetary neb.	0·000 005
Galactic cl.	0·04
Globular. cl.	0·001

Number density of stars in solar neighbourhood, using catalogues of near stars [4] giving an effective cut-off at $M_v \simeq 14\cdot3$,

$$= 0\cdot08 \text{ stars or star components pc}^{-3}$$
$$= 0\cdot06 \text{ single or multiple star systems pc}^{-3}$$

Number density in various spectral classes [1, 4, 6]

The supergiants, and subgiants are included with giants; all early stars and subdwarfs are included in the main sequence. All faint stars are cut off at $M_v = 14\cdot5$.

$$10 + \log (\text{stars pc}^{-3})$$

Sp	O	B	A	F	G	K	M	Total
Giants, etc.				5·7	6·2	6·6	5·5	6·8
Main sequence	2·4	6·0	6·7	7·4	7·8	8·0	8·7	8·8
White dwarfs		7·1	7·3	7·1	6·8	7		7·7

Emission of stellar radiation

$$= 1\cdot5 \times 10^{-3} \ (M_{bol} = 0) \text{ stars pc}^{-3}$$
$$= 4\cdot5 \times 10^{25} \text{ watts pc}^{-3} = 1\cdot5 \times 10^{-23} \text{ erg cm}^{-3} \text{ s}^{-1}$$

Emission of stellar luminous radiation

$$= 6\cdot1 \times 10^{-4} \ (M_v = 0) \text{ stars pc}^{-3}$$
$$= 6\cdot6 \times 10^{-29} \text{ lumens cm}^{-3} = 5\cdot2 \times 10^{-30} \text{ candela cm}^{-3}$$

Luminosity function, emission, and star density. Population I

Luminosity function $= \phi(M) =$ number of stars per unit volume within the magnitude range $M + \frac{1}{2}$ to $M - \frac{1}{2}$. The table gives also E, the stellar emission of light or radiation in number of zero absolute magnitude stars per unit volume; and $\mathscr{M}_d$, the total star mass per unit volume in each magnitude range. The visual magnitude ranges have been used for the column $E(\mathrm{bol})$ which expresses the number of $M_{\mathrm{bol}} = 0$ stars per unit volume. $\phi(M)$, E, and $\mathscr{M}_d$ all become doubtful beyond $M = 17$.

M	$10 + \log \phi(M)$		$\phi(M)$		E			$\mathscr{M}_d$
	pg	V	pg	V	pg	V	bol	V
		[1, 7, 8, 9, 10, 13]						
	in pc^{-3}		10^{-4} pc^{-3}		$10^{-6}(M = 0)$ pc^{-3}			$10^{-4}\mathscr{M}_\odot$ pc^{-3}
-7	1·0	0·7			1		5	0·000 3
-6	1·9	1·6			2	1	15	0·002
-5	2·8	2·6			6	4	50	0·011
-4	3·6	3·4			16	10	100	0·045
-3	4·1	4·0			20	16	140	0·10
-2	4·6	4·6			25	25	180	0·25
-1	5·2	5·28			40	48	220	1·0
0	5·84	5·98	1	1	69	96	240	4
1	6·38	6·54	2	3	96	138	220	10
2	6·64	6·76	4	6	69	91	120	13
3	6·89	7·05	8	11	49	71	78	20
4	7·15	7·32	14	21	35	52	52	25
5	7·32	7·47	21	30	21	30	33	30
6	7·42	7·56	26	36	10	14	17	30
7	7·48	7·59	30	40	5	6	10	30
8	7·53	7·65	34	45	2	3	7	26
9	7·62	7·74	42	55	1	1	4	30
10	7·82	7·89	66	78	1	1	2	40
11	7·90	7·97	80	93			1	35
12	7·95	8·06	90	115				32
13	8·04	8·11	110	130				28
14	8·11	8·15	130	140				25
15	8·15	8·10	140	130				25
16	8·1	8·0	130	100				20
17	8·0	8·0	100	90				18
18	8·0?	7·9?	100?	80?				16
19	8·0?	7·9?	100?	70?				14
20	8·0?	7·8?	100?	60?				12
Total			1 328	1 334	468	607	1 494	485
To $M = 14.5$			658	804	468	607	1 494	380

Luminosity function and stellar classification

The table gives the luminosity function $\phi(M)$ within each stellar class [1, 6, 7]. The ranges included in each classification are 0 to 9 (e.g. B0 to B9, etc.). In [7] similar information is given but with stars segregated into colours instead of spectral class. In [6] the same information is tabulated for the variable M_{bol} instead of M_v.

The upper part of the tabulation is logarithmic and the lower part linear.

M_v	O	B	A	F	G	K	M
			$10 + \log \phi(M)$ in pc^{-3}				
− 7	0·3	0·7	0·5	0·5	0·5		
− 6	0·7	1·4	1	1	0	0·6	0·6
− 5	1·0	2·4	2	1·8	1·9	1·6	2·0
− 4	1·5	3·2	2	2·2	2·4	2·1	2·1
− 3	2	3·7	2·7	2·9	2·9	3·0	2·8
− 2	2	4·4	2·9	3·3	3·5	3·8	3·6
− 1	2	5·1	4·0	4·2	4·0	4·4	4·5
0	1	5·3	5·3	4·3	4·9	5·4	5·0
			10^{-4} stars pc^{-3}				
0	0	0·2	0·2	0·02	0·08	0·25	0·1
1	0	0·3	1·0	0·3	0·3	1·2	0·1
2	0	0·2	2	1·6	0·5	1·1	0
3	0	0·1	0·8	7	1·5	1·0	0
4	0	0	0·3	12	7	1·0	0
5	0	0	0	6	20	3	0
6	0	0	0	2	15	15	0·1
7	0	0	0	1	8	30	1·0
8	0	0	0	0·1	4	25	10
9	0	0	0	0	2	15	30
10	0	0·1	0	0	0	4	80
11	0	1	0·3	0·1	0	2	90
12	0	2	4	1	0	1	100
13	0	4	6	3	1	4	100
14	0	8	10	10	6	8	100
15	0	15	20	10	15	12	80
16	0	30	50	30	30		60

Population II luminosity function [11, 12]

The absolute values are adjusted to fit population I at about $M_v = +5$. The elliptical galaxy populations are additional to a globular cluster type population and on the same scale.

M_v	Globular clusters	Elliptical galaxies
	$10 + \log \phi(M)$ in pc^{-3}	
−3	4·0	
−2	5·4	
−1	5·7	
0	6·6 (peak)	
1	6·1	
2	6·5	
3	7·0	
4	7·3	

M_v	Globular clusters	Elliptical galaxies
	$10 + \log \phi(M)$ in pc^{-3}	
5	7·5	
6	7·5	8·2
7		8·8
8	probably	9·4
9	similar	10·0
	to	
10	population	10·4
11	I	10·7
12		10·9

[1] *A.Q.* **1**, § 115.
[2] E. R. HILL, *B.A.N.*, **15**, 1, 1960.
[3] J. H. OORT, *B.A.N.*, **15**, 45, 1960; *Stellar populations*, ed. O'Connell, p. 415, Vatican, 1958.
[4] W. GLIESE, *Z. Ap.*, **39**, 1, 1956.
[5] C. PERRY, ROBERTS, and STABLEFORD, *P.A.S.P.*, **70**, 459, 1958.
[6] K. F. d'OCCHIEPPO, *Mitt. U.-S. Wien*, **6**, No. 4, 59, 1952; **7**, No. 15, 213, 1955.
[7] G. A. STARIKOVA, *A. Zh.*, **37**, 476, 1960; *Sov. A.*, **4**, 451.
[8] E. E. SALPETER, *Ap. J.*, **121**, 161, 1955.
[9] S. W. McCUSKEY, *Ap. J.*, **123**, 458, 1956.
[10] D. N. LIMBER, *Ap. J.*, **131**, 168, 1960.
[11] A. SANDAGE, *Ap. J.*, **125**, 422, 1957.
[12] M. S. ROBERTS, *A.J.*, **61**, 195, 1956.
[13] M. SCHMIDT, *Ap. J.*, **129**, 243, 1959.

§ 118. Star Densities and the Galactic Plane

Distribution of density $\rho(z)$ of stellar + interstellar material as a function of distance z from the galactic plane [1, 2, 3, 4]. $\rho(0) = 0.14 \, \mathscr{M}_\odot$ pc$^{-3} = 9.5 \times 10^{-24}$ g cm^{-3}. $K(z) =$ acceleration in the z direction.

z in pc	0	50	100	200	400	600	1 000	2 000	5 000	10 000
$\rho(z)/\rho(0)$	1·00	0·91	0·82	0·57	0·25	0·12	0·044	0·011		
$K(z)$ in 10^{-9} cm s^{-2}	0·0	1·3	2·4	4·0	6·0	6·9	7·8	8·4	7·5	5

Total equivalent thickness of Milky Way (based on densities in galactic plane near sun)
$$= 660 \text{ pc} = 2.0 \times 10^{21} \text{ cm}$$

Total density per unit area on galactic plane
$$= 0.019 \text{ g cm}^{-2}$$

Change of luminosity function with z

The tables give the logarithmic ratio of the luminosity function $\phi(z)$ (§ 117) to its value near the galactic plane $\phi(0)$ as a function of absolute magnitude and spectral class [1, 5, 6]. The tables also contain β in the approximation $\phi(z) = \phi(0) \exp(-z/\beta)$, and v_z the r.m.s. velocity in the z direction.

$$\log \phi(z) - \log \phi(0)$$

M_v	z in pc						β
	0	100	200	500	1 000	1 500	
	dex						pc
− 4	0·0	−1·1	−1·9	−3			50
− 2	0·0	−0·8	−1·2	−2·0	−2·9		80
0	0·0	−0·5	−0·8	−1·4	−2·2	−2·7	120
2	0·0	−0·27	−0·53	−1·1	−1·8	−2·3	160
4	0·0	−0·13	−0·30	−0·8	−1·4	−1·9	270
6	0·0	−0·07	−0·14	−0·5	−1·0	−1·4	450
8	0·0	−0·03	−0·09	−0·3	−0·6	−1·0	800 ?
10	0·0	−0·01	−0·04	−0·11	−0·3		2 000 ?
12	0·0	0·00	−0·02	−0·04	−0·17		4 000 ?

$$\log \phi(z) - \log \phi(0)$$

Sp	z in pc						β	v_z
	0	100	200	500	1 000	1 500		
	dex						pc	km/s
O	0·0	−1·0	−1·5				50	5
B	0·0	−0·8	−1·4	−2·2			60	5
A	0·0	−0·27	−0·73	−1·6	−2·5		115	8
F	0·0	−0·10	−0·37	−1·3	−2·3		190	11
dG	0·0	−0·05	−0·17	−0·7	−1·9		340	15
dK	0·0	−0·01	−0·14	−0·8	−2·0		350	15
dM	0·0						350	15
gG	0·0	−0·07	−0·17	−0·55	−1·1	−1·5	400	
gK	0·0	−0·15	−0·28	−0·8	−1·4	−1·8	270	15
gM	0·0							

Values of β and v_z for various objects [5, 6, 7]

Object	β	v_z
	pc	km/s
White dwarfs	280	18
Subdwarfs	3 000	60
Subgiants		25
Supergiants		13
Cepheid variables	45	5
RR Lyr var. P < 0·5 d	900	35
„ P > 0·5 d	3 000	70
W Vir variables	2 000	
U Gem stars	2 600	

Object	β	v_z
	pc	km/s
L.P.V's M0e–M4e	1 500	40
M5e–M8e	500	24
Planetary nebulae	260	20
Novae	200	20
Recurrent novae	500	
Globular clusters	4 000	70
Open clusters	80	6
Interstellar gas	125	8

[1] *A.Q.* 1, § 116.
[2] J. H. OORT, *B.A.N.*, 15, 45, 1960.
[3] R. V. D. R. WOOLLEY, *M.N.*, 117, 198, 1957.
[4] E. R. HILL, *B.A.N.*, 15, 1, 1960.
[5] P. P. PARENAGO, Coll. Internat. on *Principes Fondementaux de Classification Stellaire*, p. 13, Paris, 1953.
[6] J. H. OORT, *Stellar Populations*, ed. O'Connell, p. 415, Vatican, 1958.
[7] C. PAYNE-GAPOSCHKIN, *Variable Stars and Galactic Structure*, London, 1954.

§ 119. Motion of Sun and Neighbouring Stars

Solar motion with respect to neighbouring stars (excluding high velocity stars) [1, 2, 3]

Solar velocity
$$S = 20\cdot0 \pm 0\cdot5 \text{ km/s}$$
$$= 2\cdot05 \times 10^{-5} \text{ pc/y} = 4\cdot22 \text{ AU/y}$$

Solar apex
$$A = 271° \pm 2°, \qquad D = +30° \pm 1° \quad (1900)$$
$$L^{II} = 57° \pm 1°, \qquad B^{II} = +22° \pm 2°$$

where A, D, L^{II}, B^{II} are the coordinates α, δ, l^{II}, b^{II} of the solar apex *towards* which the sun is moving. The solar motion varies for different selections of comparison stars. Solar apex tables have been constructed on $S = 20$ km/s, $A = 270°$, $D = +30°$ [4].

Components of solar motion

Towards galactic centre, $l^{II} = 0$, $b^{II} = 0$, $X = +10\cdot1$ km/s
In galactic plane towards $l^{II} = 90$, $b^{II} = 0$, $Y = +15\cdot5$ km/s
Towards galactic pole, $b^{II} = +90$, $Z = +7\cdot5$ km/s

Solar motion as a function of stellar class [1, 3, 5, 6, 7, 8]

Sp	S	A	D	L^{II}	B^{II}	K
	km/s	°	°	°	°	km/s
B0	22	272	+33	59	+21	+5·3
A0	16	266	+25	49	+23	+1·4
F0	16	266	+23	47	+22	0·0
G0	20	271	+27	53	+20	−0·5
K0	22	274	+32	61	+17	0·0
M0	25	278	+39	67	+19	+0·4

The K term is an apparent mean velocity of recession (red shift) in all directions. Values quoted are for brighter stars ($m < 6$); for faint stars the K term is much less and close to the gravitational shift ($= 0.634\ (\mathcal{M}/\mathcal{M}_\odot)/(\mathcal{R}/\mathcal{R}_\odot)$ km/s).

Solar motion with respect to RR Lyr stars (representing high velocity stars) [1]

$$S = 130 \text{ km/s}$$
$$A = 297°, \quad D = +52°$$
$$L^{II} = 85°, \quad B^{II} = +13°$$

Motion of solar neighbouring stars with respect to galactic centre [1]

$$\text{Velocity} = 215 \pm 15 \text{ km/s}$$
$$\text{Direction: } l^{II} = 90°, b^{II} = 0°$$

Motion of solar neighbouring stars with respect to the system of globular clusters, subdwarfs, and high velocity stars [1]

$$\text{Velocity} = 175 \pm 30 \text{ km/s}$$
$$\text{Direction: } l^{II} = 94°, b^{II} = +3°$$

Velocity ellipsoid for near stars; σ_1, σ_2, σ_3 = dispersion in velocity. The dynamic axis is about 13° from the galactic centre but this discrepancy is reduced when fainter and more distant stars are analysed.

$$\text{Major axis: } \sigma_1 = 38 \text{ km/s}, \quad l^{II} = 13°, \quad b^{II} = 0°$$
$$\text{Second axis: } \sigma_2 = 24 \text{ km/s}, \quad l_2^{II} = 103°, \quad b_2^{II} = 0°$$
$$\text{Third axis: } \sigma_3 = 18 \text{ km/s}, \quad\quad\quad\quad b_3^{II} = 90°$$

Velocity ellipsoid as a function of stellar class [1, 3, 5, 9, 10]

The table gives also the mean mass and an indication of the kinetic energy

Sp	l_1^{II}	σ_1	σ_2	σ_3	$\bar{\mathcal{M}}$	$\sigma_3^2 \bar{\mathcal{M}}$
	°	km/s	km/s	km/s	$\mathcal{M}_\odot$	$\mathcal{M}_\odot$ (km/s)^2
B0	350	12	9	4	17	270
A0	22	17	9	7	3·5	170
F0	16	23	13	12	1·8	260
dG0	10	32	21	18	1·1	360
dK0	10	39	25	18	0·8	260
dM0	10	45	27	18	0·5	160
gG0	10	22	15	15	2·5	560
gK0	10	26	17	17	4·0	1 200
gM0	10	27	18	19	6	2 200

Star drift (apparent) velocities and directions [1, 6, 7]

	Proportion of stars	Velocity	Apex of drifts			
			α	δ	l^{II}	b^{II}
		km/s	°	°	°	°
Drift I	55%	31	91	−10	217	−14
Drift II	45%	16	290	−74	321	−28

[1] *A.Q.* **1**, § 117.
[2] H. C. v. d. Hulst, Muller, and Oort, *B.A.N.*, **12**, 117, 1954.
[3] R. v. d. R. Woolley, *M.N.*, **118**, 45, 1958.
[4] F. Link, *M.O. Czech. A. Soc.*, No. 9, 1948.
[5] W. Gliese, *Z. Ap.*, **39**, 1, 1956.
[6] S. R. Tannahill, *M.N.*, **114**, 460, 1954.
[7] D. G. Ewart, *M.N.*, **114**, 467, 1954.
[8] G. S. Mumford; E. R. Dyer, *A.J.*, **61**, 224, 228, 1956.
[9] I. A. Daube, *A. Zh.*, **32**, 338, 1955.
[10] A. Sandage, *Ap. J.*, **125**, 435, 1957.

CHAPTER 13

NEBULAE AND INTERSTELLAR SPACE

§ 120. Bright Diffuse Nebulae

THE bright diffuse nebulae comprise the line emission nebulae (E), and the reflection nebulae with continuous spectra (C). Of these the E nebulae are usually excited by a star of spectral class earlier than B1, and the C nebulae are illuminated by a star later than B2. Fainter E nebulae are sometimes very large and called Hα emission areas.

Size: Most nebulae are very irregular and no measurements exist from which to derive representative dimensions (§ 6). Nevertheless the diameter and size quoted is intended to be representative (i.e. $\sqrt{2} \times \frac{1}{2}$-flux-diameter).

Mass: Estimates vary greatly. The great contribution from the fainter outer regions cannot readily be estimated. Dynamic considerations sometimes give much greater values (e.g. 40 000 $\mathcal{M}_\odot$ for Orion neb [6]).

Typical sizes of nebulae and features [8]

Bright diffuse nebulae	5 pc
Bright rims	0·02 pc
Reflection filaments	0·005 pc
Filaments in Cygnus Veils	0·001 pc

Colour index of C (i.e. reflection) nebulae [1]

$$C_{\text{neb}} \simeq 0·2$$
$$C_{\text{neb}} - C_* = -0·25 \quad [C \simeq B - V - 0·1]$$

Density of reflection nebulae [1] $\quad \simeq 6 \times 10^{-23}$ g cm^{-3}

Particle density in reflection nebulae [1]

$$\simeq 2 \times 10^{-8} \text{ particles cm}^{-3}$$

Relation between nebular radius a and magnitude of illuminating star—either C or E nebulae [1],

$$2 \log a = -0·4\, m_{\text{v}} + 4·33 \quad [a \text{ in } ' \text{ arc}]$$

Here a is a limiting radius.

Median galactic latitude of E nebulae [1]

$$= 2°·0$$

Median galactic latitude of C nebulae [1]

$$= 9°$$

Selected bright diffuse nebulae

The m_v and mass are intended to represent the complete nebula. The diameters are intended to be representative dimensions.

Nebula	NGC or IC	Type	Coordinates l^{II} (°)	Coordinates b^{II} (°)	m_v [1]	Abs A_v [4]	Dist. [1, 4, 5, 9] pc	Diam. [1, 3] '	Density [1, 4] Atom cm^{-3}	Mass [4] $\mathcal{M}_\odot$	Stars involved Sp	Stars involved M_v
Near γ Cas	I59	E	124	−2			130	10	50		B0e	2·3
Pleiades neb M 45	1432–5	C	166	−23			126	40		0·05	B5	3·0
Crab neb [11] M 1	1952	E	184	−6	8·6	1·5	1 050	5			Oe	5·4
Orion neb M 42	1976	E	209	−20	4	0·1	460	30	1 000	700	B1	4·6
	1977	CE	208	−19		0·1	460	18	600		O9	2·1
Near ζ Ori (Horsehead)	I434	CE	207	−17			300	30	30	1·5	B6	10·4
M 78	2068	C	205	−14	8·3	0·1	500	4	30	0·6		
30 Dor (LMC) (Tarantula)	2070	E	280	−32		1·6	52 000	10	15	400	O6	7·4
	2174–5	E	190	0		2	1 800	15	30	9 000	O5e	7·3
Rosette, NGC 2237–38–44–46		E	206	−2			1 400	60	200		pec	7
Near η Car	3372	E	287	−1		1·0	1 600	70			O7e	6·9
Trifid neb M 20	6514	E	7	0	8·5	1·0	1 600	15	40	300	O5e	6·0
Lagoon neb M 8	6523	E	6	−1	5·8	1·1	1 500	25	30	3 000	Oe	8·3
M 16	6611	E	17	+4	6·4	2·4	1 800	12	70	300	Oe	8·3
Ω, Swan, Horseshoe M 17	6618	E	15	−1	7	3	1 800	20	80	1 000	B1 }	6·4
Cygnus loop	6960	E	73	−8			700	30				
Cyg. veil, network	6992–5	E	75	−9			700	40				
Pelican neb I 5067–68–70		CE	84	0		2·5	600	40	30	80	O6 }	6·0
North America neb	7000	CE	86	−1		1·1	800	80	10	3 000		
	7023	C	104	+14			300	5			B2p	7·2
Cocoon neb	I5146	C	94	−5		1·4	1 500	4	70	7	B1	10·0

[1] *A.Q.* 1, § 118.
[2] A. Bečvář, *Atlas Coeli Skalnaté Pleso*, ii, 1951.
[3] V. F. Gaze and G. A. Shain, *Iz. Crimea*, 15, 11, 1955.
[4] R. E. Gershberg and L. P. Metik, *Iz. Crimea*, 24, 148, 1960.
[5] H. M. Johnson, *Ap. J.*, 121, 604, 1955; 124, 90, 1956.
[6] P. P. Parenago, *Astron. News Let.*, No. 74, 20, 1954.
[7] W. W. Morgan, Whitford, and Code, *Ap. J.*, 118, 318, 1953.
[8] H. C. van de Hulst, *Rev. Mod. Phys.*, 30, 913, 1958.
[9] S. Pottasch, *B.A.N.*, 13, 77, 1956.
[10] A. D. Kuzmin and R. I. Noskova, *A. Zh.*, 39, 241, 1962.
[11] L. Woltjer, *B.A.N.*, 13, 301, 1957; 14, 39, 1958.

§ 121. Planetary Nebulae

Planetary nebulae may be recognized by their complicated disk-like structure [2, 3]. About 150 are known.

Absolute photographic magnitude of planetary nebulae [4]

$$M_n = -1 \cdot 5 + 0 \cdot 8 \, \delta \pm 1 \cdot 1$$

where $\delta = m_* - m_n$ = magnitude difference between nebula and exciting star.

Effective wavelength for photographic nebular magnitudes

$$\lambda(\text{pg, neb}) = 4800 \text{ Å}$$

Temperature of exciting star T_* in relation to δ

T_* in °K	30 000	40 000	50 000	60 000	80 000	100 000
δ in mag pg	0·4	1·6	2·6	3·5	5·0	6·3

There are various methods of measuring and expressing T_* [5].

Median electron density [12]   = 8 000 electrons cm^{-3}

Median electron temperature [12]   = 14 000 °K

Scale height of number density variation with distance from the galactic plane β
      = 260 pc

Median galactic latitude [1]   = 7°·5

Energy received outside earth atmosphere from the spectrum lines of an $m_{pg} = 10$ planetary nebula   = $6 \times 10^{-13} \times$ (intensity) erg cm^{-2} s^{-1}

where the (intensity) is from the table (with Hβ = 100).

Spectrum of planetary nebulae [1, 6]

Only the stronger lines are tabulated, and are relative to Hβ (= 100). The intensities represent planetary nebulae in general but wide differences are found, mostly concerned with T_*. t = line whose intensity increases with T_*; ~ = line whose intensity varies erratically for various nebulae; [ ] = forbidden line.

λ	Elements and line components	Intensity	λ	Elements and line components	Intensity
Å		Hβ = 100	Å		Hβ = 100
3133	O III	30 t	4686	He II	30 t
3203	He II	10 t	4725	[A IV] 4712, 40; [N IV]	6 t
3343	O III [Ne V] 3340–46	25 t	4861	H I	100
3435	[Ne V] 3425; O III 3444	20 t	4959	[O III]	300 t
3727	[O II] 3726·1, 3728·6	40 ~	5007	[O III]	800 t
3798	H I	5	5412	He II	6 t
3835	H I	7	5755	[N II]	10 ~
3869	[Ne III]	50 t	5876	He I	30
3889	H I 3889·1; He I 3888·6	15	6302	[O I] 6300; [S III] 6311	30 ~
3968	[Ne III] 3967·4; H I 3970·1	30 t	6364	[O I]	10 ~
4026	He I	2	6548	[N II]	70 ~
4073	S II 4069, 4076	4	6563	H I	400
4101	H I 4102; N III 4097, 4103	25	6584	[N II]	150
4340	H I	40	6678	He I	12
4363	[O III]	10 t	6726	[S II] 6716, 6731	15
4471	He I	5	7065	He I	20
4542	He II	2 t	7136	[A III]	50 t
4638	N III 4634, 4641	4	7325	[O II] 7319, 7330	20

[1] *A.Q.* **1**, § 110.
[2] H. D. CURTIS, *Pub. Lick Ob.*, **13**, 57, 1918.
[3] D. S. EVANS and A. D. THACKERAY, *M.N.*, **110**, 429, 1950.
[4] I. S. SHKLOVSKY, *A. Zh.*, **33**, 222, 1956.
[5] H. ZANSTRA, *B.A.N.*, **15**, 237, 249, 1960.
[6] A. BEČVÁŘ, *Atlas Coeli Skalnaté Pleso*, Praha, 1951.
[7] W. LILLER, *Ap. J.*, **122**, 240, 1955.
[8] G. A. GURZADYAN, *Burakan Ob.*, **18**, 15, 1956.
[9] N. A. RAZMADZE, *A. Zh.*, **33**, 3, 1956.
[10] L. KOHOUTEK, *B.A. Czech.*, **11**, 64, 1960; **12**, 213, 1961.
[11] L. H. ALLER, *Gaseous Nebulae*, Chapman and Hall, 1956.
[12] M. J. SEATON, *M.N.*, **115**, 279, 1955.
[13] H. ANDRILLAT, *Haut Prov. Ob.*, **3**, No. 12, 1955
[14] O. C. WILSON, *Ap. J.*, **111**, 279, 1950.
[15] C. R. O'DELL, *Ap. J.*, **135**, 371, 1962.

Selected planetary nebulae

Since planetary nebulae are somewhat irregular and not homogeneous the various measurements and means are not clearly defined. The diameters are approximately representative (§ 6).

Nebula	1900 α (h m)	1900 δ (° ')	Diam. (")	m_n (pg) [1,6,7,8]	m_* (pg) [1,6,7,8]	A (pg)	Distance (pc) [1,4,8,9,10,15]	Sp_* [1,11]	T_* (1000 °K) [1,5,6,7,8,9,12,13]	T_n (1000 °K)	ρ_n (100 atoms cm^{-3}) [8,11]	$\mathcal{M}_n$ ($\mathcal{M}_\odot$) [9,10]	Expansion vel. (km/s) [1,14]
NGC 246	0 42	−12 25	230	8.7	11.2		350	O7	40			0.12	
IC 418	5 23	−12 46	12	11.0	10.9	0.5	1 200	O7	32	14	120	0.04	0
NGC 2392	7 23	+21 07	30	8.5	10.5		700	O6	42	20	10	0.10	53
NGC 3132 8-burst	10 03	−39 57	45	8.2			600			14	1	0.12	
NGC 3242	10 20	−18 08	30	9.2		0.6	600	con	45	15	60	0.04	20
NGC 3587 Owl	11 09	+55 34	200	11.7	14.3	0.5	800		50		2	0.10	
NGC 3918	11 45	−56 37	12	8.4	14		1 000		80				
NGC 6210	16 42	+23 53	18	9.9	11.1	0.8	1 200	O7	38	11	200	0.13	21
NGC 6543	17 59	+66 38	19	8.8	11.5	0.7	650	O7	37	9	150	0.12	12
NGC 6572	18 07	+ 6 50	15	9.4		1.3	900	WN6	49	13	160	0.10	4
NGC 6720 Ring neb	18 50	+32 54	72	9.4	14.6	0.4	550	con	75	11	40	0.17	19
NGC 6826	19 42	+50 17	26	9.3	10.7	0.8	540	O6	32	11	2	0.08	
NGC 6853 Dumbell	19 55	+22 27	360	7.8	13.4	0.6	220		80	13		0.17	
NGC 7009 Saturn	20 59	−11 46	28	8.5	11.7	1.8	600	con	50	16	200	0.09	18
NGC 7027	21 03	+41 50	13	10.1	16		1 100		70		80	0.2	18
NGC 7293 Helix, Shaw	22 24	−21 21	800	6.8	13.4		140		100	17	40	0.19	
NGC 7662	23 21	+41 59	17	9.0	12.6		800	con	60	15	80	0.07	25

§ 122. Dark Nebulae

Typical dimensions of various types of dark nebulae [1]

	Globule I	Globule II	Coal sack	Large cloud
Diameter in pc	0·06	0·5	8	40
Total absorption A_{pg}	5 mag	1·5 mag	1·5 mag	1·4 mag
A_{pg} per kpc	8×10^4	3 000	200	35
Particle density in g cm^{-3}	$> 10^{-21}$	5×10^{-23}	3×10^{-24}	5×10^{-25}
Mass of absorbing material	$> 0·002 \mathcal{M}_\odot$	$0·05 \mathcal{M}_\odot$	$13 \mathcal{M}_\odot$	$300 \mathcal{M}_\odot$

Total mass of large dark cloud complexes from dynamics [2]

$$\simeq 10^6 \; \mathcal{M}_\odot$$

Some large cloud complexes [1, 3, 7]

Region	l^{II}	Area	Distance	Diameter	A_v	Mass of absorbing material
	°	deg^2	pc	pc		$\mathcal{M}_\odot$
Taurus, Orion, Auriga	180	600	150	70	0·9	80
Cepheus, Cassiopeia	117	450	500	170	0·6	1 400
Cygnus	80	80	700	130	1·2	700
Oph, Sco, Scu, Ser	0	1 000	120	80	0·7	100
Vela	270	100	600	120	1·6	500

Selected dark nebulae [1, 6]

Nebula	Coordinates		Size	Distance	A_v	$\mathcal{M}$ (solid particles)
	l^{II}	b^{II}				
	°	°	°	pc		$\mathcal{M}_\odot$
θ Ophiuchi	1	+ 5	3	250	2·0	
Scutum	28	− 2	3	220	3	
52 Cygni	72	− 7	2	500	1	
Cygnus	75	− 3	1·5	600	2	
North America	85	+ 1	1	200 and 600	2	
Cygnus	92	+ 3	4	250 and 600	1+1	
Cepheus	102	+ 2	0·6	200 to 400	0·7	
Taurus [5]	171	− 15	2	120		5
S Monocerotis	202	+ 2	1·5	600	1·5	
Orion	207	− 21	4	300	1	
η Carinae	286	0		800	0·7	
Coal sack [4]	304	0	4	170	1·8	14
ρ Ophiuchi [5]	353	+ 17	2·5	200	4	32

[1] *A.Q.* **1**, § 119.
[2] L. Spitzer and M. Schwarzschild, *Ap. J.*, **118**, 106, 1953.
[3] W. Becker, *Sterne and Sternsysteme*, 2nd ed., p. 194, 1950.
[4] A. W. Rogers, *M.N.*, **120**, 163, 1960.
[5] B. J. Bok, *A.J.*, **61**, 309, 1956.
[6] J. Sh. Khavtassi, *Atlas of Galactic Dark Nebulae*, Abastumany, 1960.
[7] B. T. Lynds, *Ap. J. Supp.*, **7**, No. 64, 1, 1962.

§ 123. Interstellar Clouds

The material of interstellar space is gathered into clouds in such a way as to make mean quantities unsuitable for many purposes. The clouds are also very irregular, and information on their size, number, density, etc. can be only approximate. Clouds of gas and clouds of interstellar grains (smoke) coincide approximately and hence dimensions are not quoted separately.

Diameter of clouds [1, 2, 5] $= 15$ pc

Number density of clouds $= 3 \times 10^{-5}$ pc^{-3}

Proportion of space near galactic plane occupied by clouds
$$= 6\%$$

Proportion of space near galactic plane where radiation from hot stars is capable of ionizing hydrogen $= 7\%$

Proportion of space near galactic plane occupied by ionized clouds (H II regions) [1, 2] $= 0.4\%$

Distance between clouds $= 40$ pc

Number of clouds penetrated per kpc $= 7$

Mean visual absorption per cloud
$$A_v = 0.25 \text{ mag}$$

Root-mean-square random velocity of clouds in the line-of-sight [1, 3]
$$= 9 \text{ km/s}$$

Mean cloud mass [3, 5] $= 1\,000\ \mathcal{M}_\odot$

Gas density in clouds [3] $= 8$ atoms cm^{-3}

Gas density between clouds [4] $= 0.01\ (\pm 0.7 \text{ dex})$

[1] *A.Q.* **1**, § 120.
[2] G. Westerhout, *B.A.N.*, **14**, 215, 1958.
[3] H. C. van de Hulst, Muller, and Oort, *B.A.N.*, **12**, 117, 1954.
[4] J. E. Baldwin, *Observatory*, **78**, 166, 1958.
[5] B. G. Clark, Radhakrishnan, and Wilson, *Ap. J.*, **135**, 151, 1962.

§ 124. Absorption and Interstellar Grains

Absorption of star light near galactic plane [1]

Stars selected within a true distance $A_v = 2.0$ mag/kpc

Stars selected by their visibility $A_v = 0.8$ mag/kpc

Avoiding interstellar clouds $A_v = 0.3$ mag/kpc

Absorption A_v, A_B and colour excess $E = A_B - A_v$ ($= E_{B-v}$)

$$A_v = (3\cdot0 \pm 0\cdot2)E \quad [2, 11, 12, 13]$$
$$A_v = 2\cdot1E + 7p \quad [3]$$

where p = linear polarization in magnitudes.

Variation of absorption A_λ with wavelength

$$A_\lambda/A_v = 0\cdot68\,(1/\lambda - 0\cdot35) \quad [\lambda \text{ in } \mu]$$

λ in μ	0·33	0·35	0·40	0·44	0·50	0·55	0·6	0·7	1·0	1·5	2·0	5·0	∞
$1/\lambda$ in μ^{-1}	3·00	2·85	2·50	2·31	2·00	1·82	1·67	1·43	1·00	0·67	0·50	0·20	0·00
A_λ/A_v [4]	1·65	1·56	1·40	1·33	1·12	1·00	0·86	0·71	0·39	0·15	0·07	0·01	0·00

Relative absorption in U, B, V [2, 5]

$$E_{U-B} = (0\cdot73 + 0\cdot06\,E_{B-V})E_{B-V}$$

Polarization (Hiltner-Hall effect)

P = degree of polarization, p = polarization in magnitudes
$$P \simeq 0\cdot46\,p$$

Maximum polarization [6, 7] relative to absorption
$$2\cdot2P = p = 0\cdot063\,A_v = 0\cdot19\,E$$

Absorption and scattering by grains: see § 36.

Mass absorption by grains (smoke) in interstellar space
$$= 4 \times 10^4 \text{ mag (vis) cm}^2\,\text{g}^{-1}$$

Radius of grains effective in absorbing stellar light [1, 8, 14]
$$= 0\cdot3\,\mu$$

Mass of a grain $= 10^{-13}$ g

Density of a grain $= 1\cdot0$ g cm^{-3} (?)

Refractive index of grain $= 1\cdot3$

Mean density of grains in space near galactic plane
$$= 1\cdot3 \times 10^{-26} \text{ g cm}^{-3}$$

Fraction by mass of interstellar matter in the form of dust [1, 9, 10]
$$= 0\cdot012$$

Mean number of grains per unit volume
$$= 2 \times 10^{-13} \text{ grains cm}^{-3}$$

Temperature of grains [8] $= 25$ °K

[1] A.Q. 1, § 121.
[2] W. A. HILTNER and H. L. JOHNSON, Ap. J., 124, 367, 1956.
[3] R. WILSON, M.N., 120, 51, 1960.
[4] A. E. WHITFORD, A.J., 63, 201, 1958.
[5] V. M. BLANCO, Ap. J., 123, 64, 1956.
[6] W. A. HILTNER, Ap. J. Supp., 2, 389, No. 24, 1956.
[7] T. SCHMIDT, Z. Ap., 46, 145, 1958.

[8] H. C. van de Hulst, Liège Symp., *Les particules solides dans les astres*, p. 390, 1955.
[9] B. J. Bok, Liège Symp., *Les particules solides . . .*, p. 480, 1955.
[10] H. Lambrecht and K. H. Schmidt, *A.N.*, **284**, 71, 1957.
[11] V. M. Blanco and C. J. Lennon, *A.J.*, **66**, 524, 1961.
[12] G. A. H. Walker, *Observatory*, **82**, 52, 1962.
[13] Th. Schmidt-Kaler, *A.N.*, **286**, 113, 1961.
[14] I. N. Minin, *A. Zh.*, **38**, 641, 1961.

§ 125. Interstellar Gas

Mean density of interstellar gas [1]

$$= 1 \cdot 2 \times 10^{-24} \text{ g cm}^{-3} = 0 \cdot 7 \text{ H atoms cm}^{-3}$$
$$= 0 \cdot 018 \, \mathscr{M}_\odot / \text{pc}^3$$

Relative abundance of atoms in interstellar gas is very similar to that in stars: § 14.

Excitation, ionization, and kinetic temperature

	H I regions	H II regions
Excitation	Atoms and molecules in ground level	
H ionization	Mainly non-ionized	Mainly ionized
Metal ionization	Mainly ionized	Completely ionized
Molecular kinetic temp.	125 °K [2]	10 000 °K

Interstellar lines

H I regions				H II regions	
Atomic absorption lines		Molecular absorption lines		Emission lines	
Atom	λ	Molecule	λ	Atom	λ
	Å		Å		Å
Na I	3302·4	CH [3]	3143·2	H	4340·5
Na I	3303·0	CH	3878·8	H	4681·5
Na I	5890·0	CH	3886·4	H	6562·8
Na I	5895·9	CH	3890·2	O II	3726·1
K I	7664·9	CH	4300·3	O II	3728·9
K I	7699·0	CN	3874·0	O III	4958·9
Ca I	4226·7	CN	3874·6	O III	5006·8
Ca II	3933·7	CN	3875·8	N II	6548·1
Ca II	3968·5	CH^+	3579	N II	6583·6
Ti II	3073·0	CH^+	3745·3		
Ti II	3229·2	CH^+	3957·7		
Ti II	3242·0	CH^+	4232·6		
Ti II	3383·8	NaH?	3934		
Fe I	3720·0				
Fe I	3859·9				

Interstellar diffuse absorption bands [1, 4]

$\Delta\lambda$ = whole-$\frac{1}{2}$-width, W = equivalent width for a well-reddened star

λ	$\Delta\lambda$	W	λ	$\Delta\lambda$	W
	Å	Å		Å	Å
4430·6	25	5	6180	40	1·9
4760	40	1·5	6203·0	7	0·5
4890	25	1·2	6270·0	5	0·2
5780·6	1·9		6283·9	8	1·7
5797·1	1·6		6614	4	

Relation between equivalent width and colour excess E

$$W(4430) = 5E \quad [W \text{ in Å}]$$

Intensity of interstellar absorption lines in relation to distance [1]

$$r = 3\cdot1\,K; \quad r = 2\cdot0\,D$$

where r = distance in kpc,

K = equivalent width in Å of the Ca II K-line,

D = mean equivalent width in Å of the two Na D-lines.

Emission measure, e.m., defining the extent of an H II region

$$\text{e.m.} = \int N_e^2\,dl = \int N_H^2\,dl$$

where l is the sight-line path within the H II region in pc

N_e = electron density in cm^{-3}

$= N_H$ = hydrogen density in atoms cm^{-3}

Hα emission from an H II region $= 3 \times 10^{-8}$ e.m. erg sterad^{-1} cm^{-2} s^{-1}

Ratio of e.m. to population of third level H atoms

$$\text{e.m.} = 400\,N_3$$

where N_3 = number of third level H atoms cm^{-2}.

Emission measure of faint extended regions of the sky

$$\text{e.m.} \simeq 1\,000$$

Radius of H II regions in relation to exciting star [5, 6, 7]

$$= s_0 N^{-2/3}$$

Star spectrum	O5	O8	B0	B2	B5	B8
s_0 in pc	110	55	26	12	3	1

Hydrogen distribution within the galaxy [8]

H I   maximum 1 atom cm^{-3} at 6·5 kpc from gal. centre

H II   maximum 0·5 ion cm^{-3} at 4 kpc from gal. centre.

Mean molecular density in interstellar space [9]

CH	110×10^{-10} molecules cm^{-3}	
CH$^+$	60×10^{-10}	,, ,,
CN	4×10^{-10}	,, ,,

[1] *A.Q.* **1**, § 122.
[2] G. WESTERHOUT, *B.A.N.*, **13**, 201, 1957.
[3] A. E. DOUGLAS and J. R. MORTON, *Ap. J.*, **131**, 1, 1960.
[4] R. WILSON, *Ap. J.*, **128**, 57, 1958.
[5] S. POTTASCH, *B.A.N.*, **13**, 77, 1956; *Ap. J.*, **132**, 269, 1960.
[6] R. E. GERSHBERG and V. I. PRONIK, *A. Zh.*, **36**, 902, 1959; *Sov. A.*, **3**, 876.
[7] J.-C. PECKER, Liège Symp. on *Spectra in Ultraviolet*, 487, 1961.
[8] J. H. OORT, Paris Symp. on *Radio Astronomy*, p. 409, 1959.
[9] D. R. BATES and L. SPITZER, *Ap. J.*, **113**, 441, 1951.

§ 126. Radiation and Fields in Interstellar Space

Density of radiation in interstellar space [1, 2]

$$= 7 \times 10^{-13} \text{ erg cm}^{-3}$$

The [2] values to 8000 Å were extended to longer wavelengths using a colour temperature of 3 500 °K.

Total radiation emission by stars near sun [3, and § 117]

$$= 1 \cdot 4 \times 10^{-23} \text{ erg cm}^{-3} \text{ s}^{-1}$$

Density of ionizing radiation ($\lambda < 912$ Å) near galactic plane

$$= 5 \times 10^{-16} \text{ erg cm}^{-3} *$$

* Though this is probably excluded from most H I regions.

Total emission of ionizing radiation near galactic plane [2, 4]

$$= 2 \times 10^{-26} \text{ erg cm}^{-3} \text{ s}^{-1}$$

Spectral distribution of radiation density [2, 8, 9]

λ	Radiation	λ	Radiation	λ	Radiation
μ	10^{-14} erg cm^{-3} μ^{-1}	μ	10^{-14} erg cm^{-3} μ^{-1}	μ	10^{-14} erg cm^{-3} μ^{-1}
0·05	4*	0·4	51	1·0	44
0·1	30	0·5	48	2·0	12
0·2	40	0·6	47	4·0	1·4
0·3	40	0·8	46	8·0	0·1

Equivalent black body temperature of space

$$= 3 \cdot 1 \text{ °K}$$

Comparison of energy densities [7]

Total radiation (star light)	$0 \cdot 7 \times 10^{-12}$ erg cm^{-3}
Turbulent gas motion	$0 \cdot 5 \times 10^{-12}$,, ,,
Total energy of galactic rotation	$1\,300 \ \times 10^{-12}$,, ,,
Cosmic rays	$1 \ \times 10^{-12}$,, ,,
Magnetic field (= 1γ)	$4 \ \times 10^{-12}$,, ,,

Interstellar magnetic field

Theoretical [5]	$= 3 \times 10^{-5}$ gauss $= 3\gamma$
Observations [6]	$< 1 \times 10^{-5}$ gauss

[1] *A.Q.* **1**, § 123.
[2] H. Lambrecht and H. Zimmermann, *Mitt. U.-S. Jena*, No. 14, 1956.
[3] K. F. d'Occhieppo, *Mitt. U.-S. Wien*, **6**, No. 4, 59, 1952.
[4] L. Spitzer, *Rev. Mod. Phys.*, **30**, 1102, 1958.
[5] L. Woltjer, *Ap. J.*, **133**, 352, 1961.
[6] R. D. Davies et al., *Nature*, **187**, 1088, 1960.
[7] P. Morrison, *Rev. Mod. Phys.*, **29**, 235, 1957.
[8] A. D. Code, *A.J.*, **65**, 278, 1960.
[9] D. McNally, *M.N.*, **124**, 155, 1962.

§ 127. Radio Emission (Cosmic)

The surface intensity I of an extended radio source is related to the equivalent temperature T and frequency ν by

$$I_\nu = 3.071\ 5 \times 10^{-40}\ T\nu^2 \text{ watt m}^{-2} \text{ sterad}^{-1} \text{ (c/s)}^{-1} \quad [T \text{ in } °K, \nu \text{ in c/s}]$$

I and I_ν include the two components of polarization.

The total radiation from an object is expressed by its flux density at the earth (earth surface flux) f, f_ν where $f = \int I \cos \theta\, d\omega \simeq \int I\, d\omega$ integrated over the angular region ω. $\theta =$ angle from centre of object.

The continuous spectral distribution is represented by a spectral index x or n such that

$$I_\nu \text{ or } f_\nu \propto \nu^x \quad \propto \lambda^{-x} \propto \lambda^{n-2} \propto \nu^{2-n}$$
$$T \propto \nu^{x-2} \propto \lambda^{2-x} \propto \quad \lambda^n \propto \nu^{-n}$$

where $x + n = 2$. The index n is always positive.

Values of x and n (near 100 Mc/s)

Mean galactic sources [2, 15]	$x = -0.71$	$n = 2.71$
Mean extragalactic sources [2]	-1.05	3.05
Mean unidentified sources [2]	-1.21	3.21
General galactic emission [4, 7]	-0.45	2.45
Cold sky	-0.60	2.60
Optically thin thermal emission	0.00	2.00
Optically thick thermal emission	$+2.00$	0.00

Mean temperature of celestial sphere at 100 Mc/s [1]
$$= 700\ °K$$

Radiation from whole celestial sphere at 100 Mc/s [1]
$$= 2.7 \times 10^{-20} \text{ watt m}^{-2} \text{ (c/s)}^{-1}$$

where m^{-2} means received on a sphere projecting 1 m^2 in any direction (i.e. of radius $\pi^{-1/2}$).

Neutral H absorption coefficient at 1420 Mc/s [1]
$$= 8.0 \times 10^3\ (N/T\ \Delta\nu)$$

where $N =$ number of H atoms cm^{-3}, $T =$ temperature in $°K$, $\Delta\nu =$ line width in c/s, and the coefficient is exponential per parsec.

Continuous absorption coefficient in a plasma (interstellar densities)

$$= 5\cdot1 \times 10^{-4}\ \lambda^2 N_e^2 T^{-3/2}\ \exp\ \mathrm{pc}^{-1}$$
$$[\lambda \text{ in cm},\ N_e \text{ in cm}^{-3},\ T \text{ in } °K]$$

Exponential absorption in H II region

$$= 5\cdot1 \times 10^{-4}\ \lambda^2\ T^{-3/2} \times \text{emission measure.}$$

Number N of radio sources per steradian having a flux density greater than f_1 at 100 Mc/s [3, 17]

f_1 in watt m^{-2} (c/s)$^{-1}$	10^{-23}	10^{-24}	10^{-25}
log N in sterad^{-1}	-1	$+0\cdot3$	$+2\cdot1$

Selected discrete sources

Discrete radio sources are labelled by various names and catalogue numbers [5] and also by an I.A.U. designation [6]. Some sources have a central nucleus and an extended halo ($+$h in the size column). There is a tendency for the halo to be included in the high frequency f measurements but not in the low, and this can account for some discrepancies between f and x values. The identifications of the sources include several supernovae SN of types I and II, colliding (or double) galaxies, peculiar galaxies, and galactic nebulosities. Thermal sources are labelled T in the x column. P = point source.

Source Name, etc.	I.A.U.	1950 α	δ	f at 100 Mc/s [2, 3, 9]	f at 1 000 Mc/s [7, 8]	x at 100 Mc/s [2, 8]	Size [2, 3, 8]	log Dist. [7, 10]	Identifications and notes
		[1, 3, 7, 8]							
		h m ° ′		10^{-26} watt m^{-2}(c/s)$^{-1}$		′	in pc		
Cas B	00N6A	0 23 +63	52	250	56	$-0\cdot7$	5·5	2·8 ?	Tycho's SN I, 1572
And A	00N4A	0 40 +40	50	190		$-0\cdot5$	140	5·68	Andr. neb., M31
Per A	03N4A	3 16 +41	21	130	22	$-0\cdot8$	2·4	7·85	Col. gal., NGC 1275
For A	03S3A	3 20 $-$37	21	240			large		Pec. gal., NGC 1316 ?
Per	04N3A	4 34 +29	36	280	70	$-0\cdot85$	P		
HB9	05N4A	4 58 +46	26	140	150	$+0\cdot1$	60$+$h		Gal. neb., SN II
Pic A	05S4A	5 18 $-$45	52	500			large		
Tau A	05N2A	5 32 +21	59	1 700	1 100	$-0\cdot26$	5	3·02	Crab neb., SN I, 1054
Ori	05S0A	5 33 $-$ 5	24	50	500		10	2·7	Orion neb., M42
Gem	06N2A	6 15 +22	38	500	200	$-0\cdot4$	30$+$h	3·1	IC443, SN II
Mon		6 29 + 4	59	500	320	$-0\cdot17$	70	3·15	Rosette neb.
Pup A	08S4A	8 21 $-$42	58	560	180	$-0\cdot8$	40$+$h	2·7 ?	Gal. neb., SN II
Hya A	09S1A	9 16 $-$11	53	400	65	$-0\cdot9$	P	8·32	Col. gal.
CVn	12N4A	12 15 +47					3		NGC 4258
Vir A	12N1A	12 28 +12	40	1 700	290	$-0\cdot73$	4	7·04	Pec. gal., M87
Cen A	13S4A	13 22 $-$42	46	1 750	2 000	$-0\cdot66$	5$+$h	6·7	Pec. gal., NGC 5128
Cen B	13S6A	13 30 $-$60		700					
Boo	14N5A	14 10 +52	26	100	30	$-0\cdot6$	P		NGC 5457 ? ?
Tr A	16S6A	16 10 $-$60	45	800					
2C 1402	16N4A	16 27 +39	38	100	7	$-1\cdot4$	1		Four gal. NGC 6166
Her A	16N0A	16 49 + 5	07	580	74	$-0\cdot8$	2·5	8·53	Pec. gal. ?
2C 1473		17 18 $-$ 0	52	400	84	$-1\cdot2$	4		
2C 1485		17 28 $-$21	16	80			P	2·8 ?	Kepler's SN I, 1604
Sgr A	17S2A	17 43 $-$28	50	3 800	2 000	$-0\cdot6$	70	3·91	Galactic centre
Sgr		18 01 $-$24	21		140	T			Gal. neb. M8
Oph	18S0A	18 13 $-$ 7		200					
Sgr	18S1A	18 18 $-$16	18		700	T	10	3·2	Gal. neb. Ω = M17
Cyg A	19N4A	19 58 +40	35	11 800	2 150	$-0\cdot68$	1·2	8·34	Col. gal.
Cyg X	20N4A	20 30 +41			900	T	100	3·1	IC1 318 (γ Cyg)
2C 1725		20 42 +50	20	510	180	$-0\cdot5$	100		SN II
Cyg loop		20 48 +30	30	430	200	$-0\cdot35$	150	2·88	Cyg. loops SN II
America		20 52 +44	00		400	T	150	3·0	America neb.
Cas A	23N5A	23 21 +58	32	19 000	3 100	$-0\cdot80$	4	3·35	Gal. neb. SN II

Intensity of general cosmic radio emission [1, 7, 11, 12]

General galactic radio emission is concentrated along the galactic equator and towards the galactic centre. Measurements are disturbed by irregularities and superimposed sources. We chose as representative regions the galactic ridge at $l^{II} = \pm 10°$ (i.e. avoiding the Sgr A source), and the coldest part of the sky near $b^{II} = \pm 90°$.

ν	λ	Galactic ridge $l^{II} = \pm 10°$		Cold sky $b^{II} = \pm 90°$	
		$\log T$	$\log I_\nu$	$\log T$	$\log I_\nu$
Mc/s	cm	in °K	in watt m^{-2} (c/s)$^{-1}$ sterad^{-1}	in °K	in watt m^{-2} (c/s)$^{-1}$ sterad^{-1}
10	3 000	5·9	−19·6	5·3	−20·2
20	1 500	5·5	−19·4	4·6	−20·3
50	600	4·8	−19·3	3·56	−20·55
100	300	4·09	−19·42	2·76	−20·75
200	150	3·36	−19·55	1·98	−20·93
500	60	2·37	−19·74	0·94	−21·17
1 000	30	1·64	−19·87	0·1	−21·4
2 000	15	0·9	−20·0		
5 000	6	−0·1	−20·2		

T on galactic equator at 100 Mc/s [1, 7, 11, 12, 13, 16]

l^{II}	T	l^{II}	T	l^{II}	T	l^{II}	T
°	°K	°	°K	°	°K	°	°K
0	12 000	90	2 600	180	1 600	270	2 000
30	9 000	120	1 900	210	1 500	300	3 500
60	3 500	150	1 800	240	1 400	330	9 000

Whole-$\frac{1}{2}$-width of galactic strip [7, 11, 12]

$$= 3·5°$$

[1] *A.Q.* **1**, § 124.
[2] G. R. WHITFIELD, *M.N.*, **117**, 680, 1957.
[3] D. O. EDGE et al.; B. ELSMORE et al., *Mem. R.A.S.*, **68**, 37, 61, 1959.
[4] C. H. COSTAIN, *P.A.S.P.*, **72**, 351, 1960; *M.N.*, **120**, 248, 1960.
[5] J. R. SHAKESHAFT et al., *Mem. R.A.S.*, **67**, 106, 1955.
[6] J. L. PAWSEY, *Ap. J.*, **121**, 1, 1955.
[7] G. WESTERHOUT, *B.A.N.*, **14**, 215, 1958.
[8] D. E. HARRIS and ROBERTS; R. W. WILSON and BOLTON, *P.A.S.P.*, **72**, 237, 331, 1960.
[9] A. BOISCHOT, Paris Symp. on *Radio Astronomy*, p. 492, 1959.
[10] J. L. STEINBERG and J. LEQUEUX, *Radioastronomie*, Dunod, Paris, 1960.
[11] B. Y. MILLS (HILL and SLEE), *Obs.*, **78**, 116, 1958; *P.A.S.P.*, **71**, 267, 1959.
[12] J. H. PIDDINGTON and G. H. TRENT, *Aust. J. Phys.*, **9**, 481, 1956.
[13] J. E. BALDWIN, *M.N.*, **115**, 684, 690, 1955.
[14] D. E. HARRIS, *Ap. J.*, **135**, 661, 1962.
[15] N. W. BROTEN and W. J. MEDD, *J.R.A.S. Canada*, **56**, 11, 1962.
[16] I. I. K. PAULINY-TOTH and J. R. SHAKESHAFT, *M.N.*, **124**, 61, 1962.
[17] B. Y. MILLS, SLEE, and HILL, *Aust. J. Phys.*, **13**, 676, 1960.

§ 128. Cosmic Rays

The kinetic energy T of cosmic ray particles is often expressed by the rigidity R through the relation

$$R = \frac{pc}{ze} = \frac{1}{ze}(T^2 + 2mc^2 T)^{1/2}$$

where p = momentum = $mv(1 - v^2/c^2)^{-1/2}$, ze = charge, v = velocity, mc^2 = rest mass.

Interrelations [2, 3, 7]

Only the $(\log T > 8.5)$ particles are regarded as cosmic rays but low energy data is included for geomagnetic purposes.

log T	in ev	2	3	4	5	6	7	8	9	Cosmic rays 10	11	12
Protons												
log R	in volts	5·64	6·14	6·64	7·14	7·64	8·15	8·65	9·23	10·04	11·00	12·00
v	in 10⁸ cm/s	0·14	0·44	1·4	4·4	14	44	133	255	300	300	300
Lat. geomag. cut-off	in °		84·5	82·7	80·4	77	72	65	54	21	0	0
Penetration height	in km			128	110	90	67	32	6	0	0	0
Penetration mass	in g cm⁻²						0·15	9	400			
Electrons												
log R	in volts	4·00	4·50	5·00	5·52	6·15	7·02	8·01	9·00	10·00	11·00	12·00
v	in 10⁸ cm/s	6	19	60	170	280	300	300	300	300	300	300
Lat. geomag. cut-off	in °			87	86	84						
Penetration height	in km		128	103	80	57						
α-particles												
log R						7·94	8·45	8·95	9·54	10·18	11·01	12·00

Log abundance of cosmic ray nuclei [2]

Scale: $\log$ H abundance = 12·0

Atom nucleus	H	He	Li, Be, B	C, N, O, F	Heavy nuclei $z \geqslant 10$	$23 \leqslant z \leqslant 30$	Very heavy
Cosmic rays	12·0	11·2	9·4	10·1	9·6	9·0	<6
Cosmic material, § 14	12·0	11·2	3	9·1	8·0	7·0	4

Radius of gyration in a magnetic field

$$a = 3.34 \times 10^{-3}\, R/B \text{ cm} \quad [R \text{ in volts}, B \text{ in gauss}]$$

Cosmic ray flux per unit surface outside influence of earth magnetic field [1, 4, 5]

Sunspot minimum

number = 0·6 primary particles $\text{cm}^{-2}\,\text{s}^{-1}$

energy = 5 Gev $\text{cm}^{-2}\,\text{s}^{-1}$ = 0·007 erg $\text{cm}^{-2}\,\text{s}^{-1}$

Sunspot maximum

number = 0·3 primary particles $\text{cm}^{-2}\,\text{s}^{-1}$

energy = 3 Gev $\text{cm}^{-2}\,\text{s}^{-1}$ = 0·004 erg $\text{cm}^{-2}\,\text{s}^{-1}$

Space density of primary cosmic rays [1]

$$\text{number} = 0.8 \times 10^{-10} \text{ particles cm}^{-3}$$
$$\text{energy} = 1.0 \times 10^{-12} \text{ erg cm}^{-3}$$

Mean energy of primary cosmic ray particles [1]

$$= 7 \text{ Gev} = 0.011 \text{ erg}$$

Distribution of primary particles with energy [2, 4, 5]. *Lower energy particles*

Energy T in Gev Intensity in 10^{-4} particles $\text{cm}^{-2}\,\text{s}^{-1}\,\text{sterad}^{-1}\,\text{Gev}^{-1}$	0·5	1·0	1·5	2	3	5	10
at Sunspot minimum	350	450	440	350	180	75	18
at Sunspot maximum	50	140	180	150	100	50	16

Higher energy particles

$\log T_1$ in ev	9	10	11	12	13	14	15	16	17	18
$\log$ (particles with $T > T_1$) in $\text{cm}^{-2}\,\text{s}^{-1}$ sterad^{-1} mean of sp. min. and max.	-0.9	-1.7	-2.8	-4.3	-6.0	-7.9	-9.7	-11.6	-13.5	-15.3

Intensities from solar proton events (particles with $T > T_1$) [7]

$\log T_1$ in ev	6	7	8	9
$\log$ (Intensity) in $\text{cm}^{-2}\,\text{s}^{-1}\,\text{sterad}^{-1}$	4·5	3·8	2·0	-2

Relative numbers of primary particles inside earth magnetic field but outside the atmosphere [1]

Geomagnetic latitude	0°	10°	20°	30°	40°	50°	60°	70°
Rel. number of particles	10	10	11	16	28	55	84	93

Ion pairs produced by cosmic rays at sea level

Geomag. lat. Ion pairs $\text{cm}^{-3}\,\text{s}^{-1}$	0°	10°	20°	30°	40°	50°	60°	70°	80°	90°
	1·61	1·61	1·63	1·68	1·77	1·84	1·84	1·84	1·84	1·84

Ion pairs as a function of height [1, 6]

Pressure in mm-Hg	760	700	600	500	400	300	200	100	50
Height in km	0	0·70	1·95	3·4	5·1	7·2	9·9	14·3	19
Ion pairs cm^{-3} s^{-1}									
Geomag. lat. 0°–15°	1·61	1·88	2·6	4·0	6·8	10·8	15	11	6
Geomag. lat. 50°–90°	1·84	2·15	3·2	5·5	10·0	19	31	33	22

[1] *A.Q.* **1**, § 125.
[2] E. P. NEY, *Ap. J., Supp.*, **4**, 369, 371, 1960.
[3] T. OBAYASHI and Y. HAKURA, *Rep. Ionosph. and Space R. in Japan*, **14**, 1, 1960.
[4] F. B. McDONALD, *Phys. Rev.*, **116**, 462, 1959.
[5] J. A. SIMPSON, *Ap. J. Supp.*, **4**, 378, 1960.
[6] F. K. RICHTMYER, KENNARD, and LAURITZEN, *Intr. to Modern Phys.*, p. 565, McGraw-Hill, 1955.
[7] D. K. BAILEY, *Proc. I.R.E.*, **47**, 255, 1959; *J. Geoph. Res.*, **67**, 391, 1962.

§ 129. Extragalactic Space

Extragalactic absorption [1] $A_v = 0·004$? mag Mpc^{-1}

Corresponding density of grain material in intergalactic space
$$= 10^{-31} ? \text{ g cm}^{-3}$$

Intergalactic gas density ρ_{IG} [2, 3]

From 21-cm absorption $\rho_{IG} < 6 \times 10^{-29}$? g cm^{-3}

From cosmological dynamical considerations
$$\rho_{IG} \simeq 2 \times 10^{-28} \text{ g cm}^{-3}$$

Radiation density in intergalactic space
$$= 10^{-14} \text{ erg cm}^{-3}$$

[1] *A.Q.* **1**, § 126.
[2] G. B. FIELD, *Ap. J.*, **129**, 525, 536, 1959; **135**, 684, 1962.
[3] F. D. KAHN and L. WOLTJER, *Ap. J.*, **130**, 705, 1959.

CHAPTER 14

CLUSTERS AND GALAXIES

§ 130. Open Clusters and Associations

IN a recent catalogue [2] (1961) there are 758 open clusters, 82 O-associations, 5 moving clusters, (119 globular clusters), and 7 stellar groups recorded within the Galaxy. In addition 41 T-associations have been listed [18]. An association, moving cluster or group is sometimes connected with an open cluster as its nucleus. These various groupings cannot always be clearly differentiated and hence we have listed the groupings separately with some duplications.

Selected open clusters

The angular and linear diameters refer to the more concentrated part of the cluster. The numbers of stars are from catalogues and cannot include fainter stars.

Name or designation	NGC or IC	Coordinates l^{II} [2]	Coordinates b^{II} [2]	Distance [1, 3, 4, 13]	Diameter Ang [1, 3]	Diameter Lin	Number of stars [1, 5]	Total m_v [1, 3]	Absorption A_v [4]	log Age [6, 7, 8]
		°	°	pc	′	pc				in y
[19]	188	123	+22	1 000	14	4		9·3		10·0
M103	581	128	− 2	2 100	7	4	30	6·9	1·5	7·4
	752	137	−23	400	45	5	60	6·2		9·2
h Persei	869	135	− 4	2 200	30	19	300	4·1	1·7	7·0
χ Persei	884	135	− 4	2 300	30	20	240	4·3	1·7	7·1
M34	1039	144	−16	480	30	5	60	5·6	0·2	8·2
Perseus		147	− 7	155	240	11	80	2·2		7·0
Pleiades		167	−24	126	120	4	120	1·3	0·2	7·8
Hyades		179	−24	40·8	400	5	100	0·6	0·6	8·6
M38	1912	173	+ 1	980	18	5	100	7·0		7·7
M36	1960	174	+ 1	1 270	17	6	50	6·3	0·7	7·5
M37	2099	178	+ 3	900	25	7	200	6·1		8·3
S mon	2264	203	+ 2	800	30	7	60	4·3		6·3
τ CMa	2362	238	− 6	1 400	7	3	30	3·9	0·4	6·1
Praesepe	2632	206	+32	159	90	4	100	3·7	0·0	8·4
o Vel	I2391	270	− 7	170	45	2	15	2·6	0·2	7·3
M67	2682	216	+32	830	17	4	80	6·5		9·6
θ Car	I2602	290	− 5	190	70	4	25	1·7	0·2	6·8
	3532	290	+ 2	430	50	6	130	3·3	0·0	8·0
Sco-Cen*		320	+10	190	2 000	100	110	−0·8		6·6
Coma		228	+84	79	300	7	40	2·8	0·0	8·5
κ Cru	4755	303	+ 2	1 100	12	5	30	5·0	0·0	7·2
Ursa Maj		110	+50	22	1 000	7	100	−0·2	0·0	8·2
M21	6531	8	0	900	12	3	40	6·8		6·8
M16	6611	17	+ 1	2 000	8	5	40	6·6	1·2	6·1
M11	6705	27	− 3	1 700	12	6	80	6·3		8·2
M39	7092	92	− 2	255	30	2	20	5·1	0·2	8·4

* The Sco-Cen B stars are listed as a cluster because they do not appear in the O-association lists.

O-associations [2, 15, 16, 17]

The associations were chosen from the catalogue [2] and then identified as far as possible with the lists [15, 16]. The first name refers to the Schmidt list [16].

Association [15, 16]	[2]	l^{II}	b^{II}	Number of stars	Distance	Associated features (NGC numbers)
		°	°		pc	
III + VII Cas	I	125	− 1	28	2 700	381, 366
I Per	I	135	− 5	180	1 900	h and χ Per
II Per	II	160	−17	100	380	ζ Per
I Aur	I	173	0	15	1 100	χ Aur
I Ori	I	206	−18	1 000	500	1976, ε Ori
II Mon	I	202	+ 1	50	510	2264
I Mon	II	207	− 1		1 400	2244
I Car	I	287	0	90	900	3293, I 2602
I Sco	I	343	+ 1	70	1 300	6231
I + II Sgr	I	7	− 1	60	1 300	6514, 6523
IV Sgr	II	14	0	120	1 700	6561
II Cyg	I	76	+ 2	200	1 800	6871, I 4996, P Cyg
I Cep	II	101	+ 5	80	680	ν Cep
I Lac	I	98	−15	70	550	10 Lac
II + IV Cep	I	107	− 1	150	2 500	7380
I + V Cas	II + V	111	0	160	2 700	7510

T-associations [14, 17, 18]

Association	l^{II}	b^{II}	Diam.	Number of stars	Dist.	Reference objects
	°	°	°		pc	
Tau T1	169	− 16	3	12	200	RY Tau
Tau T2	179	− 20	4	11	170	T Tau
Aur T1	172	− 7	7	13	170	RW Aur
Ori T2	209	− 19	4	399	400	T Ori
Mon T1	203	+ 2	3	141	800	S Mon, NGC 2264
Sco T1	354	+ 18	9	26	210	α Sco, AU Sco
Lyr T1	60	+ 20	17	13	400	LT Lyr
CrA T1	0	− 18	0·5	6	115	R CrA
Del T1	55	− 9	15	25	200	V536 Aql, WW Vul

Convergent points of moving clusters [1]

Cluster association or group	Convergent point relative to sun				Velocity	
	α	δ	l^{II}	b^{II}	rel. sun	cor- rected
	°	°	°	°	km/s	km/s
Perseus, Cas-Tau [10]	99	− 20	230	− 10	22	12
Pleiades	85	− 43	248	− 30	20	5
Hyades	94	+ 7	202	− 3	45	32
Orion	84	− 17	220	− 23	22	5
Praesepe	95	+ 4	206	− 3	41	27
Scorp-Cen	107	− 46	256	− 16	24	10
Coma Ber	121	− 47	262	− 8	8	14
Ursa Maj. Sirius group [11, 12]	302	− 34	8	− 31	18	29

Ages of clusters may be determined from the colour-magnitude or spectrum-magnitude diagram [6]. Measurements may be made on those parts of the main sequence which curl away from the zero age sequence (§§ 95, 98).

Cluster age relations [6, 7, 8]

Log age in years	6	7	8	9	9·5
Most luminous M_v on main sequence	− 6·5	− 3·7	− 0·9	+ 1·9	+ 3·3
Earliest type on main sequence	O7	B1	B7	A5	A8
Smallest $(B-V)_{\mathrm{cor}}$ on main sequence	− 0·31	− 0·23	− 0·05	+ 0·30	+ 0·52

Median galactic latitude of clusters [1]
$$\bar{b} = 3°·3$$

Space density of open clusters [1]

Distance from galactic plane	in kpc	0·0	0·1	0·2	0·3	0·4	0·5
Density	in clusters kpc^{-3}	400	120	30	15	8	4

Total number of clusters in galaxy [1]
$$= 20\ 000$$

Most probable total absolute magnitude and its dispersion [1]
$$M_t = − 3·5 \pm 1·4$$
(1·5 mag brighter if containing O stars).

Number of stars N ($M_* < 6$) in a cluster of radius R in pc [1]
$$\log N = 1·3 \log R + 2·0$$

Number of stars per cluster is 100 to 1 000, but the number of recognized cluster members is often less.

Limiting density for a stable cluster [1]

Mean cluster density $\qquad > 0{\cdot}09 \, \mathscr{M}_\odot \, \text{pc}^{-3}$

Disruption time of a cluster [9] $\qquad = 2 \times 10^8 \, \rho \; \text{year}$
where ρ is density in $\mathscr{M}_\odot/\text{pc}^3$.

[1] *A.Q.* **1**, § 127.
[2] G. ALTER, RUPRECHT, and VANÝSEK, *Catalogue of Star Clusters and Associations*, Czech. Acad. Sci., 1958; Supplements, *B.A. Czech. Appendices*, **10**, No. 3, 1959; **11**, No. 1, 1960; **12**, No. 1, 1961; **13**, No. 1, 1962.
[3] H. S. HOGG, *Handb. der Phys.*, **53**, p. 129, 1959.
[4] W. BECKER, *Z. Ap.*, **51**, 49, 151, 1960.
[5] P. COLLINDER, *Lund Ann.*, **2**, 1931.
[6] A. SANDAGE, *Stellar Populations*, ed. O'Connell, 41, Vatican, 1958.
[7] W. LOHMANN, *Z. Ap.*, **42**, 114, 1957.
[8] S. VON HOERNER, *Z. Ap.*, **42**, 273, 1957.
[9] L. SPITZER, *Ap. J.*, **127**, 17, 1958.
[10] R. M. PETRIE, *M.N.*, **118**, 80, 1958.
[11] R. M. PETRIE and B. N. MOYLS, *M.N.*, **113**, 239, 1953.
[12] O. J. EGGEN, *M.N.*, **118**, 65, 1958.
[13] H. L. JOHNSON, *Ap. J.*, **126**, 121, 1957.
[14] P. N. HOLOPOFF, *A. Zh.*, **27**, 233, 1950.
[15] W. W. MORGAN, WHITFORD, and CODE, *Ap. J.*, **118**, 318, 1953.
[16] K. H. SCHMIDT, *A.N.*, **284**, 76, 1958.
[17] *Astronomical News Letter*, No. 64, 1952.
[18] P. N. KHOLOPOV, *A. Zh.*, **36**, 295, 1959; *Sov. A.*, **3**, 291.
[19] O. STRUVE, *Sky and Tel.*, **20**, 140, 1960.

§ 131. Globular Clusters

There are 119 recently tabulated [2] globular clusters associated with the galactic system.

Number of stars in a globular cluster
$$= 10^5 \text{ to } 10^7 \text{ stars.}$$

Mean composite spectral class of globular clusters [1]
$$Sp = \text{F8}$$

Mean colour index corrected for space reddening [1]
$$B - V = +0{\cdot}6$$
For colour magnitude array: see § 98.

Median M_v of globular clusters [1]
$$\bar{M}_\text{v} = -8{\cdot}1$$

Median galactic latitude of globular clusters
$$\bar{b} = 14°$$
Globular clusters are absent from $-2° < b < +2°$ on account of space absorption.

Estimated number of globular clusters in the galactic system [6]
$$= 500$$
of which 160 belong to the detectable concentrated type.

Space density of globular clusters [6]

Distance from galactic centre	Space density	
	Galactic equator	Galactic pole
kpc	Clusters kpc^{-3}	
2	4	0·3
4	0·5	0·05
7	0·11	0·008
11	0·009	0·005
16	0·003	0·001

Selected globular clusters

Angular and linear diameters are intended to represent $2\sqrt{(2)}r_e$ where $2r_e$ is the diameter of the circle enclosing half the total luminosity (i.e. the representative diameter: see § 6). The table gives also distance, visual magnitude V_t, visual absorption A_v, number of observed variables, the radial velocity v_r, and mass.

Cluster [NGC	Coordinates		Diameter		Dis-tance	V_t	A_v	No. of vari-ables	v_r	Mass
	l^{II}	b^{II}	Ang.	Lin.	[1, 3, 4]	[1, 3]	[1, 3, 4]	[5]	[1]	[1, 7]
	[2]		[1, 3, 8, 9]							
			'	pc	kpc					$10^4\,\mathcal{M}_\odot$
47 Tuc 104	306	−45	7·6	10	4·6	4·01	0·2	11		
2419	180	+25	1·9	32	58	10·7	0·3	36	+ 14	
Δ445 3201	277	+ 9	8	9	3·7	8·0	1·8	77		
M68 4590	300	+36	2·2	8	11·8	8·31	0·4	31	−116	
M53 5024	333	+80	2·9	19	23	7·76	0·0	43	−112	
ω Cen 5139	309	+15	14·2	20	4·8	3·57	1·1	164		
M3 5272	42	+79	3·4	13	13	6·38	0·2	187	−150	21
M5 5904	4	+47	4·5	12	9·2	5·93	0·0	97	+ 45	6
M4 6121	351	+16	9·8	9	3·0	5·91	1·3	43		6
M13 6205	59	+41	4·8	11	8·2	5·87	0·2	10	−228	30
M12 6218	16	+26	6·9	14	6·8	6·72	0·8	1	+ 36	
M62 6266	354	+ 7	3·3	8	8·5	6·66	1·6	26	− 81	
M19 6273	357	+10	3·5	7	7·3	6·88	1·3	4	+102	
M92 6341	68	+35	3·3	10	10	6·53	0·1	16	−118	14
Δ366 6397	336	−11	10	7	2·4	6	1·2	3		
M22 6656	10	− 8	10	9	3·1	5·09	1·3	24	−148	700
Δ295 6752	336	−26	15	24	5·6	6·2	0·6	1	− 3	
M55 6809	9	−23	8·2	16	6·8	6·30	0·1	6		
7006	64	−19	1·2	17	48	10·68	0·3	40	−348	
M15 7078	65	−27	2·8	11	13	6·36	0·2	93	−114	600

Mean rotational velocity of system of globular clusters [6]

$$\simeq 60 \text{ km/s (direct)}$$

having no clear variation with distance from the galactic centre.

Mean mass/luminosity ratio [7]

$$\mathcal{M}/\mathcal{L} = 0\cdot8\,\mathcal{M}_\odot/\mathcal{L}_\odot$$

Spectral energy distribution [10]

$$\lambda_{max} = 5000 \text{ Å}$$

λ in Å	4000	5000	6000	8000	10000
$E_\lambda/E_{\lambda(max)}$	0·68	1·00	0·89	0·56	0·38

[1] *A.Q.* **1**, § 128.
[2] G. ALTER, RUPRECHT, and VANÝSEK, *Catalogue of Star Clusters and Associations*, Czech. Acad. Sci., 1958; Supplements, *B.A. Czech. Appendices*, **10**, No. 3, 1959; **11**, No. 1, 1960; **12**, No. 1, 1961; **13**, No. 1, 1962.
[3] G. E. KRON and N. U. MAYALL, *A.J.*, **65**, 581, 1960.
[4] T. D. KINMAN, *Radcliffe Repr.*, No. 9, 1958; *Obs.*, **78**, 122, 1958.
[5] H. B. SAWYER, *P. David Dunlap Obs.*, **2**, 35, 1955.
[6] M. SCHMIDT, *B.A.N.*, **13**, 15, 1956.
[7] M. SCHWARZSCHILD and S. BERNSTEIN, *Ap. J.*, **122**, 200, 1955.
[8] S. C. B. GASCOIGNE and E. J. BURR, *M.N.*, **116**, 570, 1956.
[9] S. VAN DEN BERGH, *Z. Ap.*, **41**, 61, 1956.
[10] M. S. ROBERTS, *A.J.*, **61**, 195, 1956.

§ 132. The Local System (Gould Belt)

N Pole of system	$l = 170°$ $b = +74°$
Centre of system	$l = 240°$ $b = -3°$
Sun's distance from centre	$\simeq 100$ pc
Sun's distance from local plane	$\simeq 12$ pc N of plane
Diameter of system	$\simeq 1\ 000$ pc

The system extends in the direction of Cygnus $l = 62°$ and Carina $l = 242°$.

Velocity of rotation $= 0·04R$ km/s pc^{-1}
where R is distance from the centre.

Mass of local system $= 1 \times 10^8 \mathscr{M}_\odot$

Absolute magnitude of system $M_v = -13$

Composition of system:

Luminous O-B5 stars within 400 pc.
A stars in HD catalogue.
Diffuse nebulae, extended dark nebulae, neutral hydrogen.
Associations: I Ori, II Per, and Sco-Cen.

[1] *A.Q.* **1**, § 129.
[2] G. S. MUMFORD, *Sky and Tel.*, **16**, 214, 1957.

§ 133. The Galaxy

Diameter	$= 25$ kpc
Thickness [3]	$= 4$ kpc
Total mass [2, 3, 4]	$= 1·1 \times 10^{11} \mathscr{M}_\odot$
Overall density	$= 0·10\ \mathscr{M}_\odot$ pc$^{-3} = 7 \times 10^{-24}$ g cm^{-3}

Diameter of extended spherical system
$$= 30 \text{ kpc}$$

Absolute magnitude (seen from the direction of the galactic pole outside the galaxy) [1]
$$M_v = -20.5$$

Ohlson galactic pole previously used to define galactic coordinates and now labelled l^I, b^I

$\alpha = 12^h 40^m = 190°.0$ $\qquad\qquad$ $\delta = +28°.0$ $\qquad$ (1900)

The ascending node on the equator (at $\alpha = 280°.00 + 1°.23T$) defined $l^I = 0$. (T in centuries from 1900·0.)

I.A.U. galactic coordinate system l^{II}, b^{II} [6]

Galactic pole ($b^{II} = +90°.0$)

$\alpha = 12^h 46^m.6 = 191° 39'$ $\qquad$ $\delta = +27° 40'$ $\qquad$ (1900)
$\alpha = 12^h 49^m.00 = 192° 15'$ $\qquad$ $\delta = +27° 24'.0$ $\qquad$ (1950)
$\qquad\qquad l^I = 347° 40'$ $\qquad$ $b^I = +88° 31'$

Point of zero longitude and latitude ($l^{II} = 0$, $b^{II} = 0$) [6]

This point agrees with the position of the galactic centre

$\alpha = 17^h 39^m.3 = 264° 50'$ $\qquad$ $\delta = -28° 54'$ $\qquad$ (1900)
$\alpha = 17^h 42^m.4 = 265° 36'$ $\qquad$ $\delta = -28° 55'$ $\qquad$ (1950)
$\qquad\qquad l^I = 327° 41'$ $\qquad$ $b^I = -1° 24'$

Galactic longitude of north pole (1950)
$$\theta = 123°.00$$

This defines the longitude zero of l^{II}.

Ascending node of galactic plane on 1950 equator

$\alpha = 18^h 49^m.0 = 282° 15'$ $\quad$ inclination $62° 36'.0$
$l^{II} = 33°.00$

Sun's distance from the galactic centre
$$R = 8.2 \pm 0.8 \text{ kpc}$$
or perhaps somewhat greater [14].

Sun's distance from the galactic plane [1, 6]
$$z_0 = 8 \pm 12 \text{ pc} \quad \text{N of plane.}$$

Oort constants of galactic rotation [1, 7, 8, 9, 10]

$A = 18.2 \pm 0.9$ (km/s) $\text{kpc}^{-1} \to P = \quad 0''.39 \text{ century}^{-1}$
$B = -8 \pm 2$ (km/s) $\text{kpc}^{-1} \quad \to Q = -0''.17 \text{ century}^{-1}$
$A - B \qquad\qquad\qquad = 26 \pm 2$ (km/s) kpc^{-1}
$P - Q = \omega \qquad\qquad = 0''.56 \text{ per century.}$

Rotational velocity in solar neighbourhood
$$v_c = R(A - B) = 215 \text{ km/s}$$

Central density of galactic system [3] $= 4 \mathscr{M}_\odot \text{ pc}^{-3}$

Escape velocity [1, 5]
  from galactic centre   = 450 km/s
  from near sun   = 290 km/s
  from rim of Galaxy   = 180 km/s

Potential energy of galactic system [1]
$$= 1 \cdot 1 \times 10^{59} \text{ erg}$$

Mean sky brightness due to stars near galactic pole
$$= 43 \ (V = 10) \text{ stars per sq. deg.}$$
$$m_v = 5 \cdot 9 \text{ per deg}^2 = 23 \cdot 7 \text{ per } ('')^2$$

Surface brightness of Galaxy near sun viewed from outside in direction of pole
$$m_v = 5 \cdot 2 \text{ per deg}^2$$

Optical thickness of Galaxy (pole to pole near sun) for random sight-line [1, 11]
$$2\tau_0 = 0 \cdot 68 \text{ mag (vis)}$$
$$= 0 \cdot 85 \text{ mag (pg)}$$
Absorption of extragalactic objects $= \tau_0 \sec b$.

Effective thickness of Galaxy (pole to pole near sun) referred to interstellar absorption
  near sun   = 300 pc

Distance between spiral arms [13] $\simeq$ 1·4 kpc

Position of spiral arms near sun.

The spiral arms are considered to be located by open clusters, O-associations, H II regions [15], and interstellar absorption [16]

  Direction of arms $l^{II} = 64°$ to $244°$
  Thickness of arm $= 0 \cdot 6$ kpc

The sun is located on the inner edge (i.e. towards galactic centre) of an arm. The concentrations of neutral hydrogen appear to fall between the arms [15].

Relaxation time t_0, i.e. time to establish a Maxwellian velocity distribution or to make the new orbit of a member star quite different from the original [1]

$$t_0 \text{ near sun} = 2 \cdot 6 \times 10^6 \ v^3 \text{ year}$$

where v is the velocity in km/s of the star relative to surrounding interstellar matter which is chiefly responsible for relaxation.

Age of Galaxy [12] $= 1 \cdot 5 \times 10^{10}$ y

Relation between rotation velocity and distance from galactic centre [13] (Leiden and Sydney)

Distance	in kpc	0	1	2	4	6	8·2
Rotation vel.	in km/s	0	150	180	210	225	215

[1] *A.Q.* **1**, § 130.
[2] W. LOHMANN, *Z. Phys.*, **144**, 66, 1956.
[3] M. SCHMIDT, *B.A.N.*, **13**, 15, 1956.
[4] J. C. BRANDT, *Ap. J.*, **131**, 293, 553, 1960.
[5] L. PEREK, *B.A. Czech.*, **10**, 15, 1959.
[6] A. BLAAUW, C. S. GUM et al., *M.N.*, **121**, 123, 132, 150, 164, 1960.

[7] B. Lindblad, *Handb. der Phys.*, **53**, 21, 1959.
[8] S. C. B. Gascoigne and O. J. Eggen, *M.N.*, **117**, 430, 1957.
[9] J. M. Mohr, Mayer, and Štohl, *B.A. Czech.*, 8, 5, 1957.
[10] R. M. Petrie, Cuttle, and Andrews, *A.J.*, **61**, 289, 1956.
[11] C. D. Shane, Wirtanen, and Steinlin, *A.J.*, **64**, 197, 1959.
[12] F. Hoyle, *Proc. Roy. Soc.*, **260**, 201, 1961.
[13] I.A.U. Symp. No. 7 on *Galactic Research*, p. 42, 1959.
[14] H. Weaver et al., *P.A.S.P.*, **73**, 88, 113, 1961.
[15] W. Becker, *Z. Ap.*, **51**, 151, 1961.
[16] J. D. Fernie, *A.J.*, **67**, 224, 1962.

§ 134. Galaxies (Extragalactic Nebulae)

Galaxies or extragalactic nebulae are classified according to the Hubble scheme [2] and include as types and subtypes:

Elliptical galaxies E_0 to E_7
 i.e. E_n where $n/10 = (a-b)/a$, and a and b are the greater and smaller diameters
Lenticular galaxies SO
Normal spirals Sa, Sb, Sc in increasing openness
Barred spirals SBa, SBb, SBc in increasing openness
Irregulars IrI, IrII of populations I and II.

Poorly defined spirals between Sc and Ir may be denoted Sd or Sm. p = peculiar. More detailed classification schemes are available [3, 4, 13].

Dimensions and type. There is a wide diversity of size and magnitude within each type. The systematic changes with type are not very regular except that Ir types are small and faint [3].

Change of colour, spectrum, and mass/luminosity with type

Type	$B-V$ [3]	Sp [3] nuclear region	$\mathcal{M}/\mathcal{L}$ [3, 13, 16]
			$\mathcal{M}_\odot/\mathcal{L}_\odot$
E	0·9	G4	80
SO	0·9	G3	50
Sa	0·9	G2	30
Sb	0·8	G0	20
Sc	0·6	F6	10
Ir	0·5		3

The *luminosity function* of galaxies [14] reveals an unrestricted number of faint galaxies and consequently it is not possible to state mean values relating to all galaxies. Instead we use the *mean* of randomly distributed galaxies selected to a limiting apparent magnitude; these apparent means are denoted by a $\overline{\text{bar}}$.

Apparent mean absolute magnitude and dispersion [14]

$$\overline{M}_v = -20\cdot3 \qquad \sigma = \pm1\cdot6 \text{ mag}$$

Stars per galaxy $= 10^{11}$

Mean mass $\bar{\mathscr{M}}$ $= 1\cdot2 \times 10^{11}\,\mathscr{M}_{\odot}$

Speed of recession and distance, the Hubble constant [§ 136]

$$v_{\mathrm{r}} = 100\ \mathrm{km/s\ Mpc^{-1}}$$
$$= 3\cdot2 \times 10^{-18}\ (\mathrm{cm/s})\ \mathrm{cm^{-1}}$$

This value of the Hubble constant is adopted as far as possible for other relations. Recent value $116\ \mathrm{km/s\ Mpc^{-1}}$ [20].

Random velocities of galaxies [1] $\simeq 100\ \mathrm{km/s}$

Velocity and magnitude [1]

$$\log v_{\mathrm{r}} \simeq 0\cdot23m_{\mathrm{c}} + 0\cdot9 \quad [v_{\mathrm{r}}\ \mathrm{in\ km/s}]$$

where $m_{\mathrm{c}} = m_{\mathrm{v}} - \Delta_{\mathrm{v}} =$ magnitude corrected for galactic absorption.

Colour of elliptic nebulae and recession velocity [1]

$$B - V = 0\cdot9 + 1\cdot3 \times 10^{-5}v_{\mathrm{r}} \quad [v_{\mathrm{r}}\ \mathrm{in\ km/s}]$$

Decrease of brightness with velocity and wavelength shift [1]

$$\Delta m = 6\cdot5\,\Delta\lambda/\lambda = 6\cdot5v_{\mathrm{r}}/c$$

Diameter measurements may depend strongly on the surface brightness defining the limiting measurement. From § 6 we use the major dimension $D_{\mathrm{i}} = \sqrt{2}\,D_{\mathrm{e}} = 2\sqrt{(2)}a_{\mathrm{e}}$ in the notation of [7] (1959). Interrelations between various measurements are:

$D_{\mathrm{e}} = 2a_{\mathrm{e}}$ in [7]	$= 0\cdot71\,D_{\mathrm{i}}$
Major diam. in [6]	$= 0\cdot9\,D_{\mathrm{i}}$
$2a_1$, i.e. to $m_{\mathrm{pg}} \simeq 25\ \mathrm{mag/(")^2}$ in [7]	$= 1\cdot7\,D_{\mathrm{i}}$
Diam. to $m_{\mathrm{v}} \simeq 26\ \mathrm{mag/(")^2}$ in [5]	$= 2\cdot0\,D_{\mathrm{i}}$

Local group of galaxies

Galaxy	Type	Coordinates		D_1		Ellipticity [5, 6, 7]	Distance [1, 7, 10, 15, 20]	V [5, 7, 9]	B−V [5, 7, 8]	M_v	v_r (observed) [9]	$\log \mathcal{M}$ [1, 3, 18]
		l^{II}	b^{II}	Ang. [5, 6, 7]	Lin.							in $\mathcal{M}_\odot$
		°	°	′	kpc		kpc				km/s	
Members												
Galactic system	Sb	—	—	—	20	—	8	—	0·8	−20·3	—	11·0
Large Magellanic cloud	IrI	280	−33	470	7·8	0·89	52	0·1	0·45	−19·1	+280	10·1
Small Magellanic cloud	IrI	303	−45	153	2·6	0·5	54	2·4	0·4	−16·8	+167	9·2
Andr. neb. M31 NGC 224	Sb	121	−21	102	16·0	0·30	570	3·5	0·98	−20·9	−270	11·5
M33 NGC 598	Sc	135	−32	34	5·7	0·64	600	5·8	0·55	−18·5	−190	10·1
M32 NGC 221	E2	121	−22	5	0·8	0·74	600	8·2	0·9	−16·0	−210	9·6
NGC 205	E5p	121	−21	12	1·7	0·5	600	8·2	0·81	−16·0	−240	9·9
Sculptor system	E	284	−84	30			110	7	0·8	−13		8·5
Fornax system	E	237	−65	40			200	7	0·8	−15	+40	9
NGC 6822	Ir	26	−19	15	1·7	0·7	400	8·7	0·5	−15·0	−40	8·6
NGC 147	Ep	120	−14	9	1·0	0·63	400	9·6	0·90	−14·5		9
NGC 185	Ep	121	−14	6	0·7	0·83	400	9·5	0·93	−14·6		9
IC 1613	IrI	129	−60	12		1·0	600	9·6	0·5	−14·1	−340	7·9
Wolf-Lundmark system	E5	74	−73	10	1·5	0·5	500?	10·8	0·5	−13·5	−240	8
Leo system I	E4	227	+49	12		0·6	400?				−80	
Leo system II	E1	222	+68	11	1·3	0·9	400?	12	0·9	−12		
Possible members												
IC 10	Sc	119	−3	4		0·9			0·8		−340	
IC 342	Sc	139	+10	30		1·0	800?	9	0·4		−10	
NGC 6946	Sc	97	+11	7	2?		1000?	13	0·4	−17	+40	
Leo system III	Ir	197	+54			0·9		11				
Sextans system	Ir	246	+40								+370	
NGC 300	Sc	299	−80	20	6?	0·5	1000?	8·5	0·5	−16	+250	

Galaxies brighter than $V \simeq 8.8$. Local group galaxies are excluded
v_{cor} = radial velocity corrected for solar motion

Galaxy	Type	Coordinates l^{II}	b^{II}	D_1 Ang. [5, 6, 7]	D_1 Lin.	Ellipticity [3, 5, 6, 7]	Distance [10, 11, 12]	V [5, 7, 9]	$B-V$ [5, 7, 8]	M_v	v_{cor} [9]	$\log \mathscr{M}$ [1, 3, 18]
		°	°	′	kpc		Mpc				km/s	in $\mathscr{M}_\odot$
NGC 55	Sc	332	−76	25	12	0·12	1·9	7·1		−19·2	+180	10·5
NGC 253	Sc	75	−89	22	13	0·27	2·2	7		−20	+70	10·0
NGC 2403	Sc	150	+29	20	12	0·57	2	8·5	0·5	−19	+190	9·7
M81 NGC 3031	Sb	141	+41	20	16	0·51	3·0	6·9	1·02	−20·9	+80	11·1
M82 NGC 3034	IrII	141	+41	8	7	0·4	3	8·2	0·91	−19·6	+400	10·4
NGC 3115	E7	248	+37	4·4	5	0·32	4	9·1	1·0	−19·4	+430	10·9
NGC 4258	Sb			15	17	0·35	5	8·4	0·82	−20·2	+490	
M87 NGC 4486	E1			4·0	13	0·85	11	8·9	0·97	−21·5	+1 220	12·6
M104 NGC 4594 Sombrero	Sa	299	+51	6·5	8	0·7	4·4	8·1	1·02	−20·4	+1 020	11·2
NGC 4736	Sb	124	+76	7	10	0·8	6	8·2	0·78	−20·6	+350	
NGC 4826	Sb	319	+83	8	12	0·58	6	8·4	0·86	−20·5	+360	
NGC 4945	S	305	+12	12	14	0·2	5	7		−22		
M63 NGC 5055	Sb	310	+19	10	15	0·5	4	8·6	0·86	−20·1	+2 600	
NGC 5128	Ep			14	15	0·80	3·8	6		−23	+260	
M51 NGC 5194 Whirlpool	Sc	105	+68	9	9	0·58	2	8·3	0·63	−19·6	+550	11·0
M83 NGC 5236	Sc	316	+33	10	12	0·8	4	7·6	0·73	−20·9	+320	
M101 NGC 5457 Pinwheel	Sc	102	+60	20	23	1·00	3	8·1	0·6	−20·2	+400	11·2
NGC 7793	Sd	4	−77	6	4	0·7	3	8·8		−18·6	+290	

Space density of galaxies $= 0 \cdot 03$ apparent mean galaxies Mpc^{-3}

Density ρ of galactic matter throughout space [19]
$$\log \rho = -30 \cdot 2 \quad [\rho \text{ in g cm}^{-3}]$$

Number N_m of galaxies per sq. degree brighter than m_v [1]
$$\log N_m = 0 \cdot 50 \ (m_v - 14 \cdot 4)$$
$$\log N_m = 0 \cdot 60 \ (m_v - \Delta m) - 8 \cdot 4$$

where Δm is the correction to the observed magnitude required by red shift, etc.

Mean sky brightness due to galaxies [1]
$$= 1 \cdot 4 \ (m_v = 10) \ \mathrm{deg}^{-2}$$

Luminous emission from galaxies [19]
$$= 3 \times 10^8 \ \mathscr{L}_\odot / (\mathrm{Mpc})^3$$

Spectral energy distribution of elliptical galaxies [17]
   (Compare globular clusters in § 131.)
$$\lambda_{\max} = 5800 \ \text{Å}$$

λ in Å	4000	5000	6000	5000	10000
$E_\lambda / E_{\lambda(\max)}$	0·48	0·91	0·98	0·82	0·73

Median galactic latitude of galaxies [1]
$$\bar{b} = 49°$$

[1] *A.Q.* **1**, § 131.
[2] E. Hubble, *Ap. J.*, **64**, 321, 1926.
[3] G. de Vaucouleurs, *Handb. der Phys.*, **53**, 275, 1959.
[4] W. W. Morgan, *P.A.S.P.*, **70**, 364, 1958; *Ap. J.*, **135**, 1, 1962.
[5] E. Holmberg, *Med. Lund.*, II, No. 136, 1958.
[6] H. Shapley and A. Ames, *Harv. Ann.*, **88**, 41, 1950.
[7] G. de Vaucouleurs, *A.J.*, **64**, 397, 1959; *Ann. Ob. du Houga*, 2/2, 1959; *Ap. J. Supp.*, **5**, 233, 1961; *Lowell Ob. Bull.*, No. 97, 4, 105; *Occ. N. R.A.S.*, **3**, No. 18, 118, 1956.
[8] E. Pettit, *Ap. J.*, **120**, 413, 1954.
[9] M. L. Humason, Mayall, and Sandage, *A.J.*, **61**, 97, 1956.
[10] S. van den Bergh, *A.J.*, **65**, 57, 1960.
[11] E. Hubble, *Ap. J.*, **84**, 270, 1936.
[12] J.-L. Sérsic, *Z. Ap.*, **50**, 168, 1960; **51**, 64, 1960.
[13] S. van den Bergh, *Ap. J.*, **131**, 215, 558, 1960.
[14] T. Kiang, *M.N.*, **122**, 263, 1961.
[15] S. Sandage, *Ap. J.*, **127**, 513, 1958.
[16] M. Schwarzschild, *A.J.*, **59**, 273, 1954.
[17] M. S. Roberts, *A.J.*, **61**, 195, 1956.
[18] V. C. Reddish, *Observatory*, 81, 19, 1961.
[19] S. van den Bergh, *Z. Ap.*, **53**, 219, 1961.
[20] J.-L. Sérsic, *Ann. d'Ap.*, **25**, 206, 1962.

§ 135. Clusters and Groups of Galaxies

As far as possible the data are adjusted to a Hubble constant of 100 km/s Mpc^{-1}.

Average diameter of clusters of galaxies [1, 2]
$$= 3 \ \mathrm{Mpc}$$

Average number of galaxies per cluster [1, 2]
$$= 130$$

Average number of cluster centres per unit volume [1, 2]

$$= 10^{-3}/\mathrm{Mpc}^3$$

Pole of local supergalaxy [4]

$$l^{\mathrm{II}} = 47° \qquad b^{\mathrm{II}} = +6°$$

with the centre of the system probably in the direction of the Virgo cluster ($l^{\mathrm{II}} = 283°$, $b^{\mathrm{II}} = +75°$).

Clusters of galaxies

Cluster (or group)	Number of galaxies [1]	Coordinates l^{II}	b^{II}	Diameter [1, 5]	Distance [1, 6]	Radial vel. [1, 3]	Gal. per volume [1]	m_{v} of 10th brightest galaxy [1, 3]
		°	°	°	Mpc	km/s	Mpc^{-3}	
Local group	16				0·4	− 100	300	8
Virgo	2 500	284	+74	12	11	+ 1 150	500	9·4
Pegasus I	100	86	−48	1	40	3 800	1 100	12·5
Pisces	100	128	−29	10	40	5 000	250	13·0
Cancer	150	202	+29	3	50	4 800	500	13·4
Perseus	500	150	−14	4	58	5 400	300	13·6
Coma	1 000	80	+88	6	68	6 700	40	13·5
Ursa Maj III	90	152	+64	0·7	80		200	14·5
Hercules		31	+44		105	10 300		14·5
Pegasus II		84	−47			12 800		15·2
Cluster A	400	144	−78	0·9	150	15 800	200	16·0
Centaurus	300	313	+31	2	150		10	15·6
Ursa Maj I	300	140	+58	0·7	160	15 400	100	16·0
Leo	300	232	+53	0·6	175	19 500	200	16·3
Gemini	200	182	+19	0·5	175	23 300	100	16·7
Cor. Bor.	400	41	+56	0·5	190	21 600	250	16·3
Cluster B	300	345	−55	0·6	200		200	16·3
Boötes	150	50	+67	0·3	380	39 400	100	18·0
Ursa Maj II	200	149	+54	0·2	380	41 000	400	18·0
Hydra II		226	+30			60 600		18·6

Groups of galaxies [6]

Group	NGC included	Distance	Radial vel.
		Mpc	km/s
Local	(§ 134)	0·4	
M81	3031, 2403, 4236, 2366, 2574, 2976	2·1	
Sculptor	55, 247, 253, 300, 7793	2·4	
UMa I	4736, 4258, 4395, 4656, 4449, 4214	3·3	+432
M101	5194, 5457, 5204, 5474, 5585, 5907	4·0	+496
NGC 1023	891, 925, 1003, 1058	4·4	+513
UMa II	4051, 5055, 4631, 4490, 4459, 4618	5·2	+620
Leo	3368, 3623, 3351, 3627, 3338, 3367, 3346, 3810, 3389, 3423	6·6	+788

[1] *A.Q.* **1**, § 132.
[2] E. Herzog, Wild, and Zwicky, *Pub. A.S.P.*, **69**, 409, 1957.
[3] M. L. Humason, Mayall, and Sandage, *A.J.*, **61**, 97, 1956.
[4] G. de Vaucouleurs, *A.J.*, **63**, 253, 1958.
[5] F. Zwicky, *Handb. der Phys.*, **53**, 373, 1959.
[6] J. L. Sérsic, *Z. Ap.*, **50**, 168, 1960.

§ 136. The Universe

Speed of recession of distant nebulae (Hubble constant) [2, 3, 4]
$$H = 100 \text{ km/s Mpc}^{-1} \ (\pm 0 \cdot 15 \text{ dex})$$
$$= 3 \cdot 2 \times 10^{-18} \text{ (cm/s) cm}^{-1} = 3 \cdot 2 \times 10^{-18} \text{ s}^{-1}$$

Life of universe for constant recession speed $= 1/H$
$$= 3 \cdot 1 \times 10^{17} \text{ s} = 9 \cdot 8 \times 10^9 \text{ y}$$

Density of galactic material throughout universe [5]
$$= 7 \times 10^{-31} \text{ g cm}^{-3}$$

Radius of observable universe
$$R = c/H = 3 \ 000 \text{ Mpc} = 0 \cdot 93 \times 10^{28} \text{ cm}$$

Volume of observable universe
$$(4\pi/3)R^3 = 3 \cdot 3 \times 10^{84} \text{ cm}^3 = 1 \cdot 1 \times 10^{11} \text{ Mpc}^3$$

Compare [6] where vol $= 2\pi^2 a^3$ and a = radius of curvature.

Galaxies in observable universe $= 3 \times 10^9$ apparent mean galaxies (§ 134).

Mass of observable universe $= 10^{54}$ g
This may increase to 3×10^{56} g if intergalactic matter of density 10^{-28} g cm^{-3} exists (§ 129).

[1] *A.Q.* 1, § 133.
[2] A. Sandage. *Ap. J.*, **127**, 513, 1958.
[3] S. van den Bergh, *J.R.A.S. Can.*, **54**, 49, 1960; *Z. Ap.*, **49**, 198, 1960.
[4] J. L. Sérsic, *Z. Ap.*, **50**, 168, 1960.
[5] J. H. Oort, Solvay Conf. on *Structure and Evolution of the Universe*, p. 163, 1958.
[6] J. B. Adams et al., Solvay Conf. on *Structure and Evolution of the Universe*, p. 97, 1958.

CHAPTER 15

INCIDENTAL TABLES

§ 137. The Julian Date

J.D. = Julian day.

Noon Jan. 1 (Julian)	4713 B.C. = J.D.	0·0
,, Jan. 1 ,,	1 B.C. = 0 A.D. = J.D.	1 721 058·0
,, Jan. 1 ,,	1 A.D. = J.D.	1 721 424·0
,, Jan. 1 ,,	1770 A.D. = J.D.	2 367 551·0
,, Jan. 1 (Gregorian)	1770 A.D. = J.D.	2 367 540·0
,, Mar. 1 ,,	1770 A.D. = J.D.	2 367 599·0

Julian day at noon (U.T.) on 1st March

Mar. 1	J.D.
1770	2 367 599
1780	2 371 252
1790	2 374 904
1800	2 378 556
1810	2 382 208
1820	2 385 861

Mar. 1	J.D.
1830	2 389 513
1840	2 393 166
1850	2 396 818
1860	2 400 471
1870	2 404 123
1880	2 407 776

Mar. 1	J.D.
1890	2 411 428
1900	2 415 080
1910	2 418 732
1920	2 422 385
1930	2 426 037
1940	2 429 690

Mar. 1	J.D.
1950	2 433 342
1960	2 436 995
1970	2 440 647
1980	2 444 300
1990	2 447 952
2000	2 451 605

[1] *A.Q.* **1**, § 134.
[2] A. K. BENNETT, *J.B.A.A.*, **57**, 144, 1947.
[3] *The Astronomical Ephemeris*, 1960+.

§ 138. The Greek Alphabet

Alpha	A	α
Beta	B	β
Gamma	Γ	γ
Delta	Δ	δ
Epsilon	E	ϵ, ε
Zeta	Z	ζ
Eta	H	η
Theta	Θ	θ, ϑ

Iota	I	ι
Kappa	K	$\kappa, \varkappa$
Lambda	Λ	λ
Mu	M	μ
Nu	N	ν
Xi	Ξ	ξ
Omicron	O	o
Pi	Π	π, ϖ

Rho	P	ρ
Sigma	Σ	σ, ς
Tau	T	τ
Upsilon	Υ	υ
Phi	Φ	ϕ, φ
Chi	X	χ
Psi	Ψ	ψ
Omega	Ω	ω

§ 139. Precession Table

Precession in R.A. for 10 years

In minutes of *time.* + ≡ R.A. increasing

Hours of R.A. for NORTHERN objects

Dec.	6	7 / 5	8 / 4	9 / 3	10 / 2	11 / 1	12 / 0	13 / 23	14 / 22	15 / 21	16 / 20	17 / 19	18	Dec.
	m	m	m	m	m	m	m	m	m	m	m	m	m	
80°	+1·77	+1·73	+1·60	+1·40	+1·14	+0·84	+0·51	+0·19	−0·12	−0·38	−0·58	−0·70	−0·75	80°
70°	1·12	1·10	1·04	0·94	0·82	0·67	0·51	0·35	+0·21	+0·08	−0·02	−0·08	−0·10	70°
60°	0·898	0·885	0·846	0·785	0·705	0·612	0·512	0·412	+0·319	+0·240	+0·178	+0·140	+0·126	60°
50°	0·778	0·768	0·742	0·700	0·645	0·581	0·512	0·444	+0·380	+0·324	+0·282	+0·256	+0·247	50°
40°	0·699	0·693	0·674	0·644	0·606	0·560	0·512	0·464	+0·419	+0·380	+0·350	+0·332	+0·335	40°
30°	0·641	0·636	0·624	0·603	0·576	0·546	0·512	0·479	+0·448	+0·421	+0·401	+0·388	+0·384	30°
20°	0·593	0·590	0·582	0·570	0·553	0·533	0·512	0·491	+0·472	+0·455	+0·442	+0·434	+0·431	20°
10°	0·552	0·550	0·546	0·540	0·532	0·522	0·512	0·502	+0·492	+0·484	+0·478	+0·476	+0·473	10°
0°	+0·512	+0·512	+0·512	+0·512	+0·512	+0·512	+0·512	+0·512	+0·512	+0·512	+0·512	+0·512	+0·512	0°
	18	19 / 17	20 / 16	21 / 15	22 / 14	23 / 13	0 / 12	1 / 11	2 / 10	3 / 9	4 / 8	5 / 7	6	

Hours of R.A. for SOUTHERN objects

Precession in Dec. for 10 years

In minutes of *arc.* + ≡ Dec. increasing and hence numerical S dec. decreasing

Hours of R.A.

12	11 / 13	10 / 14	9 / 15	8 / 16	7 / 17	6 / 18	5 / 19	4 / 20	3 / 21	2 / 22	1 / 23	0 / 24
′	′	′	′	′	′	′	′	′	′	′	′	′
−3·34	−3·23	−2·89	−2·36	−1·67	−0·86	0·0	+0·86	+1·67	+2·36	+2·89	+3·23	+3·34

§ 140. Annual Variations

Date	Sun's				Eq. of time App-mean	Transit of ♈		R.A. on meridian at 24 h, local midnight	
	R.A.	Dec.	Long.	Dist.					
	h m	°	°	AU	min	h m		h m	
Jan. 1	18 44	− 23·1	280	0·983 3	− 3·2	17	17	6	44
16	19 49	− 21·1	295	0·983 7	− 9·6	16	18	7	43
Feb. 1	20 56	− 17·3	312	0·985 4	− 13·5	15	15	8	47
16	21 56	− 12·6	327	0·987 9	− 14·2	14	16	9	46
Mar. 1	22 46	− 7·9	340	0·990 9	− 12·6	13	25	10	37
16	23 41	− 2·0	355	0·994 7	− 9·0	12	26	11	36
Apr. 1	0 40	+ 4·3	11	0·999 3	− 4·2	11	23	12	39
16	1 34	+ 9·8	26	1·003 5	0·0	10	24	13	38
May 1	2 31	+ 14·9	40	1·007 6	+ 2·8	9	25	14	37
16	3 29	+ 18·9	55	1·011 1	+ 3·7	8	26	15	37
June 1	4 34	+ 21·9	70	1·014 1	+ 2·4	7	23	16	40
16	5 35	+ 23·3	84	1·015 9	− 0·4	6	24	17	39
July 1	6 38	+ 23·2	99	1·016 7	− 3·5	5	25	18	38
16	7 39	+ 21·5	113	1·016 4	− 5·9	4	26	19	37
Aug. 1	8 43	+ 18·2	128	1·015 0	− 6·3	3	23	20	40
16	9 40	+ 14·0	143	1·012 6	− 4·4	2	24	21	39
Sept. 1	10 39	+ 8·5	158	1·009 2	− 0·2	1	22	22	42
16	11 33	+ 2·9	173	1·005 3	+ 4·8	0	23	23	41
Oct. 1	12 27	− 2·9	187	1·001 2	+ 10·0	23	20	0	41
16	13 21	− 8·6	202	0·996 9	+ 14·2	22	21	1	40
Nov. 1	14 23	− 14·2	218	0·992 6	+ 16·3	21	18	2	43
16	15 23	− 18·6	233	0·988 9	+ 15·3	20	19	3	42
Dec. 1	16 26	− 21·7	248	0·986 1	+ 11·3	19	20	4	41
16	17 32	− 23·3	264	0·984 1	+ 4·8	18	21	5	40

The sun's disk

P = position of N of sun's axis measured eastward from N point of disk
B_0 = heliographic latitude of earth or central point of disk

Date	P	B_0		Date	P	B_0
	°	°			°	°
Jan. 6	0·0	− 3·6		July 7	0·0	+ 3·5
Feb. 5	− 13·7	− 6·3		Aug. 7	+ 13·0	+ 6·2
Mar. 6	− 22·7	− 7·25		Sept. 8	+ 22·7	+ 7·25
Apr. 7	− 26·35	− 6·2		Oct. 10	+ 26·35	+ 6·2
May 7	− 23·1	− 3·5		Nov. 9	+ 23·0	+ 3·5
June 6	− 13·7	0·0		Dec. 8	+ 13·5	0·0

[1] *A.Q.* **1**, § 138.
[2] *The Astronomical Ephemeris.*

§ 141. Constellations

Constellation names, genitive ending, English meaning, 3-letter contractions, approximate positions, and areas.   Pronunciations in [3, 5].

Constellation	gen.	Meaning [3, 4, 5]	Contr.	α	δ	Area [3]
				h	°	(°)²
Andromeda	-dae	Chained maiden	And	1	40 N	722
Antlia	-liae	Air pump	Ant	10	35 S	239
Apus	-podis	Bird of paradise	Aps	16	75 S	206
Aquarius	-rii	Water bearer	Aqr	23	15 S	980
Aquila	-lae	Eagle	Aql	20	5 N	652
Ara	-rae	Altar	Ara	17	55 S	237
Aries	-ietis	Ram	Ari	3	20 N	441
Auriga	-gae	Charioteer	Aur	6	40 N	657
Boötes	-tis	Herdsman	Boo	15	30 N	907
Caelum	-aeli	Chisel	Cae	5	40 S	125
Camelopardus	-di	Giraffe	Cam	6	70 N	757
Cancer	-cri	Crab	Cnc	9	20 N	506
Canes Venatici	-num -corum	Hunting dogs	CVn	13	40 N	465
Canis Major	-is -ris	Great dog	CMa	7	20 S	380
Canis Minor	-is -ris	Small dog	CMi	8	5 N	183
Capricornus	-ni	Sea goat	Cap	21	20 S	414
Carina	-nae	Keel	Car	9	60 S	494
Cassiopeia	-peiae	Lady in chair	Cas	1	60 N	598
Centaurus	-ri	Centaur	Cen	13	50 S	1 060
Cepheus	-phei	King	Cep	22	70 N	588
Cetus	-ti	Whale	Cet	2	10 S	1 231
Chamaeleon	-ntis	Chamaeleon	Cha	11	80 S	132
Circinus	-ni	Compasses	Cir	15	60 S	93
Columba	-bae	Dove	Col	6	35 S	270
Coma Berenices	-mae -cis	Berenice's hair	Com	13	20 N	386
Corona Australis	-nae- -lis	S crown	CrA	19	40 S	128
Corona Borealis	-nae -lis	N crown	CrB	16	30 N	179
Corvus	-vi	Crow	Crv	12	20 S	184
Crater	-eris	Cup	Crt	11	15 S	282
Crux	-ucis	S cross	Cru	12	60 S	68
Cygnus	-gni	Swan	Cyg	21	40 N	804
Delphinus	-ni	Dolphin	Del	21	10 N	189
Dorado	-dus	Swordfish	Dor	5	65 S	179
Draco	-onis	Dragon	Dra	17	65 N	1 083
Equuleus	-lei	Small horse	Equ	21	10 N	72
Eridanus	-ni	River Eridanus	Eri	3	20 S	1 138
Fornax	-acis	Furnace	For	3	30 S	398
Gemini	-norum	Heavenly twins	Gem	7	20 N	514
Grus	-ruis	Crane	Gru	22	45 S	366
Hercules	-lis	Kneeling giant	Her	17	30 N	1 225
Horologium	-gii	Clock	Hor	3	60 S	249
Hydra	-drae	Water monster	Hya	10	20 S	1 303
Hydrus	-dri	Sea-serpent	Hyi	2	75 S	243
Indus	-di	Indian	Ind	21	55 S	294
Lacerta	-tae	Lizard	Lac	22	45 N	201
Leo	-onis	Lion	Leo	11	15 N	947
Leo Minor	-onis -ris	Small lion	LMi	10	35 N	232
Lepus	-poris	Hare	Lep	6	20 S	290
Libra	-rae	Scales	Lib	15	15 S	538
Lupus	-pi	Wolf	Lup	15	45 S	334
Lynx	-ncis	Lyria	Lyn	8	45 N	545
Lyra	-rae	Lyre	Lyr	19	40 N	286
Mensa	-sae	Table (mountain)	Men	5	80 S	153

Constellation	gen.	Meaning [3, 4, 5]	Contr.	α	δ	Area [2]
				h	°	(°)²
Microscopium	-pii	Microscope	Mic	21	35 S	210
Moroceros	-rotis	Unicorn	Mon	7	5 S	482
Musca	-cae	Fly	Mus	12	70 S	138
Norma	-mae	Square	Nor	16	50 S	165
Octans	-ntis	Octant	Oct	22	85 S	291
Ophiuchus	-chi	Serpent bearer	Oph	17	0	948
Orion	-nis	Hunter	Ori	5	5 N	594
Pavo	-vonis	Peacock	Pav	20	65 S	378
Pegasus	-si	Winged horse	Peg	22	20 N	1 121
Perseus	-sei	Champion	Per	3	45 N	615
Phoenix	-nicis	Phoenix	Phe	1	50 S	469
Pictor	-ris	Painter's easel	Pic	6	55 S	247
Pisces	-cium	Fishes	Psc	1	15 N	889
Piscis Austrinus	-is -ni	S fish	PsA	22	30 S	245
Puppis	-ppis	Poop (stern)	Pup	8	40 S	673
Pyxis (= Malus)	-xidis	Compass	Pyx	9	30 S	221
Reticulum	-li	Net	Ret	4	60 S	114
Sagitta	-tae	Arrow	Sge	20	10 N	80
Sagittarius	-rii	Archer	Sgr	19	25 S	867
Scorpius	-pii	Scorpion	Sco	17	40 S	497
Sculptor	-ris	Sculptor	Scl	0	30 S	475
Scutum	-ti	Shield	Sct	19	10 S	109
Serpens (Caput and	-ntis	Serpent. Head	Ser	16	10 N	429
Cauda)		Tail		18	5 S	+ 208
Sextans	-ntis	Sextant	Sex	10	0	314
Taurus	-ri	Bull	Tau	4	15 N	797
Telescopium	-pii	Telescope	Tel	19	50 S	252
Triangulum	-li	Triangle	Tri	2	30 N	132
Triangulum Australe	-li -lis	S Triangle	TrA	16	65 S	110
Tucana	-nae	Toucan	Tuc	0	65 S	295
Ursa Major	-sae -ris	Great bear	UMa	11	50 N	1 280
Ursa Minor	-sae -ris	Small bear	UMi	15	70 N	256
Vela	-lorum	Sails	Vel	9	50 S	500
Virgo	-ginis	Virgin	Vir	13	0	1 294
Volans	-ntis	Flying fish	Vol	8	70 S	141
Vulpecula	-lae	Small fox	Vul	20	25 N	268

[1] *A.Q.* **1**, § 139.
[2] *B.A.A. Handb.*, 1961, p. 25.
[3] E. G. Oravec, *Sky and Tel.*, **17**, 219, 1958.
[4] *Obs. Handb. R.A.S. Canada.*
[5] *Norton's Star Atlas*, pp. xvi, 52, last page, Gall and Inglis, 1959.

INDEX